Long-Term Monitoring and Research in Asian University Forests

This book disseminates various long-term data and research results from university forests in Asia towards realizing adaptive forest management and conservation based on a comprehensive understanding of environmental changes and ecological responses.

University forests – which refer to large, forested areas owned or controlled by universities and devoted primarily to research and teaching programs in forest-related sciences – have collected, managed and analyzed long-term meteorological, hydrological, biological and geographic data under an organizationally stable observation system. With the influence of global warming becoming apparent and extreme weather events occurring more frequently in the region, it is an important and urgent challenge to understand long-term environmental and ecosystem changes in forests and provide robust scientific knowledge on how ecosystems respond to those changes. This book is a step towards addressing the challenge.

The chapters in this book were originally published as a special feature of the *Journal of Forest Research*.

Toshiaki Owari is Associate Professor of Forest and Water Resources Management at the University of Tokyo, Japan. He is currently Director of the University of Tokyo Hokkaido Forest, Japan, and Deputy Coordinator of IUFRO Research Group 1.05.00 (Uneven-aged silviculture) and Working Party 1.01.09 (Ecology and silviculture of fir).

Sangjun Im is Professor of the Department of Agriculture, Forestry and Bioresources at Seoul National University, Republic of Korea. He is now Deputy Coordinator of IUFRO Research Group 1.06.00 (Restoration of degraded sites) and a member of the editorial board of *Landslides* and *Landscape and Ecological Engineering*.

Biing T. Guan is Professor of the School of Forestry and Resource Conservation at National Taiwan University, Taipei, Taiwan.

Long-Term Monitoring and Research in Asian University Forests

Understanding Environmental Changes and Ecosystem Responses

Edited by
Toshiaki Owari, Sangjun Im and Biing T. Guan

CRC Press
Taylor & Francis Group
Boca Raton London New York

CRC Press is an imprint of the
Taylor & Francis Group, an **informa** business

First published 2022
by CRC Press
4 Park Square, Milton Park, Abingdon, Oxon, OX14 4RN

and by CRC Press
6000 Broken Sound Parkway NW, Suite 300, Boca Raton, FL 33487-2742

CRC Press is an imprint of Informa UK Limited

British Library Cataloguing-in-Publication Data
A catalogue record for this book is available from the British Library

ISBN13: 978-1-032-17235-4 (hbk)
ISBN13: 978-1-032-17240-8 (pbk)
ISBN13: 978-1-003-25243-6 (ebk)

DOI: 10.1201/9781003252436

Typeset in Minion Pro
by codeMantra

Publisher's Note
The publisher accepts responsibility for any inconsistencies that may have arisen during the conversion of this book from journal articles to book chapters, namely the inclusion of journal terminology.

Disclaimer
Every effort has been made to contact copyright holders for their permission to reprint material in this book. The publishers would be grateful to hear from any copyright holder who is not here acknowledged and will undertake to rectify any errors or omissions in future editions of this book.

Contents

	Citation Information	vii
	Notes on Contributors	ix
	Foreword Naoto Kamata	xii
	Introduction – Long-term monitoring and research in Asian university forests: towards further understanding of environmental changes and ecosystem responses *Toshiaki Owari, Sangjun Im and Biing T. Guan*	1
1	Climate classification of Asian university forests under current and future climate *Yen-Jen Lai, Nobuaki Tanaka, Sangjun Im, Koichiro Kuraji, Chatchai Tantasirin, Venus Tuankrua, Luiza Majuakim, Fera Cleophas and Maznah Binti Mahali*	3
2	Soil conservation service curve number determination for forest cover using rainfall and runoff data in experimental forests *Sangjun Im, Jeman Lee, Koichiro Kuraji, Yen-Jen Lai, Venus Tuankrua, Nobuaki Tanaka, Mie Gomyo, Hiroki Inoue and Chun-Wei Tseng*	14
3	Analyzing the leafing phenology of *Quercus crispula* Blume using the growing degree days model *Naoto Kamata, Yuji Igarashi, Keisuke Nonaka, Hitomi Ogawa and Hisatomi Kasahara*	24
4	Effects of typhoon disturbances on seasonal and interannual patterns of litterfall on coniferous and broadleaf plantations in Xitou, central Taiwan *Chih-Hsin Cheng, Chia-Yi Lee, Hong-Ru Lee, Chiou-Pin Chen and Oleg V. Menyailo*	32
5	Differences in climate and drought response of the exotic plantation species *Abies firma*, *Cryptomeria japonica*, and *Chamaecyparis obtusa* in southern Korea *Jong Bin Jung, Hyun Jung Kim, Ji Sun Jung, Jong Woo Kim and Pil Sun Park*	40
6	Investigating the factors influencing trap capture of bark and ambrosia beetles using long-term trapping data in a cool temperate forest in central Japan *Naoto Kamata, Sunisa Sanguansub, Roger A. Beaver, Toshihiro Saito and Toshihide Hirao*	49
7	Influence of seasonality and climate on captures of wood-boring Coleoptera (Bostrichidae and Curculionidae (Scolytinae and Platypodinae)) using ethanol-baited traps in a seasonal tropical forest of northern Thailand *Sunisa Sanguansub, Sawai Buranapanichpan, Roger A Beaver, Teerapong Saowaphak, Nobuaki Tanaka and Naoto Kamata*	60

8 Spatio-temporal variation in egg-laying dates of nestbox-breeding varied tits (*Poecile varius*) in response to spring pre-breeding period temperatures at long-term study sites in South Korea and Japan 69
Min-Su Jeong, Hankyu Kim and Woo-Shin Lee

9 Modeling stand basal area growth of *Cryptomeria japonica* D. Don under different planting densities in Taiwan 79
Tzeng Yih Lam and Biing T. Guan

10 Long observation period improves growth prediction in old Sugi (*Cryptomeria japonica*) forest plantations 88
Takuya Hiroshima, Keisuke Toyama, Satoshi N. Suzuki, Toshiaki Owari, Tohru Nakajima and Seiji Ishibashi

11 Predicting individual tree growth of high-value timber species in mixed conifer-broadleaf forests in northern Japan using long-term forest measurement data 97
Kyaw Thu Moe and Toshiaki Owari

12 Evaluating relationships of standing stock, LAI and NDVI at a subtropical reforestation site in southern Taiwan using field and satellite data 105
Chiang Wei, Jiquan Chen, Jing-Ming Chen, Jui-Chu Yu, Ching-Peng Cheng, Yen-Jen Lai, Po-Neng Chiang, Chih-Yuan Hong, Ming-Jer Tsai and Ya-Nan Wang

Index 115

Citation Information

The chapters in this book were originally published in the *Journal of Forest Research*, volume 25, issue 3 (2020) and volume 25, issue 4 (2020). When citing this material, please use the original citations and page numbering for each article, as follows:

Introduction

Special feature Long-term monitoring and research in Asian university forests: towards further understanding of environmental changes and ecosystem responses
Toshiaki Owari, Sangjun Im and Biing T. Guan
Journal of Forest Research, volume 25, issue 3 (2020) pp. 134–135

Chapter 1

Climate classification of Asian university forests under current and future climate
Yen-Jen Lai, Nobuaki Tanaka, Sangjun Im, Koichiro Kuraji, Chatchai Tantasirin, Venus Tuankrua, Luiza Majuakim, Fera Cleophas and Maznah Binti Mahali
Journal of Forest Research, volume 25, issue 3 (2020) pp. 136–146

Chapter 2

Soil conservation service curve number determination for forest cover using rainfall and runoff data in experimental forests
Sangjun Im, Jeman Lee, Koichiro Kuraji, Yen-Jen Lai, Venus Tuankrua, Nobuaki Tanaka, Mie Gomyo, Hiroki Inoue and Chun-Wei Tseng
Journal of Forest Research, volume 25, issue 4 (2020) pp. 204–213

Chapter 3

Analyzing the leafing phenology of Quercus crispula *Blume using the growing degree days model*
Naoto Kamata, Yuji Igarashi, Keisuke Nonaka, Hitomi Ogawa and Hisatomi Kasahara
Journal of Forest Research, volume 25, issue 3 (2020) pp. 147–154

Chapter 4

Effects of typhoon disturbances on seasonal and interannual patterns of litterfall on coniferous and broadleaf plantations in Xitou, central Taiwan
Chih-Hsin Cheng, Chia-Yi Lee, Hong-Ru Lee, Chiou-Pin Chen and Oleg V. Menyailo
Journal of Forest Research, volume 25, issue 3 (2020) pp. 155–162

Chapter 5

Differences in climate and drought response of the exotic plantation species Abies firma, Cryptomeria japonica, *and* Chamaecyparis obtusa *in southern Korea*
Jong Bin Jung, Hyun Jung Kim, Ji Sun Jung, Jong Woo Kim and Pil Sun Park
Journal of Forest Research, volume 25, issue 4 (2020) pp. 214–222

Chapter 6
Investigating the factors influencing trap capture of bark and ambrosia beetles using long-term trapping data in a cool temperate forest in central Japan
Naoto Kamata, Sunisa Sanguansub, Roger A. Beaver, Toshihiro Saito and Toshihide Hirao
Journal of Forest Research, volume 25, issue 3 (2020) pp. 163–173

Chapter 7
Influence of seasonality and climate on captures of wood-boring Coleoptera (Bostrichidae and Curculionidae (Scolytinae and Platypodinae)) using ethanol-baited traps in a seasonal tropical forest of northern Thailand
Sunisa Sanguansub, Sawai Buranapanichpan, Roger A Beaver, Teerapong Saowaphak, Nobuaki Tanaka and Naoto Kamata
Journal of Forest Research, volume 25, issue 4 (2020) pp. 223–231

Chapter 8
*Spatio-temporal variation in egg-laying dates of nestbox-breeding varied tits (*Poecile varius*) in response to spring pre-breeding period temperatures at long-term study sites in South Korea and Japan*
Min-Su Jeong, Hankyu Kim and Woo-Shin Lee
Journal of Forest Research, volume 25, issue 4 (2020) pp. 232–241

Chapter 9
Modeling stand basal area growth of Cryptomeria japonica *D. Don under different planting densities in Taiwan*
Tzeng Yih Lam and Biing T. Guan
Journal of Forest Research, volume 25, issue 3 (2020) pp. 174–182

Chapter 10
*Long observation period improves growth prediction in old Sugi (*Cryptomeria japonica*) forest plantations*
Takuya Hiroshima, Keisuke Toyama, Satoshi N. Suzuki, Toshiaki Owari, Tohru Nakajima and Seiji Ishibashi
Journal of Forest Research, volume 25, issue 3 (2020) pp. 183–191

Chapter 11
Predicting individual tree growth of high-value timber species in mixed conifer-broadleaf forests in northern Japan using long-term forest measurement data
Kyaw Thu Moe and Toshiaki Owari
Journal of Forest Research, volume 25, issue 4 (2020) pp. 242–249

Chapter 12
Evaluating relationships of standing stock, LAI and NDVI at a subtropical reforestation site in southern Taiwan using field and satellite data
Chiang Wei, Jiquan Chen, Jing-Ming Chen, Jui-Chu Yu, Ching-Peng Cheng, Yen-Jen Lai, Po-Neng Chiang, Chih-Yuan Hong, Ming-Jer Tsai and Ya-Nan Wang
Journal of Forest Research, volume 25, issue 4 (2020) pp. 250–259

Notes on Contributors

Roger A. Beaver, Soi Wat Pranon, T. Donkaew, A. Maerim, Chiangmai, Thailand.

Sawai Buranapanichpan, Department of Entomology and Plant Pathology, Faculty of Agriculture, Chiang Mai University, Thailand.

Chiou-Pin Chen, Experimental Forest, National Taiwan University, Nantou, Taiwan.

Jing-Ming Chen, Department of Geography and Program Planning, University of Toronto, Canada.

Jiquan Chen, Department of Geography, Environment, and Spatial Sciences, Michigan State University, East Lansing, USA.

Chih-Hsin Cheng, School of Forestry and Resource Conservation, National Taiwan University, Taipei, Taiwan.

Ching-Peng Cheng, School of Forestry and Resource Conservation, National Taiwan University, Taipei, Taiwan.

Po-Neng Chiang, Experimental Forest, National Taiwan University, Nantou, Taiwan.

Fera Cleophas, Faculty of Science and Natural Resources, Universiti Malaysia Sabah, Malaysia.

Mie Gomyo, Ecohydrology Research Institute, The University of Tokyo Forests, Graduate School of Agricultural and Life Sciences, The University of Tokyo, Seto, Japan.

Biing T. Guan, School of Forestry and Resource Conservation, National Taiwan University, Taipei, Taiwan.

Toshihide Hirao, The University of Tokyo Chichibu Forest, Graduate School of Agricultural and Life Sciences, The University of Tokyo, Saitama, Japan.

Takuya Hiroshima, Department of Global Agricultural Sciences, Graduate School of Agricultural and Life Sciences, The University of Tokyo, Tokyo, Japan.

Chih-Yuan Hong, Experimental Forest, National Taiwan University, Nantou, Taiwan.

Yuji Igarashi, The University of Tokyo Chichibu Forest, Graduate School of Agricultural and Life Sciences, The University of Tokyo, Saitama, Japan.

Sangjun Im, Department of Forest Sciences, Seoul National University, Republic of Korea.

Hiroki Inoue, Arboricultural Research Institute, The University of Tokyo Forests, Graduate School of Agricultural and Life Sciences, The University of Tokyo, Minami-Izu, Japan.

Seiji Ishibashi, The University of Tokyo Tanashi Forest, Graduate School of Agricultural and Life Sciences, The University of Tokyo, Nishitokyo, Japan.

Min-Su Jeong, Department of Forest Sciences, Seoul National University, Republic of Korea.

Ji Sun Jung, Department of Forest Sciences, Seoul National University, Republic of Korea.

Jong Bin Jung, Department of Forest Sciences, Seoul National University, Republic of Korea.

Naoto Kamata, The University of Tokyo Chiba Forest, Graduate School of Agricultural and Life Sciences, The University of Tokyo, Kamogawa, Japan.

Hisatomi Kasahara, The University of Tokyo Hokkaido Forest, Graduate School of Agricultural and Life Sciences, The University of Tokyo, Furano, Japan.

Hankyu Kim, Department of Forest Sciences, Seoul National University, Republic of Korea; Department of Forest Ecosystems and Society, Oregon State University, Corvallis, USA.

Hyun Jung Kim, Department of Forest Sciences, Seoul National University, Republic of Korea; Baekdudaegan Conservation Department, Baekdudaegan National Arboretum, Bonghwa, Republic of Korea.

Jong Woo Kim, Department of Forest Sciences, Seoul National University, Republic of Korea.

Koichiro Kuraji, Executive Office, The University of Tokyo Forests, The University of Tokyo, Tokyo, Japan.

Yen-Jen Lai, Experimental Forest, National Taiwan University, Nantou, Taiwan.

Tzeng Yih Lam, School of Forestry and Resource Conservation, National Taiwan University, Taipei, Taiwan.

Chia-Yi Lee, School of Forestry and Resource Conservation, National Taiwan University, Taipei, Taiwan.

Hong-Ru Lee, School of Forestry and Resource Conservation, National Taiwan University, Taipei, Taiwan.

Jeman Lee, Department of Forest Sciences, Seoul National University, Republic of Korea.

Woo-Shin Lee, Department of Forest Sciences, Seoul National University, Republic of Korea.

Maznah Binti Mahali, Faculty of Science and Natural Resources, Universiti Malaysia Sabah, Malaysia.

Luiza Majuakim, Institute for Tropical Biology & Conservation, Universiti Malaysia Sabah, Malaysia.

Oleg V. Menyailo, Institute of Forest Research RAI SR, Krasnoyarsk, Russia.

Kyaw Thu Moe, Department of Forest Science, Graduate School of Agricultural and Life Sciences, The University of Tokyo, Tokyo, Japan.

Tohru Nakajima, Department of Forest Science, Graduate School of Agricultural and Life Sciences, The University of Tokyo, Tokyo, Japan.

Keisuke Nonaka, Department of Ecosystem Studies, Graduate School of Agricultural and Life Sciences, The University of Tokyo, Tokyo, Japan.

Hitomi Ogawa, The University of Tokyo Hokkaido Forest, Graduate School of Agricultural and Life Sciences, The University of Tokyo, Furano, Japan.

Toshiaki Owari, The University of Tokyo Hokkaido Forest, Graduate School of Agricultural and Life Sciences, The University of Tokyo, Furano, Japan.

Pil Sun Park, Department of Forest Sciences, Seoul National University, Republic of Korea.

Toshihiro Saito, The University of Tokyo Chichibu Forest, Graduate School of Agricultural and Life Sciences, The University of Tokyo, Saitama, Japan.

Sunisa Sanguansub, Department of Entomology, Faculty of Agriculture at Kamphaeng Saen, Kasetsart University Kamphaeng Saen Campus, Thailand.

Teerapong Saowaphak, Department of Highland Agriculture and Natural Resources, Faculty of Agriculture, Chiang Mai University, Thailand.

Satoshi N. Suzuki, The University of Tokyo Hokkaido Forest, Graduate School of Agricultural and Life Sciences, The University of Tokyo, Furano, Japan.

Nobuaki Tanaka, The University of Tokyo Hokkaido Forest, Graduate School of Agricultural and Life Sciences, The University of Tokyo, Furano, Japan.

Chatchai Tantasirin, Faculty of Forestry, Kasetsart University, Bangkok, Thailand.

Keisuke Toyama, The University of Tokyo Chiba Forest, Graduate School of Agricultural and Life Sciences, The University of Tokyo, Kamogawa, Japan.

Ming-Jer Tsai, School of Forestry and Resource Conservation, National Taiwan University, Taipei, Taiwan.

Chun-Wei Tseng, Division of Watershed Management, Taiwan Forestry Research Institute, Taipei, Taiwan.

Venus Tuankrua, Faculty of Forestry, Kasetsart University, Bangkok, Thailand.

Ya-Nan Wang, School of Forestry and Resource Conservation, National Taiwan University, Taipei, Taiwan.

Chiang Wei, Experimental Forest, National Taiwan University, Nantou, Taiwan.

Jui-Chu Yu, Experimental Forest, National Taiwan University, Nantou, Taiwan.

Foreword

Climate change attributed to human activity has gained general attention. In the recent past, the frequencies of violent typhoons and extreme weather events have increased. These events can trigger large-scale windthrow damages, landslides, wildfires, and the spread of forest pests. In addition to these environmental extremes, changes in temperature and precipitation have multiple influences on forest ecosystems via changes in growth and survival rates, flowering and fruiting intervals of plants, and species composition of forest vegetation. These changes in turn influence forest inhabitants, river flow, and frequencies of floods and droughts.

In Europe and North America, many studies have addressed the impact of environmental changes on forest ecosystems. In contrast, few studies based on long-term observations have been conducted in Asia, and their effects have not been completely verified. However, the effects of environmental changes have also become apparent in Asian countries. Thus, establishing a reliable and continuous long-term observation system is an important goal. The establishment of baseline data based on long-term observations for several decades or over 100 years is essential to detect environmental changes and ecosystem responses in forest ecosystems. Long-term human resources and research budget support are needed to continue long-term observations. The number of observation sites aiming at long-term research has been increasing recently in Asia. However, most sites are operated by individual researchers or project volunteers. It is expected that observations will not be conducted, or the observation sites will be abolished when the researchers retire.

Forests that are owned and/or managed by universities – in which education and research in forest science are carried out – have human resources, organizations, and technologies to stably continue long-term observations. Japan is one of the Asian countries that began early long-term forest observations. The country has developed sophisticated observation and analysis technologies, and has collected abundant data. The University of Tokyo Forests (UTF) institution has conducted long-term observations for more than 100 years. UTF activities include collaborating with other Asian universities to develop long-term observation systems; to establish cooperative research networks; and to collect, manage, and analyze the long-term data. These activities are crucial for the sustainable and adaptive management of forest ecosystems based on scientific predictions of environmental changes and ecosystem responses.

UTF has been active in establishing networks with other universities in Asia, which manage university forests under the FY2016–FY2018 and FY2019–FY2021 subsidiaries of the Core-to-Core Program (B. Asia-Africa Science Platforms) funded by the Japan Society for the Promotion of Science. This book is a collection of treaties produced by the network. I hope our project and this book will contribute to the studies in environmental science and the eternal coexistence of all species in Asia and globally.

Naoto Kamata, Ph.D.
Professor, the University of Tokyo Chiba Forest
Project Coordinator, Core-to-Core Programs (B. Asia-Africa Science
Platforms) funded in FY 2016 and 2019 by the Japan Society for the Promotion of Science

INTRODUCTION

Long-term monitoring and research in Asian university forests: towards further understanding of environmental changes and ecosystem responses

Toshiaki Owari, Sangjun Im and Biing T. Guan

Forests cover 593 million hectares of land in Asia (FAO 2016), with high biodiversity and supplying multiple ecosystem services to human society. Meanwhile, the influence of global warming becomes apparent, and extreme weather events frequently occur in the region, posing threats to forest ecosystems and serious damages to people's lives. To sustain, conserve, and manage Asian forests, it is an important and urgent challenge to understand long-term environmental and ecosystem changes in the forests and to provide robust scientific knowledge on how the ecosystems respond to those changes.

For forests, the detection of environmental changes and ecosystem responses requires baseline datasets based on long-term (e.g., 10^1–10^2 years) observations. University forests refer to forested areas owned or managed by universities and devoted primarily to research and teaching programs in forest-related sciences (Straka 2010). Such institutions have been collecting, managing, and analyzing long-term data of meteorological, hydrological, biological, and geographic information under an organizationally stable observation system.

With funding from the Core-to-Core Program (B. Asia-Africa Science Platforms) of the Japan Society for the Promotion of Science (JSPS), the University of Tokyo Forests initiated a 3-year research exchange project in 2016 entitled "Developing a network of long-term research field stations to monitor environmental changes and ecosystem responses in Asian forests" (Project Coordinator: Prof. Naoto Kamata). The project was implemented in collaboration with core institutions in five countries (Japan, Korea, Taiwan, Thailand, and Malaysia) that hold or manage university forests and research sites in different climates and vegetation zones of the Asian monsoon region. We aimed to promote the development of long-term research field stations for stable and continuous monitoring and to establish a multilateral research cooperation network among the core institutions through close collaborations. In 2019, the JSPS Core-to-Core Program further awarded the University of Tokyo Forests another 3-year research exchange project. We invited three new universities from China, Indonesia, and Sri Lanka, to strengthen and expand our multilateral research cooperation network that has been established through the previous research exchange project.

To disseminate various long-term data and research results from university forests in Asia, the Editorial Board of the Journal of Forest Research proposed a special feature entitled, "Long-term monitoring and research in Asian university forests: towards further understanding of environmental changes and ecosystem responses." We invited authors to contribute original articles regarding the latest scientific findings from university forests in Asian countries towards the realization of adaptive forest management and conservation based on a comprehensive understanding of environmental changes and ecological responses.

This special feature consists of a total of 12 articles from researchers participating in the JSPS Core-to-Core Program. Among them, two articles address the research topic of climate and water with long-term meteorological and hydrological data. Lai et al. (2020) classified the current climate types of university forests in Japan, Korea, Taiwan, Thailand, and Malaysia, and projected changes in the classification results under future climate scenarios. The author used temperature and precipitation data observed for 15–54 years at 15 weather stations. Im et al. (2020) determined Soil Conservation Service (SCS) curve number values using rainfall and runoff data measured for 6–17 years in Japan, Korea, Taiwan, and Thailand. The curve number procedure was developed by the U.S. SCS to estimate storm runoff volume on ungauged forest watersheds.

Six articles deal with forest ecosystems in Asia using long-term biological and ecological data. Kamata et al. (2020a) determined developmental periods for bud break and leaf opening of *Quercus crispula* by developing a growing degree days model with leafing phenology data over 10 and 53 years in central and northern Japan. Cheng et al. (2020) collected monthly litterfall data in 2012–2019 in coniferous and broadleaf plantations to examine the effects of typhoon disturbances on seasonal and interannual patterns of litterfall in central Taiwan. Jung et al. (2020) conducted a tree-ring analysis with monthly climate data over 50 years to examine the differences in climate and drought response of three introduced conifers (*Abies firma, Cryptomeria japonica*, and *Chamaecyparis obtusa*) in southern Korea. Kamata et al. (2020b) used trapping data collected between 1994–2003 and 2013–2014 to investigate factors influencing the number of species and abundance of bark and ambrosia beetles captured by traps in a cool temperate forest in central Japan. Sanguansub et al. (2020) captured insects every two weeks using ethanol bait traps in

2014–2016 to analyze the influence of seasonality and weather on captures of wood-boring beetles in a seasonal tropical forest of northern Thailand. Jeong et al. (2020) investigated the annual change of egg-laying dates for varied tits (*Poecile varius*) in response to spring pre-breeding period temperatures by monitoring nest boxes and climate data over 13 and 36 years in Korea and Japan.

Four articles are contributions from the research field of forest growth and mensuration based on long-term plot measurement and remote sensing data. Lam and Guan (2020) used tree census data repeatedly measured between 1950–2015 at a Sugi (*Cryptomeria japonica*) spacing trial in central Taiwan with initial densities of 400–2500 trees ha^{-1}. The authors employed a mixed-effects modelling approach to quantify Sugi stand basal area growth under different planting densities with acceptable prediction accuracy. Hiroshima et al. (2020) fitted Richards growth functions with time-series diameter at breast height data of planted Sugi trees between 14 and 108 years old in long-term growth observation sites in central Japan and confirmed that a longer observation period can improve the accuracy of growth prediction in old Sugi plantations. Moe and Owari (2020) used long-term measurement data between 1968 and 2016 from permanent plots in northern Japan to predict the individual tree growth of high-value timber species and to determine the time required to reach marketable size. To facilitate the biomass assessment of reforestation sites, Wei et al. (2020) examined the relationships between standing stock, leaf area index (LAI), and normalized difference spectral index (NDVI) in southern Taiwan, by using plot measurement records, hemispherical photos, and SPOT satellite images obtained annually between 2011 and 2015.

We hope that this special feature provides an overview of what the JSPS Core-to-Core research exchange programs have accomplished.

Acknowledgments

We wish to thank Dr. Masahiro Takagi for his careful manuscript check with huge efforts as the Coordinating Editor of this special feature. Our acknowledgements also extend to Prof. Satoshi Ito, Editor-in-Chief of the Journal of Forest Research, and Ms. Yoko Machida at the Editorial Office, for their dedicated support during the editorial process.

Disclosure statement

No potential conflict of interest was reported by the authors.

Funding

This work was supported by the Japan Society for the Promotion of Science [JPJSCCB20190007].

ORCID

Toshiaki Owari http://orcid.org/0000-0002-9227-4177

References

Cheng CH, Lee CY, Lee HR, Chen CP, Menyailo OV. 2020. Effects of typhoon disturbances on seasonal and interannual patterns of litterfall on coniferous and broadleaf plantations in Xitou, central Taiwan. J For Res.

FAO. 2016. Global forest resources assessment 2015: how are the world's forests changing? 2nd ed. Rome: Food and Agriculture Organization of the United Nations.

Hiroshima T, Toyama K, Suzuki SN, Owari T, Nakajima T, Ishibashi S. 2020. Long observation period improves growth prediction in old Sugi (*Cryptomeria japonica*) forest plantations. J For Res. 25.

Im S, Lee J, Kuraji K, Lai YJ, Tuankrua V, Tanaka N, Gomyo M, Inoue H, Tseng CW. 2020. Soil Conservation Service curve number determination for forest cover using rainfall and runoff data in experimental forests. J For Res. 25.

Jeong MS, Kim H, Lee WS. 2020. Spatio-temporal variation in egg-laying dates of nestbox-breeding varied tits (*Poecile varius*) in response to spring pre-breeding period temperatures at long-term study sites in South Korea and Japan. J For Res. in review.

Jung JB, Kim HJ, Jung JS, Kim JW, Park PS. 2020. Differences in climate and drought response of the exotic plantation species *Abies firma*, *Cryptomeria japonica*, and *Chamaecyparis obtusa* in southern Korea. J For Res. in review.

Kamata N, Igarashi Y, Nonaka K, Ogawa H, Kasahara H. 2020a. Analyzing the leafing phenology of *Quercus crispula* Blume using the growing degree days model. J For Res. 25.

Kamata N, Sanguansub S, Beaver RA, Saito T, Hirao T. 2020b. Investigating the factors influencing trap capture of bark and ambrosia beetles using long-term trapping data in a cool temperate forest in central Japan. J For Res. 25.

Lai YJ, Tanaka N, Im S, Kuraji K, Tantasirin C, Tuankrua V, Majuakim L, Cleophas F, Mahali MB. 2020. Climatic classification of Asian university forests under current and future climate. J For Res. 25.

Lam TY, Guan BT. 2020. Modeling stand basal area growth of *Cryptomeria japonica* D. Don under different planting densities in Taiwan. J For Res. 25.

Moe KT, Owari T. 2020. Predicting individual tree growth of high-value timber species in mixed conifer-broadleaf forests in northern Japan using long-term forest measurement data. J For Res. in review.

Sanguansub S, Buranapanichpan S, Beaver RA, Saowaphak T, Tanaka N, Kamata N. 2020. Influence of seasonality and weather on captures of wood-boring Coleoptera (Bostrichidae and Curculionidae (Scolytinae and Platypodinae)) using ethanol bait traps in a seasonal tropical forest of northern Thailand. J For Res. 25.

Straka TJ. 2010. Public outcry increasingly becoming safeguard of university forests. Plann Higher Edu. 38(4):52–60.

Wei C, Chen J, Chen JM, Yu JC, Cheng CP, Lai YJ, Chiang PN, Hong CY, Tsai MJ, Wang YN. 2020. Evaluating relationships of standing stock, LAI and NDVI at a subtropical reforestation site in southern Taiwan using field and satellite data. J For Res. in review.

Climate classification of Asian university forests under current and future climate

Yen-Jen Lai, Nobuaki Tanaka, Sangjun Im, Koichiro Kuraji, Chatchai Tantasirin, Venus Tuankrua, Luiza Majuakim, Fera Cleophas and Maznah Binti Mahali

ABSTRACT

Species diversity and the distribution of forests are closely related to climate, and climate classifications have been used to characterize vegetation distribution for over a century at the global scale. In contrast, climate type and dominant forest species may not be accurately classified at the forestry stand scale due to limited observational data and the influence of terrain. The collaboration of Asian university forests traverses 37.4° of latitude, from Hokkaido in Japan to Sabah in Malaysia. This study used both long-term observations and Worldclim 1-km resolution gridded datasets to classify well-managed Asian university forests according to the Trewartha climate classification method. Outputs from circulation models of the Coupled Model Inter-comparison Project Phase 5 (CMIP5) were then used to assess projected changes in future climate. Results showed that the current climate subtypes of the Asian university forests were consistent between the observations and Worldclim database. Ensemble projections of future climate suggested two likely drastic forest changes under a moderate emissions scenario during 2041–2060; parts of the Seoul National University Forests are likely to shift from a temperate to a subtropical climate, while sections of forests in Thailand are likely to shift from a subtropical to a tropical climate.

Introduction

Forest ecosystems are a complex hierarchy characterized by intricate interactions within and between different levels. These open systems are linked to, and interact with, the external environment and climate. Hence, climate change may influence these ecosystems and cause diverse ecosystem changes. In turn, forest ecosystem changes will influence the composition of the atmosphere and the state of the climate (Bonan 2008; Li 2008). Climate change impacts on forest ecosystems have been a research focus in recent years and studies have focused on abnormal plant and animal phenology (Gallinat et al. 2015; Forrest 2016; Piao et al. 2019); the ability of species to rapidly adapt or find suitable niches (Valiente-Banuet et al. 2015; García-Valdés et al. 2015a; Estes et al. 2016); abnormal migration, distribution, and composition (Gallinat et al. 2015; García-Valdés et al. 2015b; Morin et al. 2018); increased forest fire frequency (Flannigan et al. 2009; Aponte et al. 2016; Ruthrof et al. 2016); and increased likelihood of landslides (driven by increased extreme rainfall events), resulting in rapid changes to the forest landscape (Dale et al. 2001).

The fundamental drivers of forest disturbance under climate change are temperature and precipitation. According to the Intergovernmental Panel on Climate Change (IPCC) 5th Assessment Report (IPCC 2013), global surface temperatures have increased by 0.85 °C (0.65-1.06 °C) since the end of the 19th century. In East Asia, temperatures have likewise increased by approximately 1 ~ 3 °C in the last century with warming focused in the mid to high latitudes, including Japan and South Korea; besides, an inter-decadal scale weakening signal of both the summer and winter monsoon circulations has been experienced after the 1970s. Across the Southeast Asian region, the temperature has been increasing by 0.14-0.20 °C per decade since the 1960s (Tangang et al. 2007). Annual total wet-day rainfall and rainfall from extreme rain have increased by 22 and 10 mm per decade, respectively (Alexander et al. 2006; Caesar et al. 2011).

Climate zones are the classification of the global climate based on long-term climate data, and are used to generalize and compare different regions to understand ecosystem characteristics. While early classifications of climate can be traced to ancient Greece (Trewartha and Horn 1980), modern climate zones originated from the Köppen classification (Köppen 1918). A series of revisions to the Köppen classification resulted in a worldwide climate map in 1931, which has become one of the most widely used classification methods (Trewartha 1954). Subsequent classification methods have been proposed by Thornthwaite (1931), Holdridge (1947), Walter and Box (1976), and Trewartha and Horn (1980). However, during the development of these classification methods, only a small number of meteorological observation stations were used to identify global climate zones under the regional scale. Therefore, while global classification methods are an important tool they do not account for small-scale climate variations. For example, when the forest stand scale in which the area is less than 1 km^2 is considered, it is possible that the climate type will vary since complex interactions exist between the terrain and climate. Unfortunately, there are even fewer observations of high-quality long-term forest climate data that exist globally.

University forests are usually under good management without any inappropriate deforestation in order to approach their objectives, i.e. scientific research, education and field practice, forest management demonstration, and environmental conservation (Fukuda et al. 2019). Furthermore, the majority of university forests would like to maintain and collect long-term climate data over decades and in some cases, centuries. This well-maintained climate data is recognized as ground-based data and has been used for studies on climate change, hydrology, plant and animal growth, and the dynamics of forest ecosystems (Jung et al. 2019; Kamata and Suzuki 2019; Kuraji et al. 2019; Lai et al. 2019; Marod and Duengkae 2019; Im et al. 2019a). Therefore, the combination of appropriate forest management and high-quality long-term climate data makes the university forests become the most suitable baseline for understanding climate change impacts on forest ecosystems.

Cross-collaboration among the University of Tokyo Forests (UTF) and four other Asian university forests located within a wide latitudinal range of the Asian monsoon region is a platform which can be used to explore ecosystem differences between different climate and planting zones and to enhance forest management capabilities by sharing data, knowledge, and promoting innovation (Kamata et al. 2019). Based on this collaboration, the present study examined and compared the climate types of the Asian university forests using high spatial resolution climatological data (1 km) in conjunction with long-term observational data from weather stations near the forests. Data from outputs of the Coupled Model Inter-comparison Project Phase 5 (CMIP5) were also used to assess possible changes in climate classification under future climate change scenarios. By exploring changes in temperature and precipitation, this study aimed to clarify the influences of the current and future climate on the forest ecosystems based on climate type shifts in East and Southeast Asia. Furthermore, the potential shifts in the climate type may contribute towards guiding forest management policies to adapt to climate change.

Materials and methods

Study Sites

Five universities participated in the study (Table 1, Figure 1); the University of Tokyo (UTokyo), Seoul National University (SNU), National Taiwan University (NTU), Kasetsart University (KU), and Universiti Malaysia Sabah (UMS). Table 1 includes the list of abbreviation used hereafter for the Asian university forests.

UTokyo

The University of Tokyo Forests (UTF) was established in 1894 and now comprises seven university forests in Japan. The forests include (listed equatorward) the University of Tokyo Hokkaido Forest (UTHF), the University of Tokyo Chichibu Forest (UTCF), the University of Tokyo Tanashi Forest (UTTF), Fuji Iyashinomori Woodland Study Center (FIWSC), Ecohydrology Research Institute (ERI), the University of Tokyo Chiba Forest (UTCBF), and Arboricultural Research Institute (ARI). Forests range from a latitude of 43.3–34.6 °N and comprise various climate characteristics and vegetation types. Lowland (i.e. below 300 m a.s.l.) is dominated by deciduous swamp forests in the UTHF, evergreen needleleaf forest in the UTCF, evergreen broadleaf forest in the UTTF and FIWSC, deciduous and evergreen broadleaf mixed forest in the ERI and UTCBF, and evergreen broadleaf forest in the ARI. Detailed information can be found in Fukuda et al. (2019) and Kuraji et al. (2019).

SNU

The Seoul National University Forests (SNUF) were established in 1913 and own three university forests in the mid and southern regions of South Korea. The forests include Chilbosan, Taehwasan (SNUTF), and Nambu (SNUNF). This research only focused on the Taehwasan and Nambu forests since long-term climate data exists for these two forests. Vegetation types are dominated by deciduous and evergreen broadleaf and needleleaf mixed forest in SNUTF, and deciduous broadleaf forest in SNUNF. Detailed information can be found in Im et al. (2019a) and Im et al. (2019b).

NTU

The Experimental Forest of National Taiwan University (NTUEF) was originally established in 1901 during the period of Japanese occupation as the "Taiwan Practice Forest" attached to the College of Agriculture of Tokyo Imperial University.

Table 1. Locations, mean annual temperatures, and annual total precipitations of the meteorological stations within the Asian university forests, listed latitudinally. Abbreviations of universities and forests are given in parentheses.

University name Forest name	Weather station	Latitude (°)	Longitude (°)	Altitude (m)	T_{annual} (°C)	P_{annual} (mm)
The University of Tokyo (UTokyo)						
Hokkaido (UTHF)	Yamabe	43.219	142.384	230	6.5	1267.9
Chichibu (UTCF)	Koakasawa	35.937	138.804	1210	8.4	1596.1
Tanashi (UTTF)	Tanashi	35.739	139.538	60	14.7	1561.4
Fuji Iyashinomori (FIWSC)	Yamanakako	35.408	138.864	998	9.0	2840.9
Ecohydrology (ERI)	Higashiyama	35.236	137.158	352	12.0	1841.0
Chiba (UTCBF)	Kiyosumi	35.159	140.146	300	14.1	2240.8
Arboricultural (ARI)	Aono	34.691	138.838	105	15.3	2302.8
Seoul National University (SNU)						
Taehwasan (SNUTF)	Taehwasan	37.312	127.311	102	11.7	1210.7
Nambu (SNUNF)	Gwangyang	34.975	127.583	17	14.1	1504.7
National Taiwan University (NTU)						
Shuili (NTUSF)	Shuili	23.805	120.860	303	22.2	2136.1
Xitou (NTUXF)	Xitou	23.670	120.798	1180	16.5	2581.9
Kasetsart University (KU)						
Kog Ma (KUKF)	Kog Ma	18.813	98.902	1268	19.9	1863.8
Mae Mo (KUMF) [a]	Mae Mo	18.418	99.719	370	25.4	1332.3
Universiti Malaysia Sabah (UMS)						
Inobong (UMSIF) [b]	Inobong	5.856	116.137	490		3925.5
Alab (UMSAF) [b]	Alab	5.829	116.341	1952		3565.4

[a]: KUMF is managed by the Mae Mo branch office of the Forest Industry Organization.
[b]: Both UMSIF and UMSAF are managed by Sabah Parks.

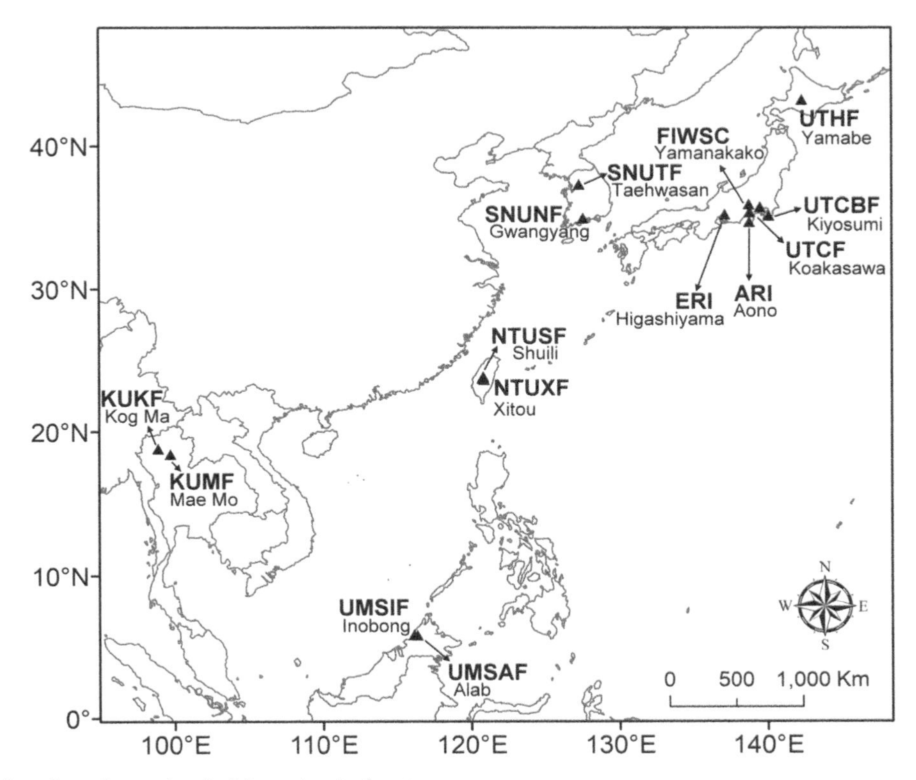

Figure 1. Locations of selected weather stations in Asian university forests.

Terrain in the forest rises from 220 m a.s.l. to 3,952 m a.s.l., covering approximately 32,770 ha (~1% of Taiwan Island). The area of the NTUEF covers an elevation range of 3,732 m with a wide variation in climate zones and vegetation types. Vegetation within the lowland Shuili Forest (NTUSF) and low-montane Xitou Forest (NTUXF) are dominated by subtropical evergreen broadleaf forest and subtropical evergreen needleleaf forest, respectively. Detailed information can be found in Tsai et al. (2019) and Lai et al. (2019).

KU

The Faculty of Forestry, Kasetsart University (KUFF) was founded as a Forestry School in 1936 in Thailand. Six forestry research and training stations have been established. Kog Ma Forest (KUKF) is located next to a national park in Doi Pui Forestry Research and Training Station, Chiang Mai Province. The dominant vegetation type is evergreen broadleaf forest. The Mae Mo Forest (KUMF) is a teak plantation (*Tectona grandis* Linn. f.) established in 1968 in the Lampang Province and is managed by the Mae Mo branch office of the Forest Industry Organization (FIO). A cross-collaboration among FIO, KU, and UTF engage in long-term climate observations. Detailed information can be found in Yamamura (2013), Tantasirin et al. (2019), and Tanaka et al. (2019).

UMS

UMS in Malaysia does not have its own experimental forest; however, the university works closely with government agencies including the Sabah Forestry Department, Sabah Foundation, and Sabah Parks to contribute their knowledge in forest science. In this study, we used data from two weather stations in the vicinity of the Crocker Range Park (CRP). The CRP is managed by Sabah Parks and is the largest terrestrial park and protected area in Sabah, covering 139,919 ha between the west coast and the interior plains of Sabah (Suleiman et al. 2007). The CRP encompasses a wide range of vegetation types; however, the dominant vegetation type in the lowlands is evergreen broadleaf vegetation whereas conifer-broadleaf forests are dominant at the upper montane forest. Two forests, Inobong (UMSIF) and Alab (UMSAF), located in lowland and upper montane areas, respectively, were assessed. Detailed information can be found in Lardizabal and Phua (2019).

Data

The diversity of ecosystems in the study sites is a consequence of marked variations in climate which are, in turn, impacted by latitude, altitude, and Asian monsoons. In this study, climate observations from 15 weather stations in the Asian university forests were evaluated (Table 1, Figure 1) covering latitudes of 5.829–43.219 °N (Alab–Yamabe), longitudes of 98.902–142.384 °E (Kog Ma–Yamabe), and altitudes of 17–1,952 m a.s.l. (Gwangyang–Alab). According to the metadata (see supplementary material S1), only Shuili and Gwangyang stations are 1.5 and 5.6 km away, respectively, from the forests, and the remaining 13 weather stations are located inside the forests where they belonged. The periods of observational data used in this study were more than 15 years at the majority of weather stations. The longest observed period is 54 years from 1963-2016 and 1964-2017 at Xitou and Gwangyang stations, respectively. The most overlapping period of observational data among all weather stations is from 2001-2015 and was considered the base year of present/current climate in this study. Temperature observations are just beginning and are incomplete at Inbong and Alab in Sabah. All weather stations update the measured method with the development of science and technology, and currently use automatic digital recording.

In the past, latitude was the main factor impacting climate zoning and altitude was not widely considered due to limited access to long-term climate data. Meteorological data can be impacted by local factors, including topography and land cover, and cannot adequately represent the entire forest, particularly within complicated topography. Technological developments in geographic information system and kriging-interpolated algorithms over the past 30 years have resulted in a consolidated, consistent, and rasterized global climate database, i.e. Worldclim. The database is available in two versions; 1.4 (-1960–1990; Hijmans et al. 2005) and 2.0 (1970–2000; Fick and Hijmans 2017). Both versions are based on data from weather stations worldwide and have a horizontal spatial resolution of 30 seconds (approximately 1 km^2). In this study, both versions were validated, and, based on the results of the validation, observational data and Worldclim Version 1.4 were used.

The future climate dataset is based on the Worldclim Version 1.4 database and is combined with downscaled data of the CMIP5 Global Circulation Models (GCMs). Both current and future datasets can be freely downloaded from the Worldclim website (https://www.worldclim.org). Two representative concentration pathways (RCPs) (RCP4.5 and RCP8.5) and two simulation periods (2050s [the mean of 2041–2060] and 2070s [the mean of 2061–2080]) were investigated. RCP4.5 and 8.5 are climate change scenarios with intermediate and very high greenhouse gas emissions, respectively. Overall, 19 GCMs were evaluated under the RCP4.5 scenario and 17 GCMs were evaluated under the RCP8.5 scenario.

The Worldclim future climate database provides monthly precipitation and minimum and maximum temperatures. The Trewartha climate classification system requires monthly mean temperatures, which we calculated using the mean minimum and maximum temperatures. Ground-based future climate data was calculated using current climate observations plus the difference between Worldclim future projections and Worldclim current climate data. The preparations of the current and future climate datasets are listed below:

(1) Ground-based current climate dataset: T_{gc} and P_{gc}
(2) Worldclim current climate dataset: T_{wc} and P_{wc}
(3) Ground-based future climate datasets: T_{gc} + (T_{wfm} + T_{wfn})/2- T_{wc} and P_{gc} + P_{wf} – P_{wc}
(4) Worldclim future climate datasets: (T_{wfm} + T_{wfn})/2 and P_{wf}

where T_{gc} is ground-based current monthly air temperature; T_{wc} is the Worldclim current monthly air temperature; T_{wfm} is the Worldclim current monthly minimum air temperature; T_{wfn} is the Worldclim current monthly maximum air temperature; P_{gc} is the ground-based monthly current monthly precipitatiorn; P_{wc} is the Worldclim monthly current monthly precipitation, and; P_{wf} is Worldclim monthly future monthly precipitation.

All details regarding current and future data used in this study are provided in the supplementary file S1.

Methods

There is a demonstrated good correspondence between Trewartha climate types and the natural climax vegetation types and soils within them (Bailey 1996). Furthermore, the Trewartha climate classification system has been used to create the Global Ecological Zones of the United Nations Food and Agriculture Organization (FAO) (FAO, 2001). This study intended to use this system for climate zoning. This system is based on the Köppen system and has undergone five revisions since it was first introduced. The scheme uses long-term monthly temperature and precipitation data to classify climate zones which are then related to plant distribution. In the first step, the global climate is divided into two parts: forested and non-forested climate. Forested climates have to provide sufficient heat (temperature) and water (precipitation) to support tree growth. With different amounts of heat and water, forested climates will result in a variety of vegetation types. Conversely, non-forest climates lack either sufficient water or heat to support tree growth, resulting in non-vegetated landscapes such as deserts or icecaps.

The Trewartha climate classification system includes six major classes (A–F) which are further subdivided into 20 subtypes and are distinguished based on climate details and vegetation types (Trewartha 1968; Trewartha and Horn 1980). Descriptions of Trewartha climate types and classified procedures are shown in Table 2 and Figure 2, respectively. Class A (tropical climate) is located at low latitudes, is winter free, and experiences a full-year rainfall pattern. The coldest monthly mean temperature is > 18.3 ° C. Class B (dry climate) extends from Class A to the mid-latitudes and the annual precipitation of this dry climate region is less than potential evapotranspiration. Class C (subtropical climate) experiences short mild winters and at least eight months of mean temperatures > 10 °C. Class D (temperate climate) experiences long cold winters and temperatures > 10 °C for four to seven months. Class E (boreal climate) experiences cold summers and one to three months with temperatures > 10 °C. Class F (polar climate) is continuously covered by snow and ice and the temperature is consistently < 10 °C.

To assess potential classification changes under future climate scenarios, both ground-based and Worldclim future climate datasets were used to identify the subtype at each monitoring weather station within or nearby the forest where it belonged. If both ground-based and Worldclim data agree, and > 75 % of future climate datasets (>14 in RCP4.5 and > 12 in RCP8.5) identify the same subtype as the present day, then there is a low likelihood that the subtype would disappear. Conversely, if ground-based and Worldclim data agree, and < 25 % of future climate datasets (< 5 in both RCP4.5 and RCP8.5) identify the same subtype as the present day, then the likelihood is high that the subtype would disappear and shift. Results that are between these two likelihoods are considered to be median and under an uncertain state. In forests with high probabilities of disappearing and shifting, further explorations are recommended.

Results and discussions

Worldclim data validation

Figure 3 showed temperature and precipitation comparisons between observations and Worldclim versions 1.4 and 2.0. Monthly data from all the stations were grouped by the universities and were represented by different symbols. The temperature R^2 of linear regressions were 0.99 and 0.98, mean absolute errors (MAEs) were 0.77 and 0.82 °C, and root mean square errors (RMSEs) were 1.00 and 1.13 °C for versions 1.4 and 2.0, respectively. Precipitation R^2 were 0.72 and 0.73, MAE were 43.31 and 45.39 mm, and RMSE were 67.79 and 66.80 mm for Versions 1.4 and 2.0, respectively. Both Worldclim databases provided satisfactory representations of climate in the study areas and could be used to evaluate climate classification, especially where long-term observational data is lacking, e.g. UMSIF and UMSAF. According to the validations, the temperature RMSE of Version 1.4 was 13 % less than that of Version 2.0. Comparatively, the precipitation RMSE of Version 1.4 was only 1.5% larger than that of Version 2.0. Version 1.4 performed slightly better in our sites and was used in the following analysis.

Table 2. Descriptions of Trewartha climate classes/types/subtypes (modified from Barry et al. 2010).

Class	Type	Subtype	Description
A			Tropical climates
	Ar		Rainy (tropical broadleaf evergreen rain forest)
	Aw		Tropical deciduous forests/woodland
	As		Summer dry; rare in type A climates
B			Dry climates
	BS		Semi-arid
		BSh	Tropical-subtropical shrubland
		BSk	Temperate-boreal steppe
	BW		Arid or desert
		BWh	Tropical-subtropical desert
		BWk	Temperate-cold desert
C			Subtropical climates
	Cw		Subtropical winter dry season
		Cwa	Mixed broadleaf deciduous and needleleaf forest
		Cwb	Needleleaf evergreen and broadleaf evergreen forest
	Cs		Dry-summer climates (Mediterranean climates) (dry steppe; hardleaved evergreen forests, open woodlands and shrub)
		Csa	Warm summer climate
		Csb	Cool summer climate
	Cf		Subtropical humid
		Cfa	Long and short needleleaf evergreen and broadleaf deciduous forests and evergreen broadleaf shrub understory
		Cfb	Needleleaf evergreen and deciduous forest
D			Temperate climates
	Do		Oceanic climates
		Doa	Warm summer climate
		Dob	Cool summer climate
	Dc		Continental climates
		Dca	Mid-latitude grassland, broadleaf deciduous forests and woodlands, mixed evergreen and broadleaf forests)
		Dcb	Needleleaf evergreen and mixed needleleaf-deciduous forest
E			Boreal climate (needleleaf deciduous forest and tundra woodland)
F			Polar climates
	Ft		Tundra, high altitude steppe
	Fi		Perpetual frost

Further comparisons (Table 3) of temperature showed that Worldclim data had $R^2 > 0.9$ at 87 % (i.e. 13) of the weather stations. R^2 results were > 0.99 for all weather stations in UTokyo, SNU, and NTU. Temperature biases within UTokyo, SNU, and NTU were reasonable, however, Worldclim agreement was lower at KUKF. Worldclim precipitation data were $R^2 > 0.8$ at 73 % (i.e. 12) of the weather stations. Precipitation correlations were considerably lower (0.68–0.99) compared to temperature due to high spatial variability of precipitation relative to temperature (Yatagai et al. 2012; Maussion et al. 2014). The Worldclim dataset provides assimilated values at a grid resolution of approximately 1 km^2; comparatively, the ground-based dataset provides point-source values that are sensitive to the surrounding environment. The discrepancies between the datasets may be a result of insufficient observed data or stations, complicated terrain, and land covers.

Current climate classification of Asian university forests

Current climate classification results of Asian university forests are shown in Table 4. Both UMSIF and UMSAF had insufficient ground-based data for identification, and only the climate subtypes from Worlclim existed. KUKF was the only forest where both ground-based and Worldclim datasets could not identify the climate type and subtype. While both datasets confirmed that it was Class C and approaching the Type Cf, precipitation in the driest summer month (26 mm from ground-based data and 20 mm from Worldclim) did not meet the Type Cf threshold of 30 mm. With the exception of UMSIF and UMSAF, the climate classes/subtypes of the remaining 13 forests were consistent between the ground-based and Worldclim datasets.

Forests in this study represented three of the six global climate classes. Seven subtypes were represented in this study: temperate continental, cool summer climate (Dcb) at UTHF, UTCF, and FIWSC; temperate continental, warm summer climate (Dca) at SNUTF; temperate oceanic, warm summer climate (Doa) at ERI, and SNUNF; subtropical, cool humid summer climate (Cfb) at NTUXF and UMSAF; subtropical, hot humid summer climate (Cfa) at UTTF, UTCBF, ARI, and NTUSF; tropical wet and dry, savanna climate (Aw) at KUMF, and; tropical humid, tropical rainforest climate (Ar) at UMSIF. The Subtype Cfa was represented at four forest locations, while Dca, Aw, and Ar were each only represented in one forest, i.e. SNUTF, KUMF, and UMSIF, respectively.

Based on the classification methodology of Trewartha and Horn (1980), this study considered the latitude and altitude variations and Asian monsoons influences, and resulted in variant climate subtypes among the Asian university forests. Table 4 shows the comparisons of climate types/subtypes among the results of three previous studies and this study. Some forests were misclassified using the same method. For example, NTUSF and NTUXF in Taiwan Island were identified as Class A and Subtype Aw, which are shown in the column "Trewartha and Horn (1980)". These results were interpreted from the hand-painted climate subtype map in Trewartha and Horn (1980). Subtype regions were identified by personal understandings and experiences. Comparatively, the remaining three used rasterized climate data (Jacob et al. 2012; Feng et al. 2014; this study) and ground-based data (this study) to identify the climate classification. All these studies identified two NTU forests as Class C, which is consistent with the vegetation types of NTU. This case showed that the rasterized data could identify a more precise climate type when compared with the hand-painted map.

Further comparing the results among Jacob et al. (2012), Feng et al. (2014), and this study, the types or subtypes of some forests

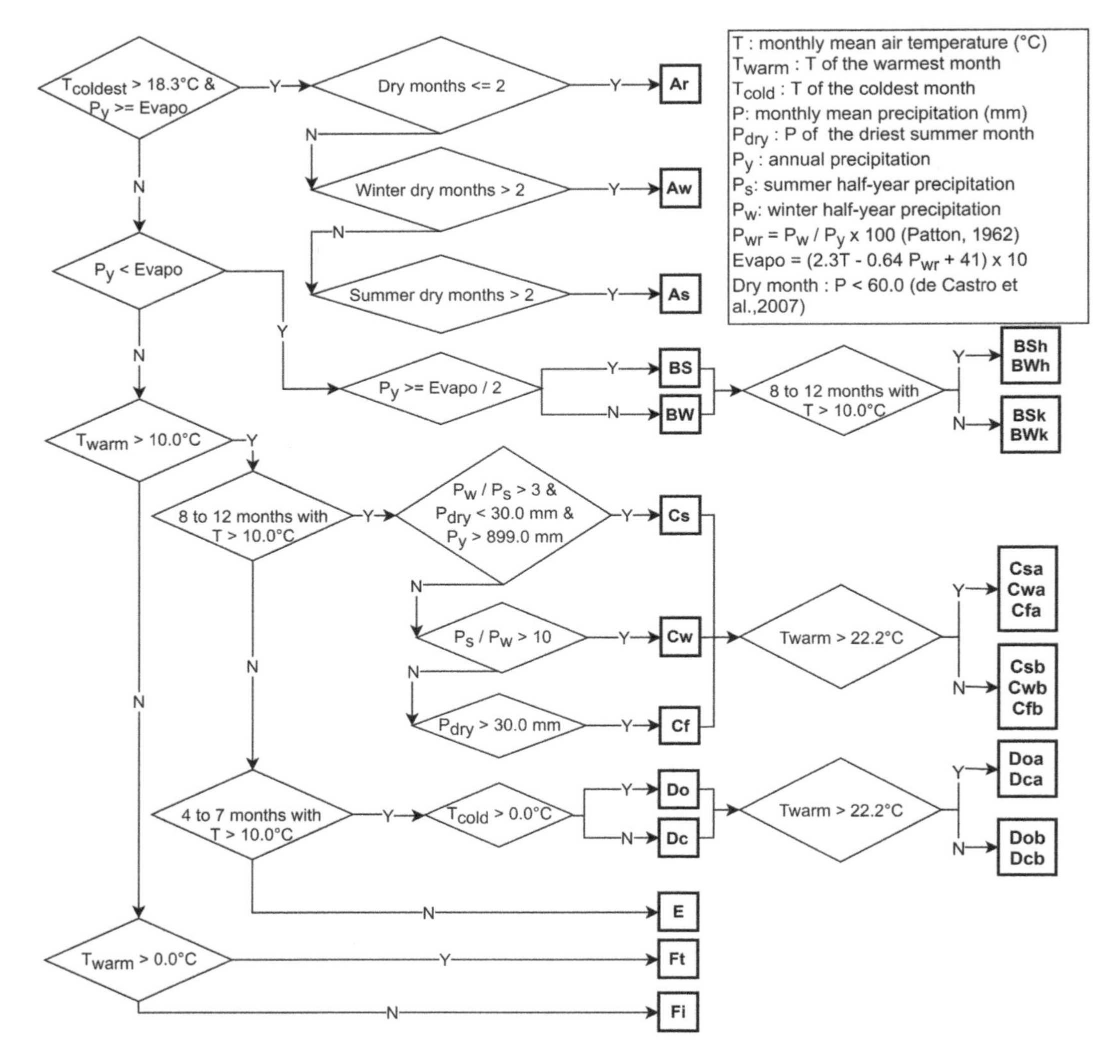

Figure 2. Flow chart for identifying Trewartha climate subtypes (based on Trewartha and Horn 1980).

remained in disagreement. Conversely, the identified subtypes of this study based on the ground-based and Worldclim datasets were consistent in all comparable forests. The disagreement in the coarse climate zones represented in Jacob et al. (2012) and Feng et al. (2014) may be a result of insufficient weather station data in the region and a lack of appropriate data interpolation. It is apparent that the precision of climate classification is improved by higher resolution rasterized data; hence, this has become a research and development focus.

Climate Projections

Figure 4 represents the mean temperature and precipitation anomalies under future climate scenarios (RCP4.5 and RCP8.5) during the 2050s and 2070s for all universities. The results show higher mean monthly temperature anomalies in the SNU forests as compared to other universities, with an increase of approximately 4 °C by the 2070s under RCP8.5. Conversely, anomalies in the UMS research areas are relatively small (up to 2.5 °C by the 2070s under RCP8.5). Projected monthly precipitation anomalies vary markedly. For example, monthly precipitation in the UMS is projected to increase by both the 2050s and 2070s under both RCP4.5 and RCP 8.5, with the highest anomalies (20 mm) occurring during January and February. Furthermore, precipitation in the 2050s in KU forests under RCP4.5 is projected to reduce by approximately 10 mm in May, and to then increase by the 2070s. Precipitation in the NTU forests under RCP8.5 is projected to decrease by approximately 20 mm in March and April and increase during the rainy season (May–September) by as much as 40 mm per month by the 2070s. Precipitation in SNU and UTokyo forests is expected to increase following a similar pattern.

Based on the future climate data, Table 5 shows the high, moderate, and low likelihoods of a subtype disappearing and shifting. Here, we first focused on the most likely class changes. ERI may gradually change from Class D (Doa) to Class C (Cfa) under the RCP4.5 scenario, and rapidly change under the RCP8.5 scenario after the 2050s. Both datasets suggest that SNUNF will change from Class D (Subtype Doa) to Class C (Subtype Cfa) and that KUKF will change from Class C to Class A during the 2050s under the RCP4.5 scenario. Meanwhile, invasive species may be more easily located in these three forests in the future and further explorations are recommended.

KUMF and UMSIF are identified as Class A due to the criteria of Class A being classified by the coldest temperature. The Worldclim future climate dataset (Figure 4) shows a warmer climate in the future for all seasons and these two forests remain in the same climate class in future scenarios. Moreover, the dataset indicates that precipitation may increase in all seasons in UMS, and also increase in KU with the exception of May; these changes will not cause any subtype to change under Class A. Overall, only 5 out of 15 forests are expected to remain as the same climate subtype under all scenarios, i.e. UTTF, UTCBF, ARI, KUMF, and UMSIF. With the exception of these forests, climate subtypes based on the Trewartha climate classification method will vary markedly as a consequence of climate change.

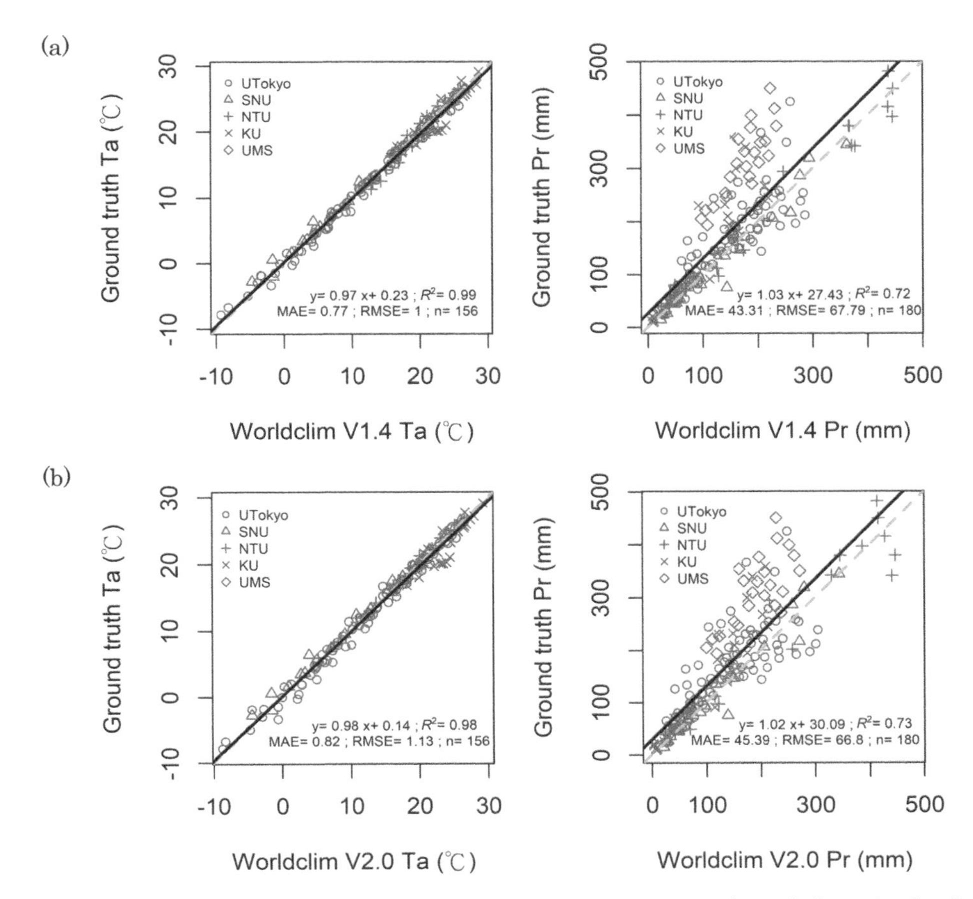

Figure 3. Comparisons of Worldclim (a) version 1.4 and (b) version 2.0 temperature (Ta) and precipitation (Pr) data with observation data. Each point represents the mean value of observational period for each month in each site, and it is grouped by the universities and represents by different symbols; black line shows the linear-regression equation based on all data; the dark dashed line shows the 1:1 ratio. UTokyo – the University of Tokyo, SNU – Seoul National University, NTU – National Taiwan University, KU – Kasetsart University, UMS – Universiti Malaysia Sabah.

Table 3. The linear-regression equations (l m eq.), mean absolute errors (MAE), and coefficient of determination (R^2) of both temperature and precipitation between observational data (y) and Worldclim version 1.4 data (x) in the Asian university forests. UTokyo – the University of Tokyo, SNU – Seoul National University, NTU – National Taiwan University, KU – Kasetsart University, UMS – Universiti Malaysia Sabah.

	Ta			*Pr*		
Weather station	lm eq.	MAE	R^2	lm eq.	MAE	R^2
UTokyo						
Yamabe	$y = 0.95x+0.74$	0.66	1.00	$y = 1.32x-21.80$	16.02	0.9
Koakasawa	$y = 0.91x+0.96$	0.78	1.00	$y = 0.89x+19.01$	19.89	0.84
Tanashi	$y = 1.04x-0.61$	0.39	1.00	$y = 0.96x+12.46$	14.52	0.87
Yamanakako	$y = 1.04x-0.84$	0.54	1.00	$y = 1.06x+70.67$	80.41	0.68
Higashiyama	$y = 0.98x-1.14$	1.44	1.00	$y = 0.64x+45.84$	27.68	0.91
Kiyosumi	$y = 0.99x-0.31$	0.25	1.00	$y = 1.01x+24.41$	31.15	0.79
Aono	$y = 1.05x-1.02$	0.40	1.00	$y = 0.80x+50.94$	27.79	0.83
SNU						
Taehwasan	$y = 0.93x+1.30$	0.86	0.99	$y = 0.90x+1.21$	16.69	0.95
Gwangyang	$y = 0.98x+0.39$	0.23	1	$y = 1.02x-0.88$	10.74	0.98
NTU						
Shuili	$y = 1.00x+0.69$	0.78	0.99	$y = 0.96x-3.94$	15.14	0.99
Xitou	$y = 1.06x-2.21$	1.10	0.99	$y = 0.97x+16.46$	21.09	0.98
KU						
Kog Ma	$y = 0.60x+7.10$	1.61	0.73	$y = 1.83x-4.65$	67.99	0.86
Mae Mo	$y = 0.76x+5.93$	1.00	0.82	$y = 1.19x+0.79$	22.31	0.96
UMS						
Inobong				$y = 1.38x+88.09$	153.63	0.73
Alab				$y = 1.32x+70.05$	124.53	0.7

Tan and Tseng (2012) indicated that temperature variations relative to latitude and altitude were 0.73 °C/° latitude and 5.21 °C/km, respectively. Hence, the difference in latitude and altitude among the forests (37.4 ° and 1,935 m, respectively) could be expected to cause temperature differences of 27.3 °C and 10.1 °C, respectively. These differences are significant in forming variant climate subtypes in the well-managed Asian university forests. Among all the subtypes in the study areas, Subtype Cfa is found in the widest latitudinal range from UTTF (35.739 °N) to NTUSF (23.805 °N) in the lowland, and the range may extend northernmost to 36.5 °N (Feng et al. 2014) and southernmost to around 23.5 °N

Table 4. Comparisons of climate classifications among the results of three previous studies and this study in the Asian university forests. UTokyo – the University of Tokyo, SNU – Seoul National University, NTU – National Taiwan University, KU – Kasetsart University, UMS – Universiti Malaysia Sabah.

	Reference			
	Trewartha and Horn 1980	Jacob et al. 2012	Feng et al. 2014	This study
	Spatial resolution			
	Region	0.44 °	0.5 °	Observation (Worldclim 1 km)
	Result in class, type or subtype			
Forest	Subtype	Type	Subtype	Subtype
UTokyo				
UTHF	Dcb	Dc	Dcb	Dcb(Dcb)
UTCF	Cf	Dc	Dcb	Dcb(Dcb)
UTTF	Cf	Do	Cfa	Cfa(Cfa)
FIWSC	Cf	Dc	Dcb	Dcb(Dcb)
ERI	Cf	Do	Doa	Doa(Doa)
UTCBF	Cf	Cf	Cfa	Cfa(Cfa)
ARI	Cf	Cf	Cfa	Cfa(Cfa)
SNU				
SNUTF	Dca	Dc	Dca	Dca(Dca)
SNUNF	Cf	Dc	Dca	Doa(Doa)
NTU				
NTUSF	Aw	Cf	Cwb	Cfa(Cfa)
NTUXF	Aw	Cf	Cwb	Cfb(Cfb)
KU				
KUKF	Aw	Aw	Aw	C(C)
KUMF	Aw	Aw	Aw	Aw(Aw)
UMS				
UMSIF	Ar	Ar	Ar	(Ar)
UMSAF	Ar	Ar	Ar	(Cfb)

(Chiou et al. 2004) in the current climate. UTTF is located near the northmost border of the Subtype Cfa. Since it is located inside the Tokyo city where urban heat island effects may have already influenced the current climate. On the other hand, NTUSF is located near the northmost and southmost borders of the Subtype Cfa and will be more sensitive to future climate change. UTCBF and ARI, which are located inside the belt of the Subtype Cfa region and locate in lowland area, will remain as typical Subtype Cfa in the future climate scenarios. On the other hand, NTUSF has a high probability that a tropical climate (Class A) will appear during the 2070s under RCP8.5, based on the ground-based dataset. Meanwhile, the southernmost of the Subtype Cfa may be shifting northward and the belt of the Subtype Cfa may become narrow in the future due to global warming.

Furthermore, the latitudinal and altitudinal differences from UTCF to ARI are 1.246 ° and 1150 m in mid-latitude UTF, respectively, and may cause approximately 0.91 °C and 5.99 °C differences, respectively. The climate zone is identified as Subtype Cfa at the lower-altitude forest in any future scenarios; however, subtypes of higher-altitude UTCF, FIWSC, and ERI may shift from Dcb to Dca, Dob or Doa, from Dcb to Dca, Doa or Cfa, and from Doa to Cfa. Comparatively, the low-latitude and low-montane NTUXF may only change from Subtype Cfb to Cfa during the 2070s under RCP8.5, and the Worldclim data indicates that this shift will occur during the 2050s under the RCP4.5. The tropical and upper-montane UMSAF may change only from Subtype Cfb to Ar during the 2070s under RCP4.5, or during the 2050s under RCP8.5. At KUKF, the Worldclim and ground-based data do not identify the subtype; however, both agree that Class C will soon change to Class A (Subtype As or Aw). These results indicated that the subtype shifting uncertainties of the montane area are higher in mid-latitudes than in low-latitude and tropical region in the future scenarios.

(a)

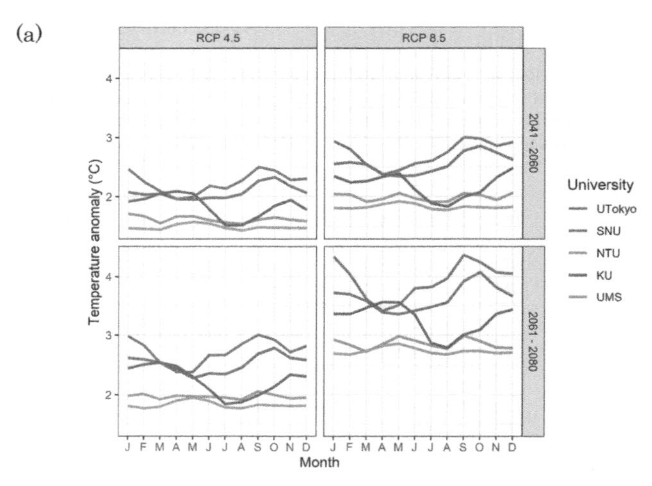

(b)

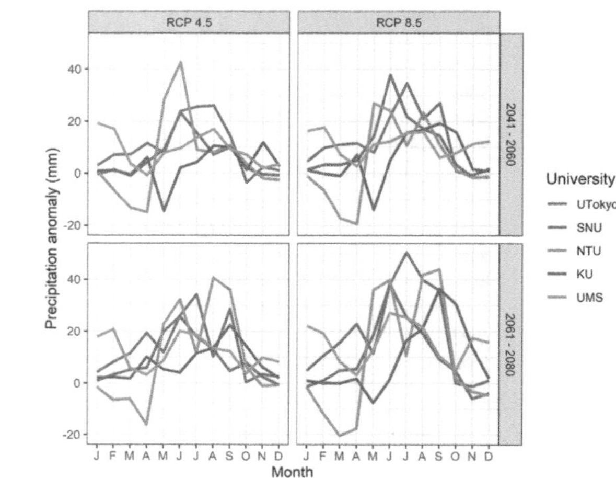

Figure 4. Projected future (a) temperature and (b) precipitation anomalies in the Asian university forests. The monthly anomaly is averaged from all global circulation models (GCMs) data of the forests of each university for each representative concentration pathway (RCP) and simulated period. UTokyo – the University of Tokyo, SNU – Seoul National University, NTU – National Taiwan University, KU – Kasetsart University, UMS – Universiti Malaysia Sabah.

Table 5. Trewartha climate types of each Asian university forests under current climate and in the 2050s and 2070s under the RCP4.5 and RCP8.5 scenarios. The total number of climate models from ground-based and Worldclim future climate datasets which were identified are represented outside and inside the parentheses, respectively. Shading in dim gray, dark gray, and white represent high, moderate, and low likelihoods, respectively, of a subtype disappearing and shifting. Unit: counts.

Forest	RCP	Year	Ar	As	Aw	Cfa	Cfb	Doa	Dob	Dca	Dcb	NA
UTHF		Present									1(1)	
	4.5	2050s								16(18)	3(1)	
		2070s								18(19)	1	
	8.5	2050s								17(17)		
		2070s								17(17)		
UTCF		Present									1(1)	
	4.5	2050s						2		2(17)	15(2)	
		2070s						3(1)	2	5(17)	9(1)	
	8.5	2050s						5	1	2(16)	9(1)	
		2070s				5(2)		9(6)		1(9)	2	
UTTF		Present				1(1)						
	4.5	2050s				19(19)						
		2070s				19(19)						
	8.5	2050s				17(17)						
		2070s				17(17)						
FIWSC		Present									1(1)	
	4.5	2050s				(1)		1(11)		13(6)	5(1)	
		2070s				(3)		1(13)		17(2)	1(1)	
	8.5	2050s				(2)		2(11)		14(4)	1	
		2070s				2(10)		8(6)		7(1)		
ERI		Present						1(1)				
	4.5	2050s				9(19)		10				
		2070s				13(19)		6				
	8.5	2050s				14(17)		3				
		2070s				16(17)		1				
UTCBF		Present				1(1)						
	45	2050s				19(19)						
		2070s				19(19)						
	85	2050s				17(17)						
		2070s				17(17)						
ARI		Present				1(1)						
	4.5	2050s				19(19)						
		2070s				19(19)						
	8.5	2050s				17(17)						
		2070s				17(17)						
SNUTF		Present								1(1)		
	4.5	2050s				1		8		10(19)		
		2070s				3		11(1)		5(18)		
	8.5	2050s				1		11		5(17)		
		2070s				7(5)		9(3)		1(9)		
SNUNF		Present						1(1)				
	4.5	2050s				19(19)						
		2070s				19(19)						
	8.5	2050s				17(17)						
		2070s				17(17)						
NTUSF		Present				1(1)						
	4.5	2050s			6	13(19)						
		2070s			9(4)	10(15)						
	8.5	2050s		1	8(5)	8(12)						
		2070s			15(12)	2(5)						
NTUXF		Present					1(1)					
	4.5	2050s				4(18)	15(1)					
		2070s				11(19)	8					
	8.5	2050s				11(17)	6					
		2070s				17(17)						
KUKF		Present										1(1)
	4.5	2050s		9	5(12)	1(1)						4(6)
		2070s		11	6(16)	(2)						2(1)
	8.5	2050s		9	7(16)	1(1)						
		2070s		11	6(17)							
KUMF		Present			1(1)							
	4.5	2050s			19(19)							
		2070s			19(19)							
	8.5	2050s			17(17)							
		2070s			17(17)							
UMSIF		Present	(1)									
	4.5	2050s	(19)									
		2070s	(19)									
	8.5	2050s	(17)									
		2070s	(17)									
UMSAF		Present					(1)					
	4.5	2050s	(13)				(6)					
		2070s	(18)				(1)					
	8.5	2050s	(16)				(1)					
		2070s	(17)									

White: < 25% models suggested disappearing and shifting.
Dark gray: 25% – 75% models suggested disappearing and shifting.
Dim gray: > 75% models suggested disappearing and shifting.

Conclusions

Global climate classifications at a coarse spatial resolution are well established. However, climate classification in montane areas remains a challenge due to the limited availability of ground-based data in these regions. This study used both long-term observational dataset and a 1-km resolution Worldclim dataset to re-identify the Trewartha climate subtypes of the Asian university forests and to assess the likelihood of subtype changes under future climate change scenarios.

Results indicate that the Worldclim dataset is reliable and fairly represents the climate subtypes within the study areas. Both temperature and precipitation showed sensitivity to differences in latitude and altitude in all forests and formed a wide variety of climate subtypes. In total, three out of six climate classes and seven out of twenty (35 %) climate subtypes were represented. Projections of future climate suggest that climate subtypes will vary markedly as a consequence of climate change. In the most sensitive forests it is likely that SNUNF will change from Class D to C and that KUKF will change from Class C to A.

Our results provide a basis for the development of adaptive forest management and conservation strategies throughout Asia at national, regional, and local levels. Findings can provide detailed climate information to facilitate further research in the Asian university forests and can be applied to hydrological, ecosystem, and management studies in the region. From the educational perspectives of university forests, since varying climate zones from tropics to temperate in the present and potential shifts in the future were found, there are greater opportunities for young scientists to become involved in adaptation projects or multi-regional monitoring activities under this platform of the Asian university forests. Furthermore, our study demonstrates the importance of high-resolution data for climate classification. Hence, future research will focus on the analysis of higher resolution gridded data to consider the influence of complex topography.

Acknowledgments

The data sharing from all the Asian university forests under the JSPS Core-2-Core project is gratefully acknowledged.

Disclosure statement

No potential conflicts of interest are reported by the authors.

Funding

Funding for the work and partial travel were supported by the NTUEF [109RG1]; partial travel and living expenses were supported by the JSPS Core-to-Core Program, B. Asia-Africa Science Platforms;Japan Society for the Promotion of Science (JP) [Core-to-Core Program, B. Asia-Africa Science Platforms];The Experimental Forest, National Taiwan University [109RG-1];

ORCID

Yen-Jen Lai http://orcid.org/0000-0002-3366-8766

References

Alexander LV, Zhang X, Peterson TC, Caesar J, Gleason B, Klein Tank AMG, Haylock M, Collins D, Trewin B, Rahimzadeh F, et al. 2006. Global observed changes in daily climate extremes of temperature and precipitation. J Geophys Res Atmos. 111 (D5109):1–22. doi:10.1029/2005JD006290.

Aponte C, de Groot WJ, Wotton BM. 2016. Forest fires and climate change: causes, consequences and management options. Int J Wildland Fire. 25:i–ii. doi:10.1071/WFv25n8_FO.

Bailey RG. 1996. Ecosystem Geography. New York (NY): Springer Verlag.

Barry B, Diaz H, Hargrove W, Hoffman F. 2010. Use of the Köppen-Trewartha climate classification to evaluate climate refugia in statistically derived ecoregions for the People's Republic of China. Clim Change. 98:113–131. doi:10.1007/s10584-009-9622-2.

Bonan GB. 2008. Forests and climate change: forcings, feedbacks, and the climate benefits of forests. Science. 320:1444–1449. doi:10.1126/science.1155121.

Caesar J, Alexander LV, Trewin B, Tse-ring K, Sorany L, Vuniyayawa V, Keosavang N, Shimana A, Htay MM, Karmacharya J, et al. 2011. Changes in temperature and precipitation extremes over the Indo-Pacific region from 1971 to 2005. Int J Climatol. 31:791–801. doi:10.1002/joc.2118.

Chiou CR, Liang YC, Lai YJ, Huang MY. 2004. A study of delineation and application of the climate zones in Taiwan. J Taiw Geogr Inform Sci. 1:41–62. Chinese.

Dale VH, Joyce LA, McNulty S, Neilson RP, Ayres MP, Flannigan MD, Hanson PJ, Irland LC, Lugo AE, Peterson CJ, et al. 2001. Climate change and forest disturbances: climate change can affect forests by altering the frequency, intensity, duration, and timing of fire, drought, introduced species, insect and pathogen outbreaks, hurricanes, windstorms, ice storms, or landslides. BioScience. 51:723–734. doi:10.1641/0006-3568(2001)051[0723:CCAFD]2.0.CO;2.

de Castro M, Gallardo C, Jylha K, Tuomenvirta H. 2007. The use of a climate-type classification for assessing climate change effects in Europe form an ensemble of nine regional climate models. Clim Change. 81:329–341. doi:10.1007/s10584-006-9224-1.

Estes JA, Burdin A, Doak DF. 2016. Sea otters, kelp forests, and the extinction of Steller's sea cow. Proceedings of the National Academy of Sciences. 113(4):880–885. doi:10.1073/pnas.1502552112.

FAO - The United Nations Food and Agriculture Organization. 2001. Global ecological zoning for the global forest resources assessment 2000 final report. accessed 2019 Dec 07. http://www.fao.org/3/ad652e/ad652e00.htm#TopOfPage.

Feng S, Hu Q, Huang W, Ho CH, Li R, Tang Z. 2014. Projected climate regime shift under future global warming from multi-model, multi-scenario CMIP5 simulations. Glob Planet Change. 112:41–52. doi:10.1016/j.gloplacha.2013.11.002.

Fick SE, Hijmans RJ. 2017. WorldClim 2: new 1-km spatial resolution climate surfaces for global land areas. Int J Climatol. 37:4302–4315. doi:10.1002/joc.5086.

Flannigan MD, Krawchuk MA, de Groot WJ, Wotton BM, Gowman LM. 2009. Implications of changing climate for global wildland fire. Int J Wildland Fire. 18:483–507. doi:10.1071/WF08187.

Forrest JR. 2016. Complex responses of insect phenology to climate change. Curr Opin Insect Sci. 17:49–54. doi:10.1016/j.cois.2016.07.002.

Fukuda K, Kuraji K, Owari T, Yasumura N, Kamata N. 2019. The University of Tokyo Forests. In: Kamata N, Kuraji K, Owari T, Guan BT, editors. Developing a network of long-term research field stations to monitor environmental changes and ecosystem responses in Asian forests. Tokyo: The University of Tokyo Forests Press; p. 3–23.

Gallinat AS, Primack RB, Wagner DL. 2015. Autumn, the neglected season in climate change research. Trends Ecol Evol. 30:169–176. doi:10.1016/j.tree.2015.01.004.

García-Valdés R, Gotelli NJ, Zavala MA, Purves DW, Araújo MB. 2015a. Effects of climate, species interactions, and dispersal on decadal colonization and extinction rates of Iberian tree species. Ecol Model. 309:118–127. doi:10.1016/j.ecolmodel.2015.04.003.

García-Valdés R, Svenning JC, Zavala MA, Purves DW, Araújo MB. 2015b. Evaluating the combined effects of climate and land-use change on tree species distributions. J Appl Ecol. 52:902–912. doi:10.1111/1365-2664.12453.

Hijmans RJ, Cameron SE, Parra JL, Jones PG, Jarvis A. 2005. Very high resolution interpolated climate surfaces for global land areas. Int J Climatol. 25:1965–1978. doi:10.1002/joc.1276.

Holdridge LR. 1947. Determination of world plant formations from simple climate data. Science. 105:367–368. doi:10.1126/science.105.2727.367.

Im S, Kim H, Eu S, Jung JB. 2019a. Long-term records of meteorological and hydrological data on Seoul National University Forests. In: Kamata N, Kuraji K, Owari T, Guan BT, editors. Developing a network of long-term research field stations to monitor environmental changes and ecosystem responses in Asian forests. Tokyo: The University of Tokyo Forests Press; p. 97–110.

Im S, Lee WS, Kim H. 2019b. Seoul National University forests. In: Kamata N, Kuraji K, Owari T, Guan BT, editors. Developing a network of long-term research field stations to monitor environmental changes and ecosystem responses in Asian forests. Tokyo: The University of Tokyo Forests Press; p. 39–49.

IPCC - Intergovernmental Panel on Climate Change. 2013. Climate change 2013: the physical science basis. Summary for policymakers. In:StockerTF,QinD,PlattnerGK,TignorM,AllenSK,BoschungJ,Nauels A, Xia Y, Bex V, Midgley PM, editors. Contribution of working group i to the fifth assessment report of the intergovernmental panel on climate change. United Kingdom and New York (NY): Cambridge University Press; p. 5.

Jacob D, Elizalde A, Haensler A, Hagemann S, Kumar P, Podzun R, Rechin D, Remedio AR, Saeed F, Sieck K, et al. 2012. Assessing the transferability of the regional climate model REMO to different coordinated regional climate downscaling experiment (CORDEX) regions. Atmosphere. 31:181–199. doi:10.3390/atmos3010181.

Jung JB, Park PS, Kim HJ, Kim JW, Jung JS, Park HK, Cho SH. 2019. Long-term growth records of cryptomeria japonica plantations at Nambu University Forest, Seoul National University, Korea. In: Kamata N, Kuraji K, Owari T, Guan BT, editors. Developing a network of long-term research field stations to monitor environmental changes and ecosystem responses in Asian forests. Tokyo: The University of Tokyo Forests Press; p. 245–252.

Kamata N, Kuraji K, Owari T, Guan BT. 2019. Developing a network of long-term research field stations to monitor environmental changes and ecosystem responses in Asian forests. Tokyo: The University of Tokyo Forests Press; p. vii.

Kamata N, Suzuki SN. 2019. Long-term ecological research sites in the University of Tokyo Forests. In: Kamata N, Kuraji K, Owari T, Guan BT, editors. Developing a network of long-term research field stations to monitor environmental changes and ecosystem responses in Asian forests. Tokyo: The University of Tokyo Forests Press; p. 169–184.

Köppen W. 1918. Klassifikation der Klimate nach Temperatur, Niederschlag und Jahreslauf. Petermanns Mitt; 64:243–248.

Kuraji K, Tanaka N, Gomyo M. 2019. Long-term meteorological and hydrological observation at Ananomiya and Shirasaka experimental watersheds, Ecohydrology Research Institute, The University of Tokyo. In: Kamata N, Kuraji K, Owari T, Guan BT, editors. Developing a network of long-term research field stations to monitor environmental changes and ecosystem responses in Asian forests. Tokyo: The University of Tokyo Forests Press; p. 81–95.

Lai YJ, Wey TH, Chang CS. 2019. Long-term meteorological and hydrological stations at National Taiwan University Experimental Forest and a review of past research. In: Kamata N, Kuraji K, Owari T, Guan BT, editors. Developing a network of long-term research field stations to monitor environmental changes and ecosystem responses in Asian forests. Tokyo: The University of Tokyo Forests Press; p. 111–124.

Lardizabal ML, Phua MH. 2019. Forestry education in Universiti Malaysia Sabah, Malaysia. In: Kamata N, Kuraji K, Owari T, Guan BT, editors. Developing a network of long-term research field stations to monitor environmental changes and ecosystem responses in Asian forests. Tokyo: The University of Tokyo Forests Press; p. 65–77.

Li PF. 2008. Impacts of climate change on ecology. National Science Council Monthly. 424:34–43. Chinese.

Marod D, Duengkae P. 2019. Montane forest dynamics based on long-term ecological research at Kog Ma watershed area in northern Thailand. In: Kamata N, Kuraji K, Owari T, Guan BT, editors. Developing a network of long-term research field stations to monitor environmental changes and ecosystem responses in Asian forests. Tokyo: The University of Tokyo Forests Press; p. 143–156.

Maussion F, Scherer D, Mölg T, Collier E, Curio J, Finkelnburg R. 2014. Precipitation seasonality and variability over the Tibetan Plateau as resolved by the high Asia reanalysis. J Climate. 27(5):1910–1927. doi:10.1175/JCLI-D-13-00282.1.

Morin X, Fahse L, Jactel H, Scherer-Lorenzen M, García-Valdés R, Bugmann H. 2018. Long-term response of forest productivity to climate change is mostly driven by change in tree species composition. Sci Rep-UK. 8:5627. doi:10.1038/s41598-018-23763-y.

Patton CP. 1962. A note on the classification of dry climate in the Köppen system. California Geogr. 3:105–112.

Piao S, Liu Q, Chen A, Janssens IA, Fu Y, Dai J, Liu L, Lian X, Shen M, Zhu X. 2019. Plant phenology and global climate change: current progresses and challenges. Glob Change Biol. 25:1922–1940. doi:10.1111/gcb.14619.

Ruthrof KX, Fontaine JB, Matusick G, Breshears DD, Law DJ, Powell S, Hardy G. 2016. How drought-induced forest die-off alters microclimate and increases fuel loadings and fire potentials. Int J Wildland Fire. 25:819–830. doi:10.1071/WF15028.

Suleiman M, Ishida H, Spait M, Said IM, Sugawara A, Repin R. 2007. An introduction to the crocker range permanent research plot project. Universiti Malaysia Sabah Kota Kinabalu. Universiti Malaysia Sabah. p. 1–65.

Tan PH, Tseng YC. 2012. The characteristics of temperature in taiwan during 1997-2010. Atmos Sci. 40:371–406. Chinese.

Tanaka N, Tantasirin C, Aranyabhaga N, Thitirojanawat P, Saphaokham S, Arunpraparut W, Kuraji K. 2019. Long-term ecohydrological data at Kog-Ma, Mae Moh and rainfall data at Mae Chaem watershed in northern Thailand. In: Kamata N, Kuraji K, Owari T, Guan BT, editors. Developing a network of long-term research field stations to monitor environmental changes and ecosystem responses in Asian forests. Tokyo: The University of Tokyo Forests Press; p. 125–140.

Tangang FT, Juneng L, Ahmad S. 2007. Trend and interannual variability of temperature in Malaysia: 1961–2002. Theor Appl Climatol. 89:127–141. doi:10.1007/s00704-006-0263-3.

Tantasirin C, Khlangsap N, Jumwong N, Lumyai P, Wongprom J, Chandaeng W, Tara A, Teejuntuk S. 2019. Forestry research and training stations, Faculty of Forestry, Kasetsart University. In: Kamata N, Kuraji K, Owari T, Guan BT, editors. Developing a network of long-term research field stations to monitor environmental changes and ecosystem responses in Asian forests. Tokyo: The University of Tokyo Forests Press, Tokyo; p. 51–63.

Thornthwaite CW. 1931. The climates of North America according to a new classification. Geogr Rev. 21:633–655. doi:10.2307/209372.

Trewartha GT. 1954. An introduction to climate. New York (NY): Mcgraw-Hill.

Trewartha GT. 1968. An introduction to climate. New York (NY): Mcgraw-Hill.

Trewartha GT, Horn LH. 1980. An introduction to climate. New York (NY): Mcgraw-Hill.

Tsai MJ, Liu SW, Wei C. 2019. National Taiwan University Experimental Forest: its past, present, and future. In: Kamata N, Kuraji K, Owari T, Guan BT, editors. Developing a network of long-term research field stations to monitor environmental changes and ecosystem responses in Asian forests. Tokyo: The University of Tokyo Forests Press; p. 25–37.

Valiente-Banuet A, Aizen MA, Alcántara JM, Arroyo J, Cocucci A, Galetti M, Galetti MB, García D, Gómez JM, Jordano P, et al. 2015. Beyond species loss: the extinction of ecological interactions in a changing world. Funct Ecol. 29:299–307. doi:10.1111/1365-2435.12356.

Walter H, Box E. 1976. Global classification of natural terrestrial ecosystems. Vegetatio. 32:75–81. doi:10.1007/BF02111901.

Yamamura R 2013. Management system of CO_2 and H_2O flux measurement in Kiryu (Japan), KogMa and MaeMo (Thailand) experimental forest. Report of Internship FOLENS Program Tokyo University of Agriculture and Technology. p.1–5.

Yatagai A, Kamiguchi K, Arakawa O, Hamada A, Yasutomi N, Kitoh A. 2012. APHRODITE: constructing a long-term daily gridded precipitation dataset for Asia based on a dense network of rain gauges. B Am Meteorol Soc. 93:1401–1415. doi:10.1175/BAMS-D-11-00122.1.

Soil conservation service curve number determination for forest cover using rainfall and runoff data in experimental forests

Sangjun Im, Jeman Lee, Koichiro Kuraji, Yen-Jen Lai, Venus Tuankrua, Nobuaki Tanaka, Mie Gomyo, Hiroki Inoue and Chun-Wei Tseng

ABSTRACT

Using the Soil Conservation Service (SCS) curve number (CN) procedure for estimating runoff volume on an ungauged forest watershed remains controversial because little guidance has been provided for defining appropriate CN values. In this study, alternative methods for assigning CN values (CNs) were assessed to determine whether these methods provide acceptable estimates of runoff on forested watersheds. The estimated CNs varied between the methods employed, showing the highest CN values when derived from a probabilistic method and lowest when derived from a graphical method. The tabulated CN values in Section 4 of the National Engineering Handbook (NEH-4) had relatively higher bias compared to those derived from measured rainfall-runoff data. The storm runoff volume was predicted using the assigned CNs and compared with the observations. The coefficients of determination and RMSE values between the measured and estimated runoff volumes varied with the methods employed. The highest watershed average RMSE value was obtained by the use of the tabulated CN values in NEH-4 (51.19 mm), while arithmetic mean approach provided the lowest average RMSE value of 24.38 mm, even though this method requires intensive data collection. Among the alternatives, probabilistic method was found to be the most reliable in determining CNs for forest cover with limited data. The estimated runoff largely agreed with the observations. Therefore, the revised CNs can be used for estimating storm runoff from ungauged, mountainous forests.

Introduction

Forests have a longer response time for storm runoff, a lower peak discharge, and a lower runoff volume than agricultural or urbanized watersheds because of dense vegetation and deep soil stratum. Because of a thick, porous litter floor, high permeability and infiltration capacity are maintained through the soil surface (Mulungu et al. 2005). Therefore, a better understanding of stormflow responses in forested watersheds is required for the proper management of mountainous regions.

The actual physical processes that convert rainfall to runoff are both complex and highly variable. There are numerous simulation models in hydrologic literature to simulate these processes and predict resultant runoff volumes and rates in ungauged small watersheds (Singh 1995), but the usage of the most models is limited because of their intense input data and the large computational burden. Therefore, simple and unpretentious approaches are preferred for predicting runoff volumes on small forest watersheds, with few data requirements and clearly stated assumption.

The curve number (CN) procedure developed by the U.S. Soil Conservation Service (SCS; now the National Resource Conservation Service) has been widely used in estimating the storm runoff volume from small ungauged watersheds, owing to its simplicity and easy to use (SCS, 1972). The SCS CN procedure was originally developed from measured rainfall–runoff data collected mostly from agricultural watersheds in the United States (SCS 1972). More recently, this procedure has been extended to stormflow analysis of urban, rangeland, and mixed land use watersheds (Mishra et al. 2005; Im et al. 2007; Patil et al. 2008); however, it performs poorly when applied to forests (Hawkins 1993).

Using the CN procedure for a forested watershed remains controversial and uncertain because little guidance has been provided for defining appropriate CNs with respect to vegetation type and geographical characteristics (Hawkins 1993). The poor estimation of CNs has led to large errors in direct runoff prediction. Therefore, care must be taken when defining CN values for reasonable results (Ponce and Hawkins 1996; Silveira et al. 2000).

Many methods have been proposed to calibrate CNs from measured rainfall and runoff data (SCS 1972; Hjelmfelt 1980; Ritter and Gardner 1991; Hawkins 1993; Yoo et al. 1993; Simanton et al. 1996). The SCS (1972) graphically defined median CNs as the best fit to rainfall–runoff data (Rallison and Cronshey 1979; Ritter and Gardner 1991). Springer et al. (1980) and Montgomery (1983) used a least squares procedure to estimate watershed CN values from rainfall and runoff data. Hjelmfelt (1980) proposed a statistical approach to determine CNs using the frequency distributions of measured rainfall and runoff pairs. Hauser and Jones (1991) developed a procedure to define CNs from the log-normal probability distribution of maximum retention storage according to antecedent moisture condition. Hawkins (1993) developed an asymptotic method from rank-ordered rainfall and runoff data pairs. However, there is no consensus on how accurately the CN values can be estimated from observed data (Bonta 1997).

An accurate CN value is essential for estimating stormflow from a given rainfall depth. This study aimed to examine the relative accuracy of different methods in assigning CNs for forest cover from a measured rainfall and runoff dataset. The simulated runoff volumes corresponding to the assigned CNs were compared with the observations to determine the reliability of the SCS procedure.

Materials and methods

Curve number determination from measured data

The SCS CN procedure was originally described in Section 4 of the National Engineering Handbook, hereinafter abbreviated as NEH-4 (SCS 1972). The SCS CN procedure is based on the water balance equation and two fundamental hypotheses. One hypothesis is that the ratio of actual soil retention after runoff begins to maximum retention storage is equal to the ratio of runoff to effective rainfall. The second hypothesis relates the initial abstraction to the maximum retention storage.

The total volume of excess rainfall or runoff Q can be expressed in terms of the rainfall depth P as follows.

$$Q = \frac{(P - I_a)^2}{(P - I_a) + S} \tag{1}$$

Here, I_a is the rainfall lost as initial abstractions, and S is the maximum retention storage of the soil. P-I_a is also regarded as effective rainfall. The initial abstraction accounts for all water losses due to interception, depression storage, surface detention, evaporation, and infiltration before runoff begins. The maximum retention storage conceptually represents a potential amount of water retained in the soil column.

Based on the second hypothesis, the amount of initial abstraction is normally set to 20% of maximum retention storage. That is,

$$I_a = 0.2S \tag{2}$$

When substituted for I_a into Equation (1), Equation (1) becomes

$$Q = \frac{(P - 0.2S)^2}{P + 0.8S} \tag{3}$$

The maximum retention storage S, which varies with the antecedent soil moisture and other variables, is related to the CN value as follows.

$$S = \frac{25400}{CN} - 254 \tag{4}$$

Here, S is expressed in mm, and CN is a non-dimensional quantity ranging from 0 (no runoff) to 100 (all effective rainfall becomes runoff). The relation between S and CN is a pure mathematical transformation for convenience in practical use (SCS 1972).

The CN parameter in Equation (4) is related to soil type, soil infiltration capability, land use, and soil wetness. To account for infiltration capacity of different soils, the SCS (1972) identified four hydrologic soil groups A, B, C, and D, according to their infiltration and transmission rates when saturated. The land use describes not only what is on the land, but in some cases its condition from a hydrologic standpoint (good, fair, or poor). CN value is further adjusted according to the antecedent moisture condition (AMC) that refers to the preceding wetness condition of soils. Soil moisture varies with the antecedent rainfall of certain duration, and thus, NEH-4 (SCS 1972) provided the quantitative criteria to define the AMC with the cumulated total rainfall over five consecutive days prior to runoff. Soil moisture condition of a given rainfall event is divided into three classes, namely AMC I, II, and III. AMC II is the average condition, while AMC I and III represent the lowest (dried) and highest (saturated) runoff potentials, respectively.

In this study, the CN values for forest land cover were practically determined from measured rainfall–runoff data using different methods such as the mean formula (arithmetic and geometric), graphical method, and probabilistic method.

The mean formula is used to measure the central tendency of quantitative values in data. When rainfall and runoff data are available, the value of S can be transformed by rearranging Equation (3), which can be given as a quadratic formula (Hawkins 1993):

$$S = 5(P + 2Q - \sqrt{4Q^2 + 5PQ}) \tag{5}$$

The S value for a specific event can be determined using Equation (5) with measured rainfall and runoff volume. Prior to arithmetic mean calculation, all storm events need to be divided into three groups, AMC I, II, and III, respectively, according to 5-day antecedent rainfall totals. The arithmetic mean of S values for each AMC condition was determined by taking the sum of individual S values, and then dividing the sum by the total number of rainfall events that belong to each AMC group. The arithmetic mean of S values is then substituted into Equation (4) to compute the corresponding CN values (Hauser and Jones 1991).

It is well known that arithmetic mean yields central tendency bias when dataset is not normally distributed. To compensate this, geometric mean is proposed to estimate the central tendency of individual S values. The geometric mean can be derived from the lognormal distribution of the maximum retention storage using Equation (6) (Yuan 1933).

$$CN = \frac{25400}{254 + 10^{\overline{\log S}}} \tag{6}$$

Here, log S is the arithmetic mean of the logarithm of the event maximum retention storage. Three datasets describing AMC I, II and III conditions are separately used in Equation (6) to define the corresponding CN I, CN II, and CN III, respectively.

The CN values were also estimated from rainfall–runoff data by using a graphical method (SCS 1972; Rallison and Cronshey 1979). The rainfall–runoff data were plotted with rainfall in the abscissa and runoff in the ordinate (see Figure 4). The CN value that divides the plot into two equal halves was taken as the median CN or CN for AMC II on the given site. The CN values associated with AMC I and AMC III were simultaneously defined by the lower and upper enveloping curves, respectively.

Hjelmfelt (1980) and Hauser and Jones (1991) proposed a probabilistic method to define the CN values from the lognormal distribution of maximum retention storage. Since the mean logarithm of *S* values corresponds to the median value, CN II was calculated from *S* value at probability 50% of fitted lognormal distribution. CN values at AMC I and III were also estimated from *S* values at probabilities 10% and 90%, respectively.

NEH-4 has published CNs for woodlands and rangelands; however, the CN values for forest land cover in tropical or temperate climate have not been validated. Nevertheless, in this study, the CNs were extracted from NEH-4 (NRCS 2001) and compared with the values derived from rainfall and runoff data for further comparison.

Data collection and compilation

The experimental forests have been operated by the universities and institutes for educational and research activities. Universities in Asia have built the university forests network to share their experiences in hydrological and ecological studies (Kamata et al. 2019). As shown in Figure 1, eight experimental forests were selected in this study, including the Ananomiya experimental watershed (AEW) and Shirasaka experimental watershed (SEW) of the Ecohydrology Research Institute, the University of Tokyo Forests (Japan), the Jyugei weir No. 2 watershed (Jyugei #2) and Jyugei weir No. 3 watershed (Jyugei #3) of the Arboricultural Research Institute, the University of Tokyo Forests (Japan), the upper Bukmoongol (U-Bukmoongol) and Baramgol (Baramgol) experimental watersheds of Seoul National University Forests (South Korea), the Lienhuachih weir No. 3 watershed (Lienhuachih #3) in the Lienhuachih Research Center of Taiwan Forestry Research Institute (TFRI), where the data were reconsolidated by the Experimental Forests of National Taiwan University (Taiwan), and the Kog Ma watershed (Kog Ma) in Kasetsart University (Thailand).

Table 1 summarizes the watershed characteristics of eight forested watersheds. The size of the watersheds ranges from 1.6 ha (Jyugei #3) to 88.5 ha (SEW), and the slope ranges from 19.0% (AEW) to 69.0% (Lienhuachih #3). The watersheds are completely covered by forest, except for the AEW (95% land area) and SEW (98% land area). The Kog Ma watershed is characterized by a tropical monsoon climate and the Lienhuachih #3 by a monsoon influenced humid sub-tropical climate. The others are located in a warm temperate climate zone. Annual mean rainfall and air temperature varies 2,229 mm and 20.8°C, respectively, in the Lienhuachih #3, and 1,654 mm and 14.5°C in the AEW, according to the geographic location. The Inceptisols is found to be dominant in the U-Bukmoongol, Baramgol, Jyugei #2 and #3, while Regosols is the major soil type in the AEW and SEW. Based on USDA soil taxonomy, soil of the Lienhuachih #3 is classified as Typic Paleudults. Readers can refer to Kamata et al. (2019) for more detailed information on the watersheds.

There is no single standard procedure for defining a minimum amount of hours with no or negligible rainfall when delineates independent rainfall events. This minimum inter-event time is never unique but closely related to the type of analysis or observation of a particular natural phenomenon (Carbone et al. 2015). In this study, six-hour period was used as minimum inter-event time criteria to delineate rainfall events from consecutive rainfall data regarding watershed size and internal structure of rainfall events (Gyasi-Agyeiand and Melching 2012).

A tipping bucket rain gauge was used to measure the rainfall depth for all watersheds. Rectangular weirs were installed to measure the water discharge from the watersheds, except for V-notch weirs in the Lienhuachih #3 and Kog Ma watersheds. The runoff volume was calculated by integrating the area under the hydrograph and subtracting the base flow. The base flow was visually separated from the

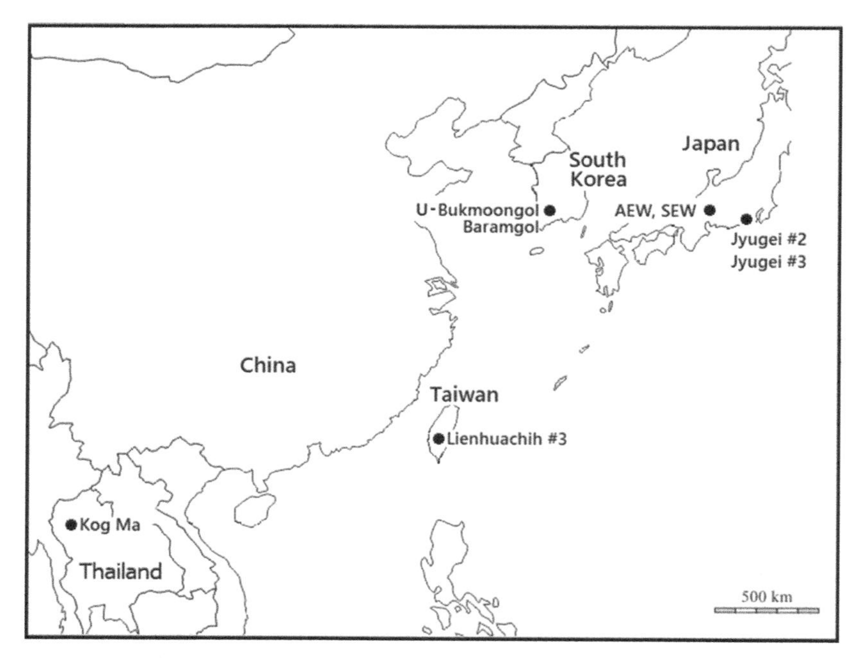

Figure 1. Location of selected watersheds (U-Bukmoongol = the upper Bukmoongol experimental watershed; Baramgol = Baramgol experimental watershed; AEW = Ananomiya experimental watershed; SEW = Shirasaka experimental watershed; Jyugei #2 & #3 = Jyugei weir No. 2 & No. 3 watersheds; Lienhuachih #3 = Lienhuachih weir No. 3 watershed; Kog Ma = Kog Ma watershed).

Table 1. Hydrological and geomorphological characteristics of eight watersheds.

Watershed[a] (University)[b]	Area (ha)	Slope (%)	Annual Rainfall (mm)	Climate Zone (Tmp, °C)[c]	Land Cover	Soil type	Dominant Tree species
U-Bukmoongol (SNUF)	15.0	29.1	1,664	Temperate (14.7)	Forest 100%	Inceptisols	*Cryptomeria japonica, Pinus densiflora*
Baramgol (SNUF)	14.6	31.0	1,664	Temperate (14.7)	Forest 100%	Inceptisols	*Pinus densiflora, Pinus rigida*
AEW (ERI)	13.9	19.0	1,654	Temperate (14.5)	Forest 95% wetland 4% denuded 1%	Regosols	*Quercus serrata, Ilex pedunculosa*
SEW (ERI)	88.5	25.0	1,831	Temperate (12.5)	Forest 98% road 1% denuded 1%	Regosols	*Quercus serrata, Pinus densiflora*
Jyugei #2 (ARI)	8.9	29.0	2,228	Temperate (15.5)	Forest 100%	Inceptisols	*Cryptomeria japonica, Chamaecyparis obtusa*
Jyugei #3 (ARI)	1.6	35.0	2,228	Temperate (15.5)	Forest 100%	Inceptisols	*Cinnamomum camphora*
Lienhuachih #3 (NTUEF/ TFRI)	3.4	69.0	2,229	Sub-tropical (20.8)	Forest 100%	Typic paleudults	*Cryptocarya chinensis*
Kog Ma (KU)	8.63	39.7	1,931	Tropical (25.1)	Hill evergreen forest 100%	Orthic Acrisols	*Castanopsis acuminatissima, Castanopsis armata*

[a]U-Bukmoongol and Baramgol = the upper Bukmoongol and Baramgol experimental watersheds; AEW = Ananomiya experimental watershed; SEW = Shirasaka experimental watershed; Jyugei #2 and #3 = Jyugei weir No 2 and No 3 watersheds; Lienhuachih #3 = Lienhuachih weir No 3 watershed; Kog Ma = Kog Ma watershed
[b]SNU = Seoul National University Forests; ERI = Ecohydrology Research Institute, The University of Tokyo; ARI = Arboricultural Research Institute, The University of Tokyo; NTUEF = National Taiwan University Experimental Forest; TFRI = Taiwan Forestry Research Institute; KU = Kasetsart University
[c]Tmp. means annual mean temperature (°C)

total runoff volume for each storm event using the constant discharge method (Linsley et al. 1958).

The measured rainfall–runoff data were used to determine the CN values for mountainous forests. The SCS (1972) used annual maximum runoff events and associated rainfall to develop CNs in their example. However, there are some difficulties in using annual flood series to estimate CNs because there is only one dataset per year of measurement (Ponce and Hawkins 1996). Many attempts have been made in recent decades to determine CNs using datasets for only a few years of records (Ritter and Gardner 1991; Yoo et al. 1993; Simanton et al. 1996; Silveira et al. 2000). While this approach provided considerably more data for analysis, the CNs associated with low rainfall are biased toward the high amount because some rainfall produces no runoff (Hjelmfelt 1991). To overcome this challenge, Hawkins et al. (1985) proposed conservative criteria for selecting storm events whose P/S values are greater than 0.46. Therefore, this study used a partial duration series of storm events with $P/S > 0.46$.

Hydrologic responses across the study watersheds were simply compared by storm runoff coefficient. Storm runoff coefficient, or event-based runoff coefficient, is a widely used and often reported parameter describing the portion of rainfall amount that appears as runoff during, or directly following, a rainfall event (Blume et al. 2007). This is numerically determined as the ratio of runoff volume, after hydrograph separation, over total rainfall during a storm period.

Accuracy assessment

No "gold standard" exists for defining CNs from measured rainfall and runoff data (Tedela et al. 2012). Accuracy assessment was conducted to find a suitable method that defines CN values for forest land cover. In this study, the runoff volumes derived from assigned CNs were compared with the measured runoff to judge the reliability of the various approaches.

The strength of closeness between the measured and estimated runoff volumes was measured using the coefficient of determination D (Aitken 1973). This statistical index determines the number of data points that fall within the line formed by the regression equation. The D value ranges from 0 to 1, zero being no correlation and one being perfect correlation. This coefficient is always less than unity, and the higher the value, the more accurate the runoff estimate.

An additional error statistic, namely the root-mean-square error (RMSE), was used to measure the difference between the measured and estimated runoff volumes. It expresses the average magnitude of the error in the unit of the variable of interest. The RMSE increases with the variance in the frequency distribution of the error magnitudes and is, therefore, more appropriate for statistical analyses.

A statistical test was also conducted to compare the measured and estimated means using the Wilcoxon signed-rank test, because some data used in the study were not normally distributed (Safeeq et al. 2014; Tancreto 2015). The Wilcoxon signed-rank test is a nonparametric alternative to the two sample *t*-test which is based solely on the order in which the observations from the two samples fall (Diebold and Mariano 1995). All statistical analysis was performed by using R Statistical Software (version 3.6.2, the R Foundation for Statistical Computing).

Results and discussion

Rainfall and runoff relationship

Table 2 lists the rainfall and runoff events for the eight watersheds, including the range of rainfall, runoff, and storm runoff ratio for each dataset. A total of 140 events over the eight watersheds were used in this study. As listed in Table 2, significant variations in the rainfall and runoff amounts can be observed. The runoff response to rainfall is complex and varied. The storm runoff ratios averaged across each watershed varied from 0.07 in the Kog Ma to 0.37 in the U-Bukmoongol. The relatively low runoff coefficient in the

Table 2. Hydrologic summary of rainfall and runoff data used in the study.

Watershed	No. of events (Data period)	Rainfall, mm (Mean)	Runoff, mm (Mean)	Storm runoff ratio (Mean)
U-Bukmoongol	38 (1992–1998)	34.0–286.0 (112.3)	3.6–182.0 (46.5)	0.08–0.87 (0.37)
Baramgol	36 (1992–1998)	32.0–264.0 (108.5)	5.3–131.3 (38.1)	0.10–0.62 (0.33)
AEW	13 (2001–2009)	20–108 (45.8)	3.2--45.0 (12.5)	0.14–0.42 (0.24)
SEW	14 (2003–2010)	26–89 (42.5)	2.7–36.1 (9.2)	0.10–0.41 (0.19)
Jyugei #2	10 (2011–2016)	19.5–91.5 (46.7)	0.8–31.5 (11.0)	0.04– 0.44 (0.18)
Jyugei #3	10 (2011–2016)	19.5–91.5 (46.7)	1.2–29.4 (12.9)	0.05–0.53 (0.22)
Lienhuachih #3	9 (1976–1992)	94.5–1607.5 (537.0)	11.0–756.1 (281.8)	0.10 –0.84 (0.50)
Kog Ma	10 (1999–2008)	34.5–88.1 (60.1)	2.4–9.9 (4.4)	0.05–0.13 (0.07)

Kog Ma is due to higher topsoil depth (1.3–15.9 m) and thicker floor litter (Chunkao et al. 1979). Figure 2 demonstrates the scatter plots between storm runoff and rainfall depth for eight watersheds. Runoff response for each watershed can be implicitly presented by the slope of straight line. The U-Bukmoongol, Baramgol, AEW, and SEW had a similar trend in rainfall and runoff plots, but the Kog Ma watershed produced a relatively lower runoff.

The SCS procedure cannot account for the temporal variation (i.e. intensity and duration) in rainfall (Hawkins 1993; Ponce and Hawkins 1996). Nevertheless, when rainfall increases, the corresponding retention storage S increases for various types of watersheds. The same is true in the data from the eight watersheds, as shown in Figure 3.

Determination of curve numbers for forest cover

Table 3 lists the CNs derived from arithmetic mean, geometric mean, graphical and probabilistic methods. The NEH-4 tabulated CNs for woodland use, associated with hydrologic soil group, and fair hydrologic conditions are also included in Table 3 for comparison.

The mean CN values corresponding to AMC II were not estimated for the Jyugei #2, Jyugei #3, and Lienhuachih #3 because of the lack of data for numerical computation. Moreover, these mean values in the U-Bukmoongol were inaccurate because of the limited data. The AEW showed the highest mean values among the study watersheds.

Figure 4 is an example of graphical method that draws the median and envelope curves on the U-Bukmoongol. The median CN values under the average condition AMC II varied according to the watershed characteristics, from 47 in the Lienhuachih #3 to 82 in the AEW. When it comes to the NEH-4 table on the condition of fair woodlands, the corresponding CN II values were 73, 60, and 36, respectively, for hydrologic soil groups B, C, and D.

The probability distribution of S derived from rainfall and runoff data of the U-Bukmoongol watershed was fitted, as shown in Figure 5. A lognormal distribution was used to fit the measured data with good results. The mean of the probability function was taken as the representative of AMC II. As shown in Figure 5, the S value associated with 50% probability is 89.2 mm and those associated with 10% and 90% probabilities are 254.0 and 31.4 mm, respectively. The CNs can be obtained from the derived S values. The CN II value corresponding to S at a probability of 50% on the U-Bukmoongol was 74. The corresponding CN I and CN III are 50 and 89, respectively. The CNs assigned by the probabilistic method are presented in Table 3 for all the watersheds. The CN II values vary from 56 to 81 for eight watersheds.

The CNs derived from the mean, graphical median, and probabilistic methods seem to be largely similar for the watersheds in temperate climates. However, the CNs of the Kog Ma and Lienhuachih #3 watersheds are clearly different from those of the other watersheds regardless of the method used to calculate the CNs from the measured rainfall and runoff volumes. The Kog Ma and Lienhuachih #3 are situated in tropical and sub-tropical climate zones, respectively.

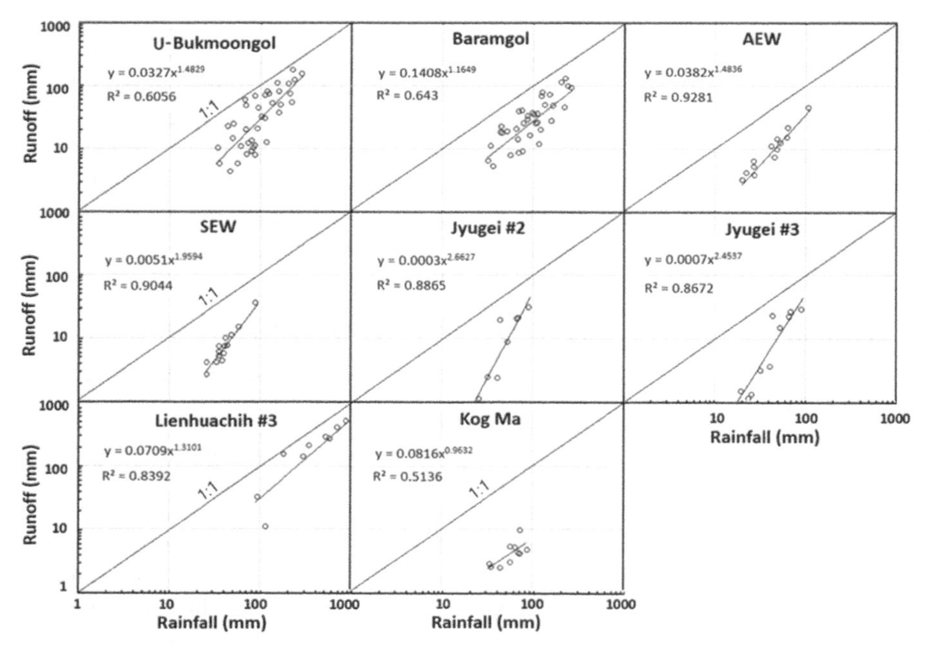

Figure 2. Scatter plots between rainfall and runoff for a storm period.

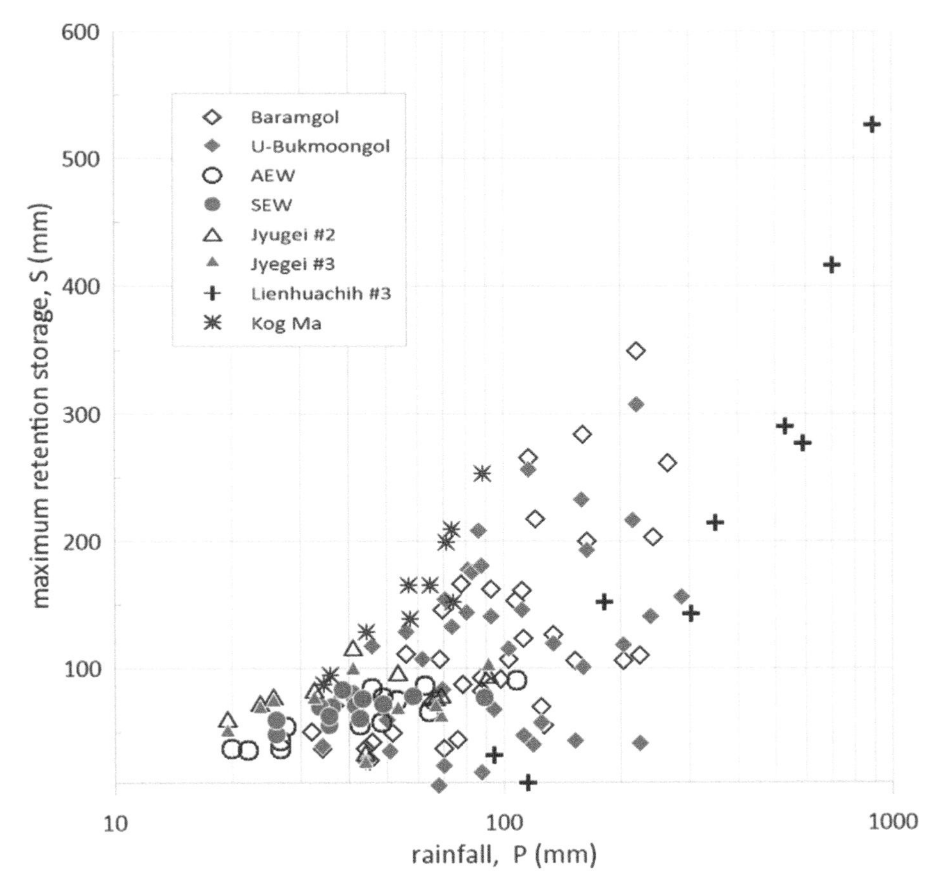

Figure 3. Relationships between rainfall and maximum retention storage for eight watersheds.

Table 3. Curve numbers of forest cover derived from different methods on eight watersheds.

Watershed	Arithmetic mean	Geometric mean	Graphical method	Probabilistic method	Tabulated NEH-4[3)]
U-Bukmoongol	69/57/77[1)]	71/57/82	45/68/97	50/74/89	39/60/78
Baramgol	67/71/75	68/74/77	42/70/90	50/72/85	39/60/78
AEW	80/82/81	81/82/81	74/82/87	74/81/87	53/73/86
SEW	78/76/79	79/76/79	75/78/84	75/79/82	53/73/86
Jyugei #2	75/NA/80	75/NA/81	69/76/88	69/77/84	39/60/78
Jyugei #3	77/NA/83	77/NA/84	72/79/91	70/79/86	39/60/78
Lienhuachih #3	47/NA[2)]/64	47/NA/67	37/47/90	30/56/80	19/36/56
Kog Ma	75/62/60	75/62/61	50/62/75	52/63/72	19/36/56

1) forward slash-separated values represent the curve numbers in sequence for AMC I, AMC II, and AMC III conditions, 2) NA means "no data for analysis", and 3) The CN values were obtained from in the NEH-4 table NRCS (2001) for wood land use, associated with hydrologic soil group, and fair hydrologic conditions

In these watersheds, rain water can be easily intercepted by vegetation canopy and litter floor, and quickly evaporated into atmosphere (Tanaka et al. 2005). In addition, deep soils with a thick humus layer can retain more water and, in turn, decrease runoff potential (Chunkao et al. 1979). It resulted in relatively low CN values compared to other watersheds in temperate climate.

The geometric mean CNs of the watersheds were relatively greater than the CN values based on the other calculation procedures. The arithmetic and geometric mean CNs do not seem to be significantly different as expected, despite the normal and lognormal distribution assumption. Many previous studies found the probabilistic method to be the most reliable; however, some of the probability CNs may be different from the mean and median CNs.

The results showed that the CN values derived from the mean, graphical median, and probability values are not significantly different, but are relatively higher than the tabulated CN values for all the watersheds. The tabulated CNs in NEH-4 were derived assuming that the reference land use and cover was the same for all the watersheds as "wood" with fair cover; however, the hydrologic soil condition was explicitly defined for each watershed. The CN procedure has been rarely implemented in forest land use category, because the tabulated curve numbers for "forest" are missing or not valid with the observations (Tedela et al. 2012).

Table 3. Curve numbers of forest cover derived from different methods on eight watersheds.

Performance evaluation of methods employed

The assigned CNs, listed in Table 3, were used to calculate the runoff volume from the corresponding measured rainfall amount. The estimated and measured runoff volumes were compared to measure how consistently a method determined the CN value of forest cover for all watersheds. Table 4 lists the magnitude of the errors and degree of correlation between the estimated and measured runoff volumes.

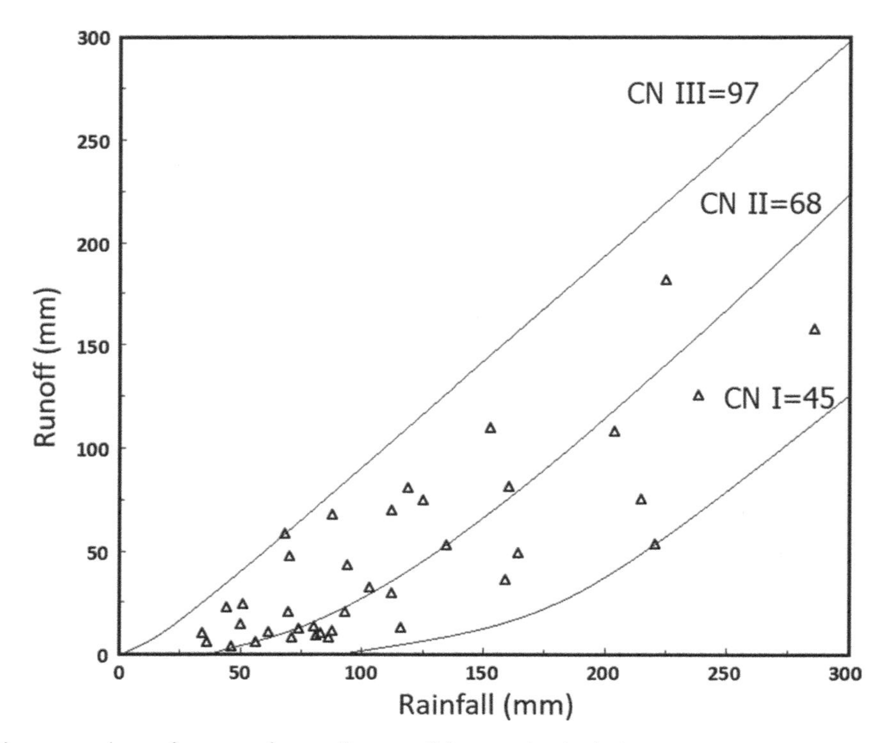

Figure 4. Mean, lower, and upper envelopes of curve numbers on the upper Bukmoongol watershed.

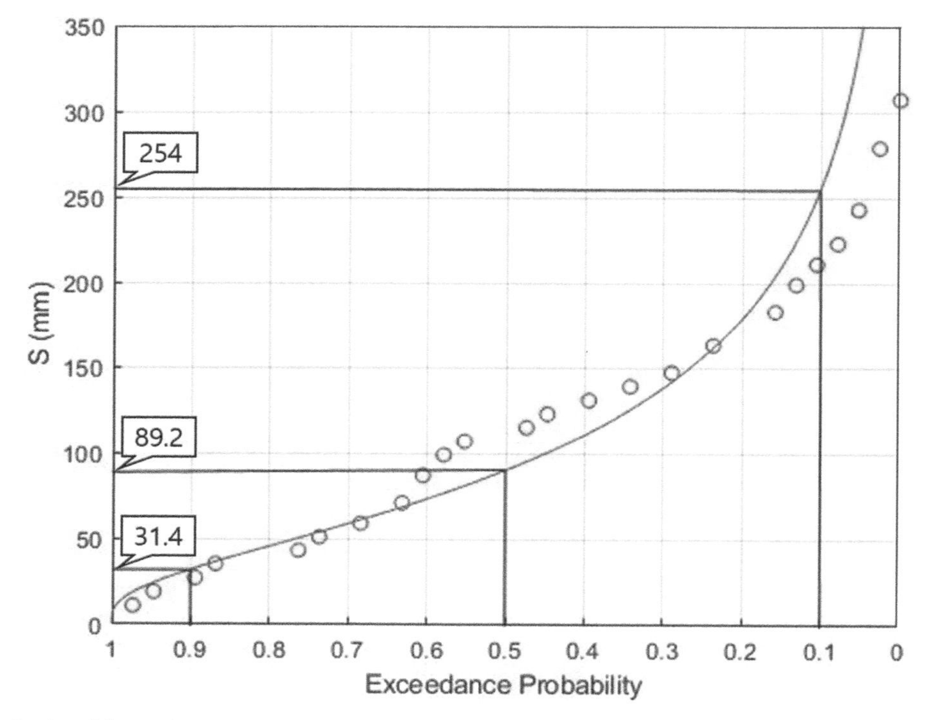

Figure 5. Lognormal distribution of the maximum retention storage on the upper Bukmoongol watershed.

Figure 6 compares the measured runoff with the estimated runoff from the derived CNs for all the watersheds.

The lower the RMSE and the closer the coefficient of determination D to a value of one, the more appropriate the method in estimating the CN value. As listed in Table 4, the differences in the runoff derived using the five methods are in general; these findings highlight that one method was as good as another. Based on the RMSE and D values, the SEW showed good reproductivity in runoff estimation with the derived CNs from all the methods, followed by the AEW and Jyugei #3. The coefficients of determination for eight watersheds ranged from 0.57 in the NRCS NEH-4 table to 0.92 in the arithmetic mean, while the RMSE values vary in the methods between 24.38 mm to 51.19 mm. Among the methods for defining CNs, the mean formula ranked first for all the watersheds, and the second was the probabilistic method. Although the simple average of individual *S* values provides a better estimate, its reliability or accuracy may vary, mainly depending on data sufficiency. Dataset size is very important consideration in estimating statistical estimators, such as arithmetic or geometric means. It is difficult to decide the minimum number of datasets required to

Table 4. Accuracy assessment of methods employed to define the curve numbers for forest cover.

Watershed	Arithmetic mean		Geometric mean		Graphical method		Probabilistic method		Tabulated NEH-4	
	D	RMSE (mm)	D	RMSE (mm)	D	RMSE (mm)	D	RMSE (mm)	D	RMSE (mm)
U-Bukmoongol	0.69	25.05	0.68	26.36	0.17	48.47	0.32	41.11	0.26	46.14
Baramgol	0.69	24.08	0.69	25.44	0.27	35.62	0.45	28.88	0.33	31.55
AEW	0.97	5.14	0.97	5.24	0.96	10.43	0.96	10.44	0.90	4.84
SEW	0.98	0.98	0.99	1.69	0.93	5.01	0.95	3.53	0.85	6.84
Jyugei #2	0.84	4.48	0.84	4.48	0.82	6.65	0.82	6.65	0.04	11.76
Jyugei #3	0.88	5.02	0.89	5.20	0.83	9.24	0.85	5.80	0.08	12.03
Lienhuachih #3	0.94	63.02	0.93	64.90	0.75	88.51	0.67	101.47	0.51	165.04
Kog Ma	0.33	13.76	0.33	13.76	0.09	3.74	0.17	3.41	0.03	11.14
All watersheds	0.92	24.38	0.92	25.41	0.75	38.61	0.75	36.78	0.57	51.19

D and RMSE mean the coefficient of determination and the root mean square error, respectively, between the measured and estimated runoff volumes.

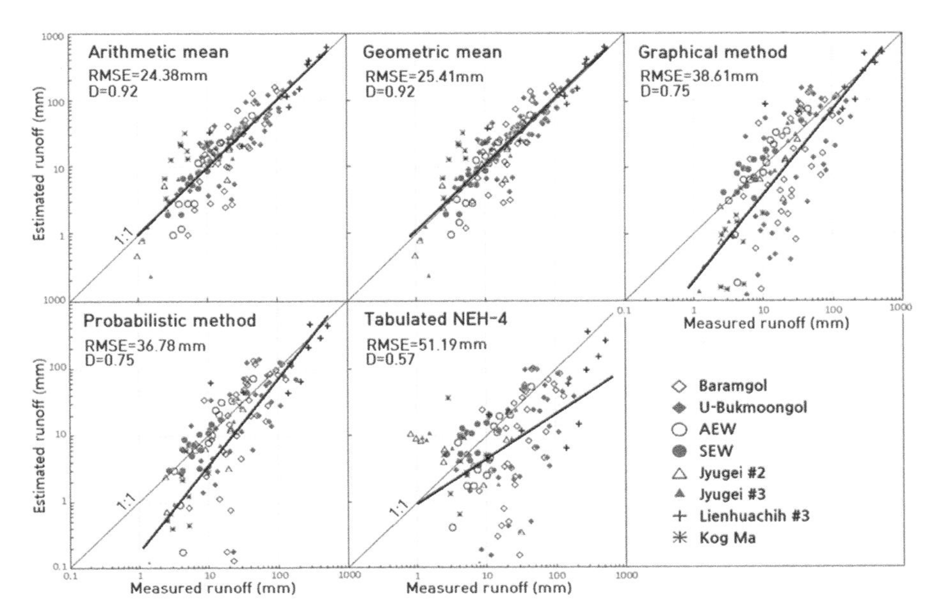

Figure 6. Relationship between measured and estimated runoff for eight watersheds (D = the coefficient of determination, RMSE = the root mean square error).

guarantee the estimator of mean value, but small dataset size is problematic because the mean value is not usually statistically significant (Adcock 1997). In this study, insufficient data or no data could lead to biased results or missing values when derived CN values from statistical averages. As a matter of practice, the probabilistic method is well applicable to define CN values for forest watersheds, where little data are available.

Wilcoxon signed-rank tests were also used to determine any significant differences between the measured and estimated runoff volumes. The probability, listed in Table 5, is a measure of the evidence against the null hypothesis. A probability less than 0.05 is evidence that the measured and estimated runoff volumes are significantly different, while a probability greater than or equal to 0.05 confirms that the measured and estimated runoff volumes are from the same population.

As listed in Table 5, the measured and estimated runoff volumes are significantly different at 95% significance for the Kog Ma watersheds. In contrast, the estimated runoff volume statistically matches with the observations for other watersheds. Although the tabulated CNs adequately estimated the runoff on the Kog Ma, the same values predicted the storm runoff with the highest RMSE and a lower coefficient of determination. Results showed that the tabulated CNs for woods give poor estimation in the U-Bukmoongol and Baramgol watersheds. The reason for the inaccurate runoff when using the tabulated CNs in these watersheds remains unclear. Wilcoxon test results also suggested that there was

Table 5. Probability of Wilcoxon signed-rank test for eight watersheds.

Watershed	Arithmetic mean	Geometric mean	Graphical method	Probabilistic method	Tabulated NEH-4
U-Bukmoongol	0.98	0.62	0.08	0.12	0.00*
Baramgol	0.98	0.73	0.09	0.23	0.00*
AEW	0.86	0.91	0.95	0.95	0.36
SEW	0.94	0.80	0.35	0.59	0.19
Jyugei #2	0.63	0.63	0.32	0.32	0.85
Jyugei #3	0.99	0.99	0.97	0.63	0.85
Lienhuachih #3	0.99	0.99	0.93	0.73	0.11
Kog Ma	0.00*	0.00*	0.00*	0.01*	0.63

* indicates statistically different at 95% significance level.

no significant improvement of runoff simulation when using the derived CNs, except for the U-Bukmoongol and Baramgol watersheds, as compared to the tabulated CNs in NEH-4 (NRCS 2001).

Conclusions

The SCS CNs for forest cover were determined using several methods from measured rainfall and runoff data. The arithmetic mean, geometric mean, graphical median, and probability-derived values were computed from large storm events collected at eight experimental forests in Japan, Korea, Thailand, and Taiwan. The reliability of the methods employed was verified by comparing the observed and estimated runoff volumes with statistical parameters such as the coefficient of determination, root-mean-square error, and Wilcoxon signed-rank test.

The CN values corresponding to antecedent precipitation were estimated from measured rainfall and runoff data. The estimated CNs varied with the methods and watershed characteristics, ranging from 47 to 82 for AMC II condition. The CN values derived from the graphical method were lowest for all watersheds, implying the watershed average CNs for AMC II was 70. The highest watershed average CN values for AMC II was 73, which was obtained from the probabilistic method. The CNs values published in the NRCS NEH-4 gave quite poor correspondence with those estimated from rainfall and runoff data. The coefficients of determination in runoff estimation for the study watersheds varied 0.57 in NRCS NEH-4 table to 0.92 in the arithmetic mean, while the RMSE values vary in the methods between 24.38 mm to 51.19 mm. By comparing the statistical parameters, the probabilistic method was found to be the most practical way to determine CNs for forest cover with limited data.

The CN is revised to satisfy hydrometeorological and geographical characteristics of specified land cover. The CN of forest cover is rarely investigated compared with agricultural or urban land use and cover. Moreover, there is no agreement on the methodology to determine the CNs from measured storm events. This study will help engineers to adopt a reliable and practical method for determining CN values from measurements. The SCS CN procedure provides a consistent basis for estimating the amount of runoff under varying landuse and soil types in ungauged forest watersheds. It was used primarily for developing design hydrographs for hydraulic structures and conservation works, such as check dam, bridge, and hillslope and road drainage structures.

Disclosure statement

No potential conflict of interest was reported by the authors.

Funding

This study was carried out with the support of 'R&D Program for Forest Science Technology (Project No. 2017061B10-1919-AB01)' provided by Korea Forest Service (Korea Forestry Promotion Institute). The JSPS Core-to-Core Program (B. Asia-Africa Science Platform) project collaborated in the research described in this paper.

ORCID

Yen-Jen Lai http://orcid.org/0000-0002-3366-8766

References

Adcock CJ. 1997. Sample size determination: A review. J Royal Stat Soc D. 46(2):261–283. doi:10.1111/1467-9884.00082.

Aitken AP. 1973. Assessing systematic errors in rainfall-runoff models. J Hydrol. 20(2):121–136. doi:10.1016/0022-1694(73)90035-8.

Blume T, Zehe E, Bronstert A. 2007. Rainfall—runoff response, event-based runoff coefficients and hydrograph separation. Hydrol Sci J. 52 (5):843–862. doi:10.1623/hysj.52.5.843.

Bonta JV. 1997. Determination of watershed curve number using derived distributions. J Irrigat Drain Eng. 123(1):28–35. doi:10.1061/(ASCE)0733-9437(1997)123:1(28).

Carbone M, Turco M, Brunetti G, Piro P. 2015. A cumulative rainfall function for subhourly design storm in Mediterranean urban areas. Adv Meteorol. 2015:1–10. doi:10.1155/2015/528564

Chunkao K, Makarabhirom P, Boonyawat S. 1979. Summer flow of hill evergreen forest at Doi Pui, Chiangmai province (in Thai). Bangkok (Thailand): Department of Conservation, Faculty of Forestry, Kasetsart University. Kog-Ma Watershed Research Bulletin 34. Thai.

Diebold FX, Mariano RS. 1995. Comparing predictive accuracy. J Bus Econ Stat. 13:253–265.

Gyasi-Agyeiand Y, Melching CS. 2012. Modelling the dependence and internal structure of storm events for continuous rainfall simulation. J Hydrol. 464-465:249–261. doi:10.1016/j.jhydrol.2012.07.014.

Hauser VL, Jones OR. 1991. Runoff curve numbers for the southern high plains. Transact ASAE. 34(1):142–148. doi:10.13031/2013.31636.

Hawkins RH. 1993. Asymptotic determination of runoff curve numbers from data. J Irrigat Drain Eng. 119(2):334–345. doi:10.1061/(ASCE) 0733-9437(1993)119:2(334).

Hawkins RH, Hjelmfelt AT, Zevenbergen AW. 1985. Runoff probability, storm depth, and curve numbers. J Irrigat Drain Eng. 111 (4):330–340. doi:10.1061/(ASCE)0733-9437(1985)111:4(330).

Hjelmfelt AT. 1980. Empirical investigation of curve number technique. J Hydraul D-ASCE. 106(9):1471–1477.

Hjelmfelt AT. 1991. Investigation of curve number procedure. J Hydraul Eng. 117(6):725–737. doi:10.1061/(ASCE)0733-9429-(1991)117:6(725).

Im S, Park S, Jang T. 2007. Application of SCS curve number method for irrigated paddy field. KSCE J Civil Eng. 11(1):51–56. doi:10.1007/BF02823372.

Kamata N, Kuraji K, Owari T, Guan BT. 2019. Developing a network of long-term research field stations to monitor environmental changes and ecosystem responses in Asian forests. Tokyo: The University of Tokyo Forests Press.

Linsley RK, Kohler MA, Paulhus JLH, Wallace JS. 1958. Hydrology for engineers. New York (NY): McGraw Hill.

Mishra SK, Jain MK, Bhunya PK, Singh VP. 2005. Field application of the SCS-CN-based Mishra-Singh general model and its variants. Water Res Manage. 19:37–62. doi:10.1007/s11269-005-1076-3.

Montgomery RJ. 1983. Advances in irrigation and drainage: A databased evaluation of the curve number method. New York (NY): ASCE; p. 290–297.

Mulungu DMM, Ichikawa Y, Shiiba M. 2005. A physically based distributed subsurface-surface flow dynamics model for forested mountainous catchments. Hydrol Proc. 19:3999–4022. doi:10.1002/hyp.5868.

[NRCS] National Resources Conservation Service. 2001. National engineering handbook, section 4: hydrology. Washington (DC):US Department of Agriculture.

Patil JP, Sarangi A, Singh AK, Ahmad T. 2008. Evaluation of modified CN methods for watershed runoff estimation using a GIS-based interface. Biosyst Eng. 100(1):137–146. doi:10.1016/j.biosystemseng.2008.02.001.

Ponce VM, Hawkins RH. 1996. Runoff curve number: has it reached maturity? J Hyd Eng. 1(1):11–19. doi:10.1061/(ASCE)1084-0699-(1996)1:1(11).

Rallison RE, Cronshey RC. 1979. Discussion of Hawkins. J Irrig Drain D-ASCE. 105(IR4):439–441.

Ritter JB, Gardner TW. 1991. Runoff curve numbers for reclaimed surface mines in Pennsylvania. J Irrigat Drain Eng. 117(5):657–666. doi:10.1061/(ASCE)0733-9437(1991)117:5(656).

Safeeq M, Mauger GS, Grant GE, Arismendi I, Hamlet AF, Lee S-Y. 2014. Comparing large-scale hydrological model predictions with observed streamflow in the Pacific Northwest: effects of climate and groundwater. J Hydrometeorol. 15(6):2501–2521. doi:10.1175/JHM-D-13-0198.1.

Silveira L, Charbonnier F, Genta JL. 2000. The antecedent soil moisture condition of the curve number procedure. Hydrol Sci J. 45(1):3–12. doi:10.1080/02626660009492302.

Simanton JR, Hawkins RH, Mohseni-Saravi M, Renard KG. 1996. Runoff curve number variation with drainage area, Walnut Gulch, Arizona. T ASAE. 39:1391–1394. doi:10.13031/2013.27630.

Singh VP. 1995. Computer models of watershed hydrology. Highlands Ranch (CO): Water Resources Publication.

[SCS] Soil Conservation Service. 1972. National engineering handbook, section 4: hydrology. Washington (DC):US Department of Agriculture.

Springer EP, Coltharp GB, Hawkins RH, McGurk BJ 1980. Curve numbers from watershed data. Proceedings of the Symposium on Watershed Management; 1980 Jul 21-23; Boise, ID. New York (NY): ASCE. p. 938–950.

Tanaka N, Tantasirin C, Kuraji K, Suzuki M, Tangtham N. 2005. Inter-annual variation in rainfall interception at a hill evergreen forest in northern Thailand. B Tokyo U For. 113:11–44.

Tancreto AE 2015. Comparison of hydrologic model performance statistics using Thiessen polygon rain gauge and NEXRAD precipitation input methods at different watershed spatial scales and rainfall return frequencies [master's thesis]. Jacksonville(FL): University of North Florida.

Tedela NH, McCutcheon SC, Rasmussen TC, Hawkins RH, Swank WT, Campbell JL, Adams MB, Jackson CR, Tollner EW. 2012. Runoff curve numbers for 10 small forested watersheds in the mountains of the eastern United States. J of Hydrol Eng. 17(11):1188–1198. doi:10.1061/(ASCE)HE.1943-5584.0000436.

Yoo KH, Yoon KS, Soileau JM. 1993. Runoff curve numbers determined by three methods under conventional and conservation tillages. Transact ASAE. 36(1):57–64. doi:10.13031/2013.28314.

Yuan P-T. 1933. On the logarithmic frequency distribution and the semi-logarithmic correlation surface. Annals Math Stat. 4(1):30–74. doi:10.1214/aoms/1177732821.

Analyzing the leafing phenology of *Quercus crispula* Blume using the growing degree days model

Naoto Kamata, Yuji Igarashi, Keisuke Nonaka, Hitomi Ogawa and Hisatomi Kasahara

ABSTRACT

In the growing degree days (GDD) model for plants, 0°C or 5°C have been empirically used as base temperature (BT) for the GDD model, without experimental determination. In this study, developmental periods for bud break and leaf opening of mizunara oak, *Quercus crispula* were determined by using samples from locations separated by 900 km, cut branches from central Japan and potted saplings from northern Japan. The samples from each location were then grown in growth chambers under the four constant temperatures in different years. The relationships between the developmental rate and temperature were determined, BTs were calculated by regression analyses, and the required GDDs were determined. Multiple regression was applied to compare model fittings for bud break and leaf opening. Observational data were fitted with a logistic curve to empirically determine the BT and GDD for bud break. Better fitting was obtained for bud break than for leaf opening, in the growth chamber experiment as well as in the multiple regression, probably because bud break was controlled by the GDD accumulation, while the rate of leaf opening was directly and exponentially influenced by temperature. The BT for bud break obtained by the growth chamber experiments varied from 0.09°C–4.88°C between the two locations, and also within one location by year. A large variation in the GDD accumulation was recognized in the field observation at each location. These results indicate additional environmental factors not included in the GDD calculation likely influenced the leafing phenology of *Q. crispula*.

Introduction

Potential impacts of climate change on plants are a concern, and changes in plant phenology are a good indicator of climate change (Menzel 2002), so research that incorporates measures of plant phenology when assessing the responses of plants to environmental changes are particularly valuable. In the case of insect pests, the growing degree days (GDD) model has been commonly used to predict the timing of an event associated with the development of the pest, in order to determine the right time for insecticide application (Hokyo 1972; Umeya and Yamada 1973; Tsugane 1975). To develop this model, insects are reared in growth chambers under constant temperatures. It is known that the development periods of the larval (nymphal) stage of insects and mites are inversely proportional to the temperature (e.g. Stamp 1993). In other words, the inverse of the developmental periods (i.e., the developmental rates) increase linearly with temperature. The intercept on the x-axis (temperature) is the base temperature (BT, or developmental zero) at which the insect starts to develop, and below which no development occurs. Required GDD are then obtained by accumulating the difference between the temperature experienced and the BT. Using the BT and the required GDD, the timing of an event, such as adult emergence, can be predicted. After climate change became an environmental concern, an increasing number of pest life cycles, under a particular scenario of climatic change, have been studied (e.g. Yamamura and Kiritani 1998).

It has previously been established that the timing of plant bud break is controlled by the GDD accumulation (Lyr et al. 1967; Kramer and Kozlowski 1979; Valentine 1983), however, few studies have been conducted for woody plants to determine both the BT and the required GDD accumulation. Some studies, based on the concept of GDD, have demonstrated a relationship between the timing of bud break and the average temperature during a given period (Kai et al. 1993; Kimura et al. 1995), under an assumption that the BT was 0°C. Fujimoto (2007) speculated that some studies used 5°C as the BT (e.g. Sawada et al. 1999) because it is the threshold temperature in the warmth index proposed by Kira (1945, 1949, 1977), an index which is closely related to the distribution of vegetation.

For a reliable prediction of plant responses to climate change, methodologies are needed that are based on ecophysiological mechanisms, rather than on empirical correlations. Studies of phenotypic plasticity in plant phenology are also required.

Mizunara oak, *Quercus crispula* Blume, is widely distributed in Japan and one of the dominant species in cool-temperate forests in northern and central Japan (JAFTA 1964). In the present study, leafing phenology of *Q. crispula* was observed with special reference to bud break and leaf opening. First, by observing leafing phenology of *Q. crispula* using time lapse cameras, developmental periods for bud break and leaf opening were determined under four constant temperatures using growth chambers, in order to determine the role of GDD accumulation in the leafing phenology process. Relationships between the developmental rate and temperature were determined by fitting with a linear model. The BT was obtained from the regression line. The required GDD accumulation was also obtained. Second, multiple regressions were applied to compare model fitting between bud break and leaf opening. Third, field observation data were fitted with a logistic curve to obtain the BT and required GDD for bud break from field observations. The results from these three methods were then compared to assess contributions of GDD accumulation and potential contributions of other unaccounted environmental factors to the leafing process.

Materials and methods

Terminology and criteria for leafing phenology

Table 1 shows the terminology and criteria for leafing phenology used in this study. Due to asynchrony of leafing phenology among individual buds/leaves within an individual tree, each stage of leafing phenology needs definitions for both individual bud/leaf and individual tree levels. The important criteria in this study were as follows:

- Stage II: Green foliage appeared among scales (=bud break) in 50% of the buds.
- Stage III: Foliage opened with exposed petiole (=leaf opening) in 80% of the leaves.
- Stage IV: Leaf area fully developed in 100% of the leaves.

The stages II and III are equivalent to 20% and 50% budburst in Kamata et al. (2019), respectively.

Field observation and temperature data

Leafing phenology of three *Q. crispula* trees, in the University of Tokyo Chichibu Forest (UTCF or Chichibu, 35°56′N, 138°49′E, 955 m a.s.l.), located in Chichibu, Saitama in central Japan, approximately 100 km west of Tokyo, was observed from 2002 to 2011. Temperature data from the Koakazawa weather station (35°56′14"N, 138°48′14"E, 1,195 m a.s.l.), located c. 1,500 m west-southwest of the observation site, were used for analyses. Leafing phenology of three individuals of *C. crispula* was observed at irregular intervals (3–10 days) from late April to mid-May. On each observation date, the individual-tree level of leafing phonology was recorded for each of the three trees as the percentage of leafing between stage I (0%) and stage IV (100%). The percentage was determined by assessing the degree of greenness of the canopy using binoculars.

Table 1. Criteria of leafing phenology of *Quercus crispula* used in this study for an individual bud/leaf level and an individual tree level (following Kamata et al. (2019)).

Stage	Status at the individual bud/leaf level (*)	Criterion for the stage at the individual tree level
I	No change in winter buds (A)	
II	Green folige appeared among scales (C)(bud break)	50% of canopy buds have reached this stage
III	Foliage opening with exposed petiole (E) (leaf opening)	80% of canopy foliage has reached this stage
IV	Full sized in leaf area (H)	100% of canopy foliage has reached this stage

(*): Category by Kamata et al. (2019)

Similarly, leafing phenology data of *Q. crispula* from the arboretum of the University of Tokyo Hokkaido Forest in Furano, Hokkaido in northern Japan (UTHF or Hokkaido, 43°13′N, 142°23′E, 225 m a.s.l., approximately 900 km from UTCF), observed since 1931 (Kamata et al. 2019), were considered. Forty-six years of data between 1931 and 2010 (the rest were lacking or problematic) published in Kamata et al. (2019) and seven years of unpublished data from 2011–2017, were used for analyses. Temperature for this site was available from the Yamabe weather station, c. 100 m south-southeast of the observatory trees (225 m a.s.l.). However, this weather station had been moved several times between the arboretum and the main office of the UTHF (43°13′N, 142°23′E), c. 2.7 km north of the arboretum. Measuring instruments (thermometers, thermal sensors, manual observation units, analog chart recorders, digital data loggers, etc.) and time of observations had changed several times, so the temperature data were calibrated according to Tanaka et al. (2013).

Growth chamber experiments

Experiments were conducted in four growth chambers (inner dimensions 2 m × 2 m × 2 m), at the Kagemori nursery of the UTCF. Three 20 W fluorescent bulbs on the ceiling were used as the light source in each chamber.

On 15 February 2013 and 2014, four approximately 1-m-long branches of *Q. crispula* were cut from upper part of each of six trees (about 5 m in height) growing on slopes beside a forest road in the UTCF, and placed in the growth chambers under constant environmental conditions: temperatures (12, 15, 18, and 21°C, respectively), humidity (70% RH), and photoperiod (12:12 h light:dark period). Six branches, one from each of the six trees, were used for each chamber, and hence, for each temperature.

In early November 2018, 5-yr-old *Q. crispula* saplings (about 1 m in height) were individually transplanted to plastic pots (diameter 30 cm, depth 30 cm), kept outdoors in the arboretum of UTHF, and were transported to UTCF on 3 March 2019. On 4 March 2019, these potted saplings were placed in the growth chambers under constant temperatures (5, 12, 19, and 26°C, respectively), humidity (70% RH), and photoperiod (12: 12 h light:dark period). Six to seven saplings were set in each chamber.

Photoperiod for the experiment were determined as an approximate average photoperiod during the estimated period of the experiment to avoid any influence of photoperiod on the leafing phenology. Because of the limited number of chambers, no chamber replications were possible, but the lack of replication was somewhat compensated for by increasing replications of branches and saplings.

Required low temperature of bud dormancy was enough for making experiments in both the materials from UTCF and UTHF.

The leaves were automatically photographed, once every day, to determine the degree of leaf opening, using time lapse cameras (GardenWatchCam, Brinno Inc., Taipei, Taiwan). More than one camera was set in each chamber. Times of photographing differed among cameras (9:00 a.m. – 11:00 a.m.) depending on the time of restart after retrieving data from a USB stick installed in each camera.

Data analyses

Fitting results of the growth chamber experiments with a linear model

The BT (°C) and required GDD accumulation (degree days) were calculated from a linear regression of the inverse of the growth period ($days^{-1}$) against temperature. The intercept of the x-axis was calculated as the BT. The required GDD accumulation was calculated by multiplying the difference between the chamber temperature and BT with the growth period (days). The models obtained from UTCF data in 2013 and 2014 were defined as Model2013 and Model2014, respectively.

Application of the GDD models to field observation

DOYs for the stage II (bud break), as predicted from field temperature data using the GDD models, were compared to field observation data. The GDD accumulations for the three models (Model2013 and Model2014 for UTCF and one for UTHF) were calculated from January 1 of each year, by accumulating the difference between each daily mean temperature (T_{mean}) and the BTs. In cases where T_{mean} was smaller than the BT, but the daily maximum (T_{max}) of the date was greater than the BT, the GDD of the date was obtained using the following equation (Hokyo 1972):

$$\mathrm{GDD} = \frac{(T_{max} - \mathrm{BT})^2}{2T_{max} - T_{min}}$$

where T_{min} is the daily minimum temperature of the date. This GDD was also accumulated. The date when the GDD accumulation became greater than the required GDD accumulation was the predicted date of the event.

Kamata et al. (2019) published dates of 20%, 50%, and 80% budburst of *Q. crispula* in the UTHF using different terminology but comparable criteria. Stage II in this study corresponded to 20% budburst in Kamata et al. (2019), allowing a relationship between prediction from the model and 20% budburst in Kamata et al. (2019) to be analysed using a linear regression model. The differences between the observed and predicted DOY of the stage II were averaged. Forty-six years during 1931–2020 in Kamata et al. (2019) and seven years (2011–2017) of unpublished data were used for the analysis. The same analyses were employed for 10-yr data from 2002 to 2011 in UTCF.

Fitting field observation data with a logistic curve

For field observation data, the percentage of leafing (0--100%) was converted to a binomial (0, 1) dataset with 1,000 samples. The logistic regression was fitted to the relationship between the binomial dataset (a response variable) and the GDD accumulation (an explanatory variable) by changing the BT value from −2°C to 8°C with 0.2°C stepwise, following an algorithm proposed by Nam et al. (2013) (Figure 1). The GDD accumulation was calculated from January 1 to the date of observation by the same methodology as above. The BT value that minimized Akaike's Information Criterion (AIC) was determined. Kamata et al. (2019) published DOYs of 20%, 50%, and 80% of budburst by organizing data according to ledgers archived at the UTHF, but these DOY percentages were not appropriate for the curve fitting used in this study, and the original data of many years were no longer available. So data available for three individual trees for six years (2000, 2003, 2005–2008) were used instead, providing the six years of data used for the curve fitting for UTHF. Those for ten years (2002–2011) were used for UTCF. Using the BT value

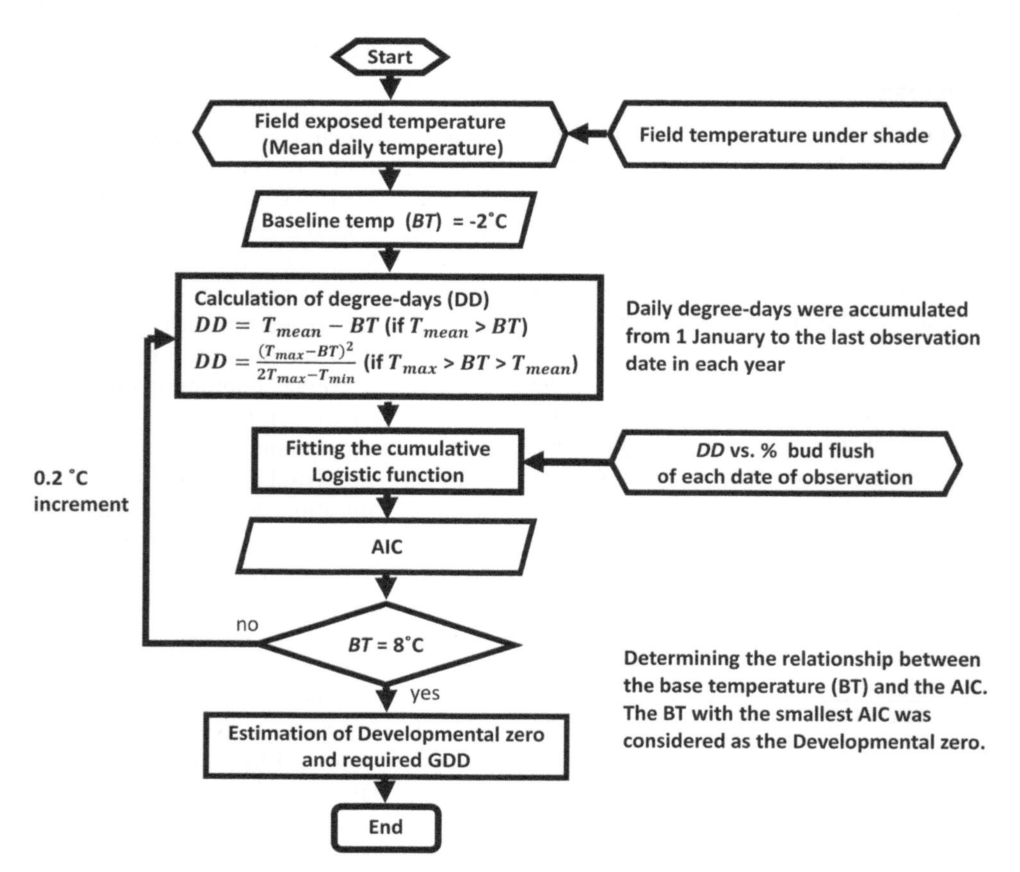

Figure 1. The scheme for estimating the base temperature (BT) of leafing phenology from field observation data (following Nam et al. 2013).

of the best model in UTHF, mean required GDD accumulations for stage II were averaged for the three observation trees over the six years, which was an estimation of required GDD accumulation in the UTHF. The proportion of leafing for the required GDD was calculated from the logistic function, which was recognized as the same status as stage II. The required GDD accumulation in UTCF providing the same proportion of leafing as in UTHF, which was recognized as the same status as stage II in UTHF, was obtained from a logistic curve of the best model in the UTCF. These BT and required GDD accumulation values were compared to those obtained from the growth chamber experiment.

Multiple regression models

We used a sequential process to develop the best multiple regression model. Using a stepwise regression approach, we first determined the most important monthly temperature variable based on the Akaike's Information Criterion (AIC). The monthly variables included the averages of the homogenized daily minimum (T_{min}), daily mean (T_{mean}), daily maximum (T_{max}), and diurnal temperature range (DTR), from January to June (The month of each variable is shown by a numeral following each variable). We then replaced the monthly average of the selected variable by the average of that variable on the day of year (DOY) and ran a stepwise regression again to find the next monthly variable that minimized AIC by changing both ends of the window. The process stopped when the model AIC could not be minimized further, and all the independent variables were DOY temperature averages.

Results

Hokkaido

GDD model from growth chamber experiment

The relationship between temperature and the development rate is shown in Figure 2. As the base temperatures obtained from the x-axis intercept were close to 5°C, the data at 5°C were not included in the regression. Stronger correlation was found for stage II (r = 1.000) than for stage III (r = 0.964). The BT and required GDD accumulation for stage II, obtained from the regression analysis, were 4.88°C and 297.9 degree days, respectively. The BT and required GDD accumulation for stage III, obtained from the regression analysis, were 3.63°C and 541.6 degree days, respectively.

A significant correlation was observed in the DOYs between observed stage II and that predicted from the GDD model (BT = 4.88°C, GDD = 297.9 degree days) using the temperature data of Yamabe (n = 53, r = 0.66, $p < 0.001$) (Figure 3). However, the predicted DOY (mean = 157.2) were on average 22.9 days later than the observed DOY (mean = 134.3).

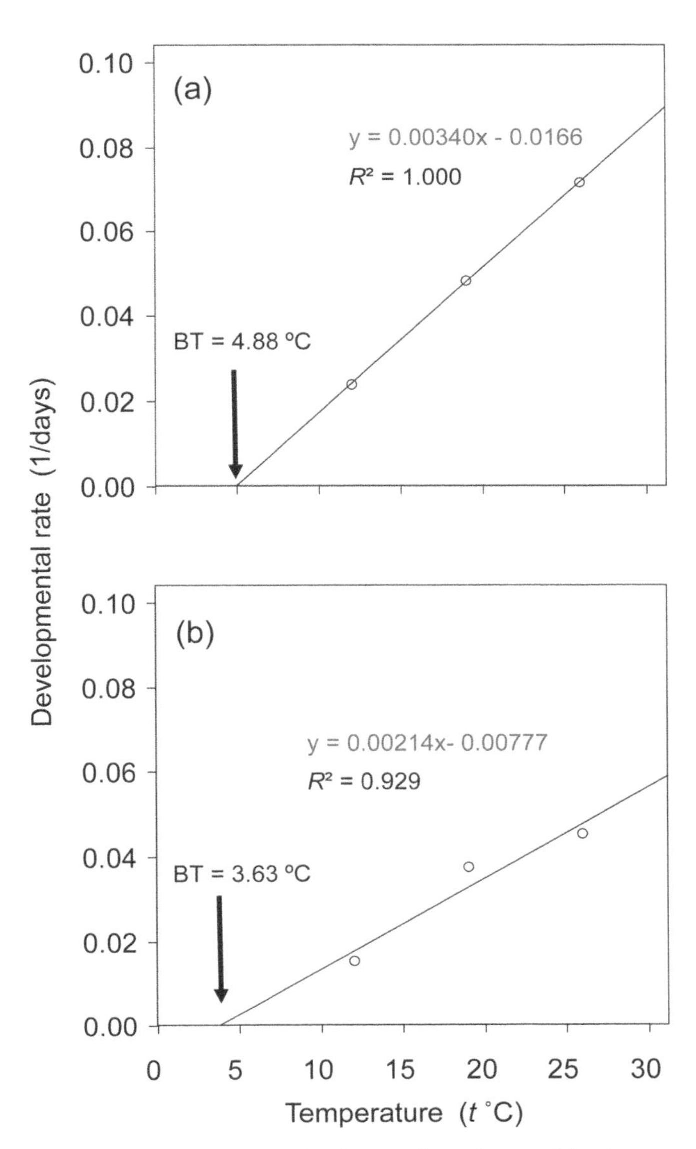

Figure 2. Relationship between developmental rate (inverse of development period) and temperature, for determining base temperature (BT) of *Quercus crispula*, in the University of Tokyo Hokkaido Forest, Furano, Hokkaido, Japan, using a growth chamber experiment. (a) Stage II (bud break), (b) stage III (leaf opening).

Multiple regression models

The best models by a multiple regression model for stage II and stage III are shown in Tables 2 and 3, respectively. To obtain the best model, four and five intermediate steps were needed for stage II and stage III, respectively (Table A1). The best model for stage II included variables of May and before, whereas that for stage III included June and before. The model fitting was better for stage II (R^2 = 0.932, Adjusted R^2 = 0.916) than stage III (R^2 = 0.897, Adjusted R^2 = 0.880). For both stage II and stage III, an average difference of 0.000 days was found between the observed and predicted DOY

GDD model obtained by fitting field observation data with a logistic curve

By fitting field observation data with a logistic curve, a minimum AIC was obtained at BT = 5.2°C (Figure A1). Using BT = 5.2°C, the average GDD for stage II during the six years used in the analysis was 82.5 degree days (n = 18, SD = 38.3, min = 37.3, max = 118.4). The percentage of leafing for the GDD was estimated as 0.0576 (5.76%) from the same logistic curve (Figure 4).

Chichibu

GDD models (Model2013 and Model2014) from growth chamber experiments

The relationship between temperature and the development rate is shown in Figure 5. As all buds died before reaching stage III probably due to cavitation, only the results for stage II are shown. For stage II, BT and required GDD accumulation obtained from the regression analysis were 2.40°C and 330.4 degree days, respectively (R^2 = 0.998) for Model2013

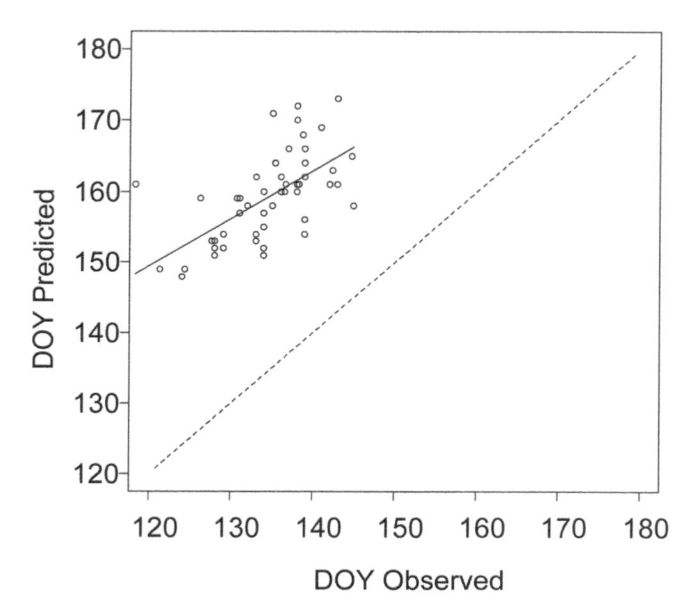

Figure 3. Relationship between observed and predicted DOY of stage II (bud break) of *Quercus crispula* trees for 53 years among 1931–2017, in the University of Tokyo Hokkaido Forest, Furano, Hokkaido, Japan. The prediction was made by accumulating growing degree days (GDD) using 4.88°C as a base temperature until the cumulative GDD became equal to or greater than the required GDD accumulation (297.9 degree days).

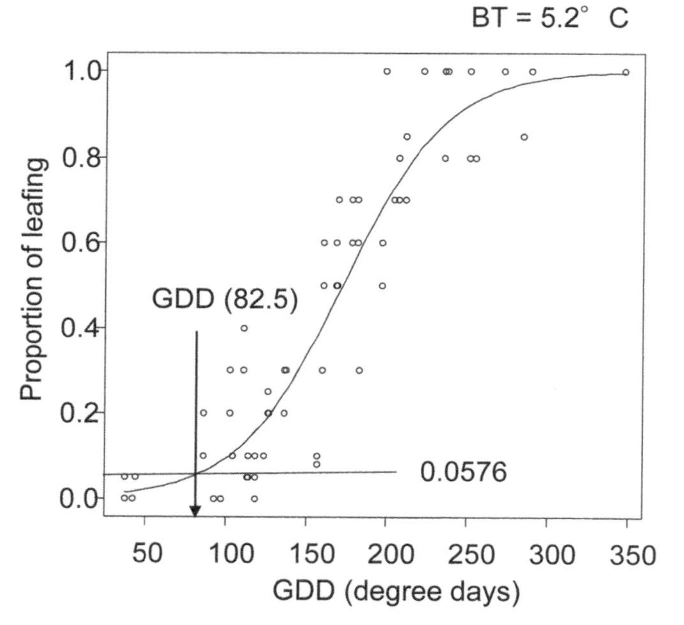

Figure 4. Relationship between growing degree days (GDD) accumulation and the proportion of leafing of three individual trees for six years (2000, 2003, 2005–2008) at the University of Tokyo Hokkaido Forest, Furano, Hokkaido, Japan. A logistic curve was fitted to the relationship. Model selection was done using Akaike's Information Criterion by changing the base temperature (BT) from −2°C to 8°C with 0.2°C stepwise. A logistic curve of the best model (BT = 5.2°C) is shown. The mean of the GDD accumulation with the 5.2°C of BT by the date of observed stage II (bud break) for each of the three observed trees of the six years averaged 82.5 degree days. The proportion of leafing at the 82.5 degree days was 0.0576 from the logistic curve.

(Figure 5(a)) and 0.09°C and 526.9 degree days, respectively (R^2 = 0.966) for Model2014 (Figure 5(b)).

A significant correlation was found in the DOYs between observed stage II and that predicted from the GDD models using the temperature data at Koakazawa (Model2013, $n = 10$, $r = 0.85$, $p < 0.001$; Model2014, $n = 10$, $r = 0.75$, $p = 0.012$) (Figure 6). However, for the 10 years from 2002 to 2011, the predicted DOYs in Model2013 (mean = 132.7) and Model2014 (mean = 136.2) were on average 6.0 and 9.5 days later than the DOYs of observed stage II (mean = 126.7), respectively.

Table 2. The best model by a multiple regression model to explain stage II (bud break) (R^2 = 0.932, Adjusted R^2 = 0.916). The averages of the homogenized temperatures (daily minimum (T_{min}), daily mean (T_{mean}), daily maximum (T_{max}), and diurnal temperature range (DTR)) were used as dependent variables. For the monthly average of the variables, the month of each variable is shown by a numeral following each variable. When the monthly average of the variable selected in the first step was replaced by the average of that variable on the day of year (DOY), month(s) is (are) indicated by an initial letter(s) of the month(s). A numeral follows the initial letter for "J" or "M" to distinguish January and June or March and May, respectively.

Variable	Estimate	SE	*t*-value	*p*-value
(Intercept)	169.596	3.794	44.706	< 0.001
TmaxMAM	−5.292	0.766	−6.910	< 0.001
TminAM	−0.895	0.187	−4.779	< 0.001
TminM3	−1.365	0.247	−5.523	< 0.001
DTRM5	0.524	0.125	4.174	< 0.001
Tmax4	1.662	0.530	3.133	< 0.01
TminJ1	0.934	0.241	3.871	< 0.001
TmeanJF	−1.850	0.637	−2.905	< 0.01
Tmean1	0.860	0.541	1.589	0.12
Tmax5	0.532	0.332	1.602	0.12
TminMA	1.390	0.327	4.249	< 0.001

Table 3. The best model by a multiple regression model to explain stage III (leaf opening) (R^2 = 0.897, Adjusted R^2 = 0.880). The averages of the homogenized temperatures (daily minimum (T_{min}), daily mean (T_{mean}), daily maximum (T_{max}), and diurnal temperature range (DTR)) were used as dependent variables. For the monthly average of the variables, the month of each variable is shown by a numeral following each variable. When the monthly average of the variable selected in the first step was replaced by the average of that variable on the day of year (DOY), month(s) is (are) indicated by an initial letter(s) of the month(s). A numeral follows the initial letter for "J" or "M" to distinguish January and June or March and May, respectively. An initial letter "A" indicates April because August was not included in the analysis. A numeral following a hyphen (-) distinguish two different periods in the same month.

Variable	Estimate	SE	*t*-value	*p*-value
(Intercept)	158.079	2.702	58.508	< 0.001
TmeanAM	−4.024	0.242	−16.595	< 0.001
TmaxFM	−1.895	0.253	−7.489	< 0.001
DTRM3	1.695	0.257	6.585	< 0.001
TmaxF	0.623	0.113	5.495	< 0.001
TmeanMJ	0.663	0.146	4.545	< 0.001
TminFM	1.117	0.257	4.347	< 0.001
DTRJ6	0.241	0.062	3.896	< 0.001
TminA-1	−1.747	0.506	−3.451	< 0.01
TminA-2	1.584	0.572	2.771	< 0.01

GDD model obtained by fitting field observation data with a logistic curve

By fitting field observation data with a logistic curve, a minimum AIC was obtained at BT = 7.2°C (Figure A2). The required GDD for stage II (Proportion of leafing = 0.0576, which was estimated from Hokkaido) was estimated as 98 degree days from the logistic curve (Figure 7).

Discussion

Quercus crispula has a ring-porous xylem wood with large size vessels (IAWA Committee 1989), which is highly susceptible to cavitation and drought (Koike et al. 1986; Tyree and Zimmermann 2002). Actually, all buds on cut branches from Chichibu died before reaching stage III, probably due to cavitation.

The proximate control of bud break in most temperate deciduous trees is usually GDD accumulation (Lyr et al. 1967; Kramer and Kozlowski 1979; Valentine 1983). However, the rate of leaf expansion is directly and exponentially influenced by the temperature (Koike et al. 1984). This

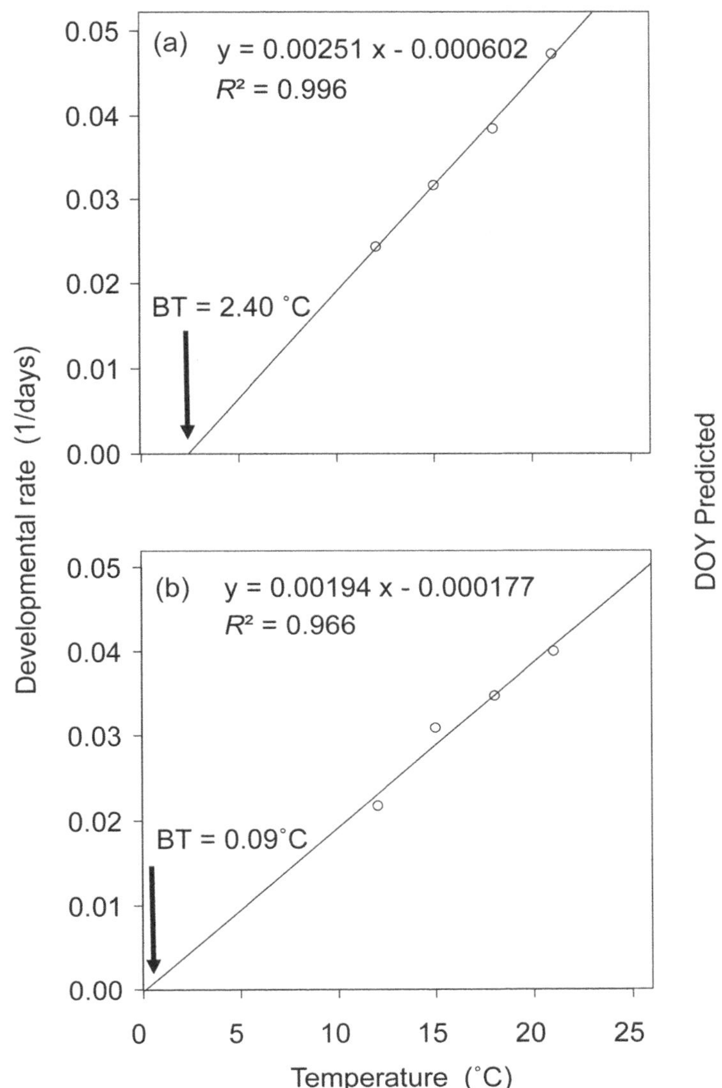

Figure 5. Relationship between developmental rate (inverse of development period) and temperature, for determining base temperature (BT) for stage II (bud break) of *Quercus crispula*, in the University of Tokyo Chichibu Forest, Chichibu, Saitama, Japan, using the growth chamber experiment. (a) Model2013, (b) Model2014.

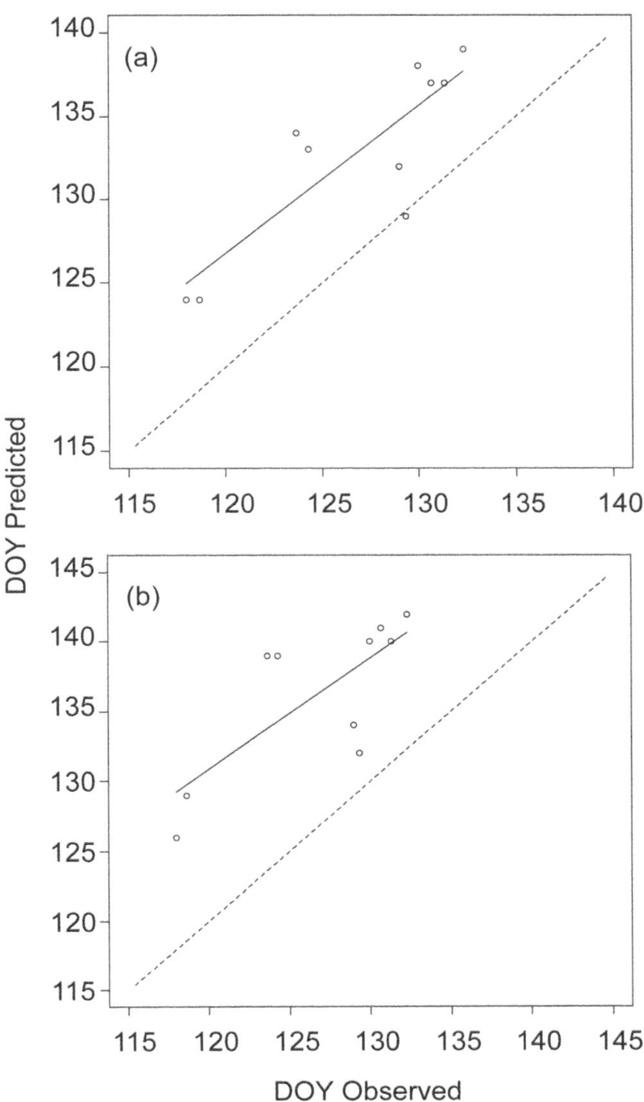

Figure 6. Relationship between observed and predicted DOY of stage II (bud break) of *Quercus crispula* trees for 10 years from 2002 to 2011, in the University of Tokyo Chichibu Forest, Chichibu, Saitama, Japan. (a) Model obtained from the growth chamber experiment 2013 (Model2013). The prediction was made by accumulating growing degree days (GDD) using 2.40°C as a base temperature until the cumulative GDD became equal to or greater than the required GDD accumulation (330.4 degree days). (b) The model obtained from the 2014 experiment (Model2014), with 0.09°C as a base temperature and 526.9 degree days as a required GDD accumulation.

is a likely cause for the better estimates obtained for stage II than for stage III in Hokkaido, by both linear regression (temperature vs. growth rate), using results of the growth chamber experiment, and multiple regression models. Hence, the discussion hereafter will focus on stage II.

In each growth chamber experiment, the growth rate (=1/growth period) obtained by the growth chamber experiments was highly correlated with temperature. It was previously reported that the timing of bud break was genetically determined, and that it differed among local populations of Siebold's beech, *Fagus crenata* (Osada et al. 2018). As Kikuzawa (1999) pointed out, in this study, the resulting BT differed even between disjunct populations of *Q. crispula*. Yet, it was strange that BT obtained from the growth chamber experiment was lower in Chichibu (BT = 2.40°C in Model2013, BT = 0.09°C in Model2014) than in Hokkaido (BT = 4.88°C), even though Chichibu is more southern and warmer than Hokkaido. On the other hand, BT obtained by fitting the field observation data with a logistic curve was lower in Hokkaido (BT = 5.2°C) than in Chichibu (BT = 7.2°C) (Figures 4 and 7, A1 and A2), which is more reasonable according to their latitudes than results from the growth chamber experiments. However, the slope of the logistic curve in Chichibu was so steep that the range of 0% and 100% of leafing overlapped at the GDD with 109.9–119.5. The slope of the curve for Hokkaido was shallower than for Chichibu so that no overlap between 0% and 100% leafing was found, whereas the variation of the GDD at a certain proportion of leafing was similar to that in Chichibu. All results from the growth chamber experiments provided a good fitting with a linear model, with a high correlation coefficient, indicating GDD accumulation control leafing phenology (especially bud break (stage II)) under a constant environment. However, regression lines differed not only between the locations but also between years within Chichibu (Model2013 and Model2014). DOYs of stage II predicted from the models obtained by growth chamber experiments and observed temperature data were much later than the observed DOYs (6–10 days and 23 days in Chichibu and in Hokkaido, respectively). Also, graphs of logistic curve fitting indicated great variation in the GDD

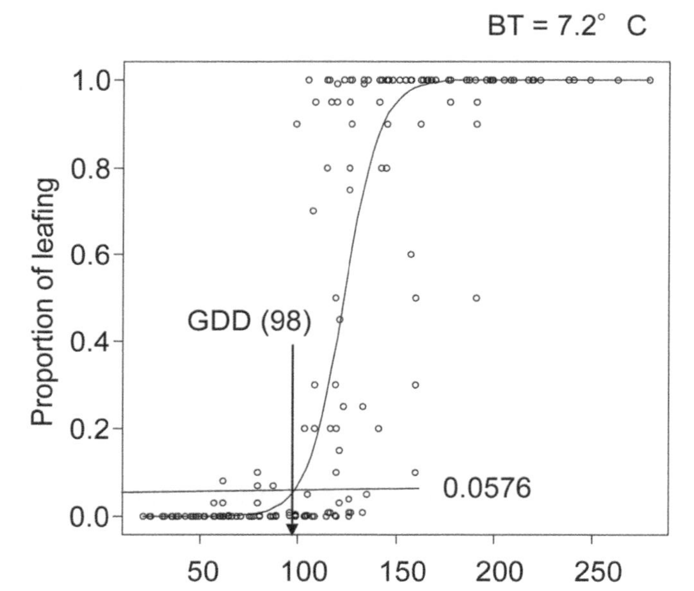

Figure 7. Relationship between growing degree days (GDD) accumulation and proportion of leafing of three individual trees for ten years (2002–2011) at the University of Tokyo Chichibu Forest, Chichibu, Saitama, Japan. A logistic curve was fitted to the relationship. Model selection was done using Akaike's Information Criterion by changing the base temperature (BT) from −2°C to 8° C with 0.2°C stepwise. A logistic curve of the best model (BT = 7.2°C) is shown. The required GDD accumulation for stage II (bud break) estimated from the logistic curve was 98 (proportion of leafing = 0.0576).

accumulation, even in the best model, so that environmental factors other than the GDD accumulation, factors unaccounted for in these experiments, likely influenced the leafing phenology of *Q. crispula*. Light condition is the most likely cause.

Leaf phenology is known to differ between the different life stages of plants (Richardson and O'Keefe 2009). Leafing is earlier for subcanopy individuals than for canopy individuals (Augspurger and Bartlett 2003), and for juveniles than for adults (Richardson and O'Keefe 2009). The demand for light, in relation to carbon gain, is believed to be a likely cause of these differences (Kikuzawa 1995). Therefore, the benefits of earlier leafing must decrease with increasing tree height (Seiwa 1999a, 1999b). Furthermore, spring phenology differs within juveniles, depending on the light condition (Augspurger and Bartlett 2003). Saplings from Hokkaido that were used in the growth chamber experiment were grown in nursery under full light, while branches from Chichibu were obtained from young subcanopy trees beside forest roads. It is possible that light conditions in the year before the experiment influenced the results. Phenotypic plasticity in the timing of bud break should be studied in relation to environmental factors, especially light conditions.

A large difference in the date of stage II was found between field observation and predictions from GDD model obtained from the growth chamber experiments (Figure 3). Duffková (2006) reported that the canopy surface temperature was higher than the air temperature 2 m above ground under full sunlight, but lower without sunlight. So actual temperatures that buds in the field experienced were likely higher than air temperatures observed in the solar radiation shield (Stevenson screen). Also, short days are known to stop shoot expansion of many woody plants in the temperate zone (Kozlowski and Pallardy 1997). While the response of shoot expansion to photoperiod is species specific, we must consider the possibility of deceleration in the leafing phenology as caused by the photoperiod chosen for the growth chamber experiment (12:12 h light:dark period). Such a deceleration as caused by higher latitude and later dates of the event is consistent with the greater difference between the observed DOY and the predictions from the GDD model obtained by the growth chamber experiment in Hokkaido (22.9 days) as compared to Chichibu (6.0 and 9.5 days).

Seasonal changes in photoperiod and light intensity as well as the GDD likely influenced leafing phenology of *Q. crispula*.

Acknowledgments

This study was supported by Grant-in-Aid for Scientific Research (B) (17H03826) and JSPS Core-to-core Project (FY2016–FY2018 and FY2019–2021) to NK. We thank William E Wright for English editing and his helpful comments. We also express our sincere thanks to the two reviewers for their valuable comments to the earlier versions of this manuscript.

Disclosure statement

No potential conflict of interest was reported by the authors.

Funding

This work was supported by the Japan Society for the Promotion of Science [Grant-in-Aid for Scientific Research 17H03826]; Japan Society for the Promotion of Science [Core-to-core Project (FY2019—FY2021)]; Japan Society for the Promotion of Science [Core-to-core Project (FY2016—FY2018)].

References

Augspurger CK, Bartlett EA. 2003. Differences in leaf phenology between juvenile and adult trees in a temperate deciduous forest. Tree Physiol. 23:517–525.

Duffková R. 2006. Difference in canopy and air temperature as an indicator of grassland water stress. Soil & Water Res. 2006:127–138.

Fujimoto S. 2007. Analysis of prediction methods for budburst days based on the phenological observation in 29 broad-leaved tree species for 10 years. J Jpn For Soc. 89:253–261. Japanese with English summary.

Hokyo N. 1972. Studies on the life history and the population dynamics of the green rice leafhopper, *Nephotettix cincticeps* Uhler. Bull Kyushu Agric Exp Stn. 16:283–382. Japanese with English summary.

IAWA Committee. 1989.IAWA list of microscopic features for hardwood identification. Wheeler EA, Baas P, Gasson PE, editors. IAWA Bulletin n.s: Vol. 10. Leiden (Netherlarnds): National Herbarium of the Netherlands; p. 219–312.

JAFTA (Japan Forestry Technical Association). 1964. Illustrated important forest trees of Japan. Tokyo:Chikyu Shuppan. Japanese.

Kai K, Kainuma M, Murakoshi M, Omasa K. 1993. Potential effects on the phenological observation of plants by global warming in Japan. J Agr Met. 48:771–774.

Kamata N, Kimura N, Iguchi K, Fukuoka S, Ogawa H, Kasahara H, Shibano S, Takahashi Y, Inukai M, Sasaki C, et al. 2019. Long-term phenology data on woody plants at The University of Tokyo Hokkaido Forest from 1930 to 2010. Misc Info Univ Tokyo For. 61:45–63. Japanese with English summary.

Kikuzawa K. 1995. Leaf phenology as an optimal strategy for carbon gain in plants. Can J Bot. 73:158–163.

Kikuzawa K. 1999. Global change and phenology of woody plants. Kawano S, Imura O, editors. Environmental changes and populations. Tokyo: Kaiyusha; 36–52. Japanese.

Kimura N, Kisanuki H, Kurahashi A. 1995. Some phenological characters on 25 broad-leaved deciduous tree species in Hokkaido. Annual fluctuations and effect of monthly mean temperature. Proc Ann Mtg Jpn For Soc. 106:367–370. Japanese.

Kira T. 1945. A new classification of climate in eastern Asia as the basis for agricultural geography. Kyoto: Horticultural Institute, Kyoto Imperial University. Japanese.

Kira T. 1949. Forest zones in Japan. Tokyo: Japan Forestry Technology Association. Japanese.

Kira T. 1977. A climatological interpretation of Japanese vegetation zones. In: Miyawaki A, Tüxen R, Okuda S, editors. Vegetation science and environmental protection. Tokyo: Maruzen; p. 21–30.

Koike T, Sakagami Y, Fujimura Y. 1984. Leaf expansion rate and leaf survival on different crown position of three birch species in Hokkaido. Proc Ann Mtg Jpn For Soc. 95:371–372. Japanese.

Koike T, Sakagami Y, Fujimura Y. 1986. A method for measuring photosynthesis with detached parts of deciduous broad-leaved trees in Hokkaido. J Jpn For Soc. 68:425–428.

Kozlowski TT, Pallardy SG. 1997. Growth control in woody plants. New York (NY): Academic Press.

Kramer PJ, Kozlowski TT. 1979. Physiology of woody plants. New York (NY): Academic Press.

Lyr H, Polster H, Fiedler HJ. 1967. Gehölzphysiologie [Physiology of woody plants]. Jena (German): Sustav Fischer Verlag.

Menzel A. 2002. Phenology: its importance to the global change community. Clim Change. 54:379–385.

Nam Y, Koh S-H, Won D-S, Kim J-K, Choi WI. 2013. An empirical predictive model for the flight period of *Platypus koryoensis* (Coleoptera: platypodinae). Appl Ent Zool. 48:515–524.

Osada N, Murase K, Tsuji K, Sawada H, Nunokawa K, Tsukahara M, Hiura T. 2018. Genetic differentiation in the timing of budburst in *Fagus crenata* in relation to temperature and photoperiod. Int J Biometeorol. 62:1763–1776.

Richardson AD, O'Keefe J. 2009. Phenological differences between understory and overstory: A case study using the long-term Harvard forests. In: Noormets A, editor. Phenology of ecosystem processes: applications in global change research. New York (NY): Springer; p. 87–117.

Sawada H, Kabaya H, Omura K, Chishima T. 1999. The fluctuations of some characters of six trees of *Quercus mongolica* var. *grosseserrata* in the Tokyo University Forest in Chichibu. Proc Ann Mtg Kanto Br Jpn For Soc. 50:79–80. Japanese.

Seiwa K. 1999a. Changes in leaf phenology are dependent on tree height in *Acer mono*, a deciduous broad-leaved tree. Ann Bot. 83:355–361.

Seiwa K. 1999b. Ontogenetic changes in leaf phenology of *Ulmus davidiana* var. *japonica*, a deciduous broad-leaved tree. Tree Physiol. 19:793–797.

Stamp NE. 1993. A temperate region view of the interaction of temperature, food quality, and predators on caterpillar foraging. In: Stamp NE, Casey TM, editors. Caterpillars: ecological and evolutionary constraints on foraging. New York (NY): Chapman and Hall; p. 478–508.

Tanaka N, Kamata N, Shibano H, Owari T, Ohkawa A, Igarashi Y, Arakida K. 2013. Estimation of long-term data sets of annual mean temperature in ecohydrology research institute, the University of Tokyo Hokkaido Forest, and the University of Tokyo Chichibu Forest. Bull Univ Tokyo For. 128:1–19. Japanese.

Tsugane R. 1975. The life cycle of *Amphipyra livida corvina* Matschulsky (Lepidoptera: noctuidae), with special reference to the termination of aestivation in the adult stage. Jap J Appl Ent Zool. 19:169–175. Japanese with English summary.

Tyree MT, Zimmermann MH. 2002. Xylem structure and the ascent of sap. Berlin Heidelberg: Springer.

Umeya K, Yamada H. 1973. Threshold temperature and thermal constants for development of the diamond-back moth, *Plutella xylostella* L., with reference to their local differences. Jap J Appl Ent Zool. 17:19–24. Japanese with English summary.

Valentine HT. 1983. Budbreak and leaf growth functions for modelling herbivory in some gypsy moth hosts. For Sci. 29:607–617.

Yamamura K, Kiritani K. 1998. A simple method to estimate the potential increase in the number of generations under global warming in temperate zones. Appl Ent Zool. 33:289–298.

Effects of typhoon disturbances on seasonal and interannual patterns of litterfall on coniferous and broadleaf plantations in Xitou, central Taiwan

Chih-Hsin Cheng, Chia-Yi Lee, Hong-Ru Lee, Chiou-Pin Chen and Oleg V. Menyailo

ABSTRACT

Many environmental and climatic disturbances can significantly change the magnitude and pattern of litterfall. This study investigated the effects of typhoon disturbances on the seasonal and interannual patterns of litterfall on coniferous and broadleaf plantation stands in Xitou, central Taiwan. Throughout the study period from 2012 to 2018, typhoon disturbances were recorded in 4 of these 7 years, whereas only minor or even no typhoon disturbances occurred in the other 3 years. Our results demonstrated that the pattern of monthly litterfall varied substantially between the coniferous and broadleaf stands. The coniferous stands exhibited a substantial litterfall pulse due to typhoon disturbances. By contrast, typhoon disturbances exerted a minor impact on the broadleaf stands. The litterfall seasonality of the coniferous stands was higher than that of the broadleaf stands, especially in the years with typhoon disturbances. Furthermore, the yearly variation caused by typhoon disturbances was distinct at the coniferous stands; the annual litterfall mass at the coniferous stands in the years with typhoon disturbances was more than twice as high as that in the years without typhoon disturbances, namely 6,000 kg ha^{-1} yr^{-1} versus 2,500 kg ha^{-1} yr^{-1}. By contrast, the annual litterfall mass at the broadleaf stands did not differ significantly among the study years. Because of high interannual variation, long-term sampling is essential for accurate estimation of annual litterfall at coniferous stands. For broadleaf plantations, interannual litterfall variation seems less critical, and spatial variability should be considered because of higher variability in terms of site conditions.

Introduction

Litterfall is a vital component of forest ecosystems that is linked to net primary production and the return of nutrients and organic matter from vegetation biomass to soil (Brown and Lugo 1982; Vitousek 1984). Litterfall is also essential for maintaining the statuses of soil decomposers and pools of soil organic matter (Brown and Lugo 1982). The amount and pattern of litterfall are crucial determinants of the regulation of these forest ecosystem functions.

Both local and regional factors greatly influence the magnitude and pattern of litterfall. Temperature and precipitation are the two main variables used to predict litterfall on a regional scale (Bray and Gorham 1964; Chave et al. 2010; Zhang et al. 2014). For example, one review study reported that the litterfall mass of a boreal forest was on the low end, whereas that of a tropical forest was on the high end (Bray and Gorham 1964). Many studies have demonstrated that on a local scale litterfall in forest ecosystems is dependent on forest type, species composition, forest age, soil fertility, and disturbances (Bray and Gorham 1964; Liu et al. 2004; Wang et al. 2016; Lin et al. 2017; Feng et al. 2019). A disturbance, which refers to a temporary change in environmental conditions, may have the most profound effects on the amount and pattern of litterfall because of the changes caused to the ecological and physiological processes of the forest (Lodge et al. 1991; Lin et al. 2017).

Studies on natural disturbances in tropical and subtropical forests tend to focus on typhoon events. Owing to their strong winds and heavy rainfall, typhoon events markedly affect litterfall mass and patterns (Lodge et al. 1991; Lin et al. 2003, 2017; Wang et al. 2013; Liu et al. 2018). Most related studies conducted in Taiwan have investigated the short-term impact on litterfall from typhoon disturbances (Chiang and Liu 1989; Wang et al. 2013; Liu et al. 2018); few have considered long-term litterfall to determine interannual litterfall patterns (Lin et al. 2003; Chin 2008). Further information is required to determine how litterfall responds to typhoon disturbances seasonally and interannually; such information could enhance understanding of the dynamics of litter input and related carbon and nutrient cycles.

In this study, seven coniferous (CP) and two deciduous broadleaf (BR) plantation stands with stand age ranged from 14 to 92 years in Xitou, central Taiwan, were selected for analysis of seasonal and annual litterfall patterns from 2012 to 2018. Typhoon disturbances were recorded in 4 of the 7 years of the study period. Only minor or even no typhoon disturbances occurred in the other 3 years. We aimed to determine the effects of typhoon disturbances on the seasonal and interannual litterfall patterns. With seven years of litterfall collection among years with and without typhoon disturbances, two forest types, and a wide range of stand age of the selected stands, we hypothesized that:

(i) Both the CP and BR stands would be severely affected by typhoon disturbances, and the litterfall mass in the month with typhoon disturbance would dominate the annual litterfall mass irrespective of forest type.

(ii) The litterfall peaks derived from typhoon disturbances would result in higher litterfall seasonality, thus deviating the litterfall patterns between years with and without typhoon disturbances.
(iii) Annual litterfall masses would proportionate to stand age. Lower litterfall masses would be found at the younger stands compared to the older ones.

Materials and methods

Study site

This study was conducted in the National Taiwan University Experimental Forest in Xitou, central Taiwan (23°40′N, 120° 47′E). The study site is classified as montane wet forest (Holdridge 1967). *Machilus* and *Castanopsis* trees originally dominated the native vegetation but have been replaced by forest plantings over the preceding 100 years (Cheng et al. 2013). The first tree species planted was *Cryptomeria japonica* (Japanese cedar); later, native CP species were planted (e.g., *Cunninghamia lanceolata* [Chinese fir] and *Taiwania cryptomerioides*) after 1970. Subsequently, BR species were planted after 1985 to enhance the site's biodiversity. Plantations in Xitou can be approximately classified as CP and BR stands.

This study investigated litterfall for nine plantation stands ranging from 14 to 92 years of age to remain faithful to the background of the silvicultural policy (Table 1). The oldest stands, namely CP1 to CP4, were Japanese cedar, and the middle-aged stands, namely CP5 to CP7, were Chinese fir and *T. cryptomerioides*. The two youngest BR stands were planted with the deciduous tree species *Cerasus campanulata* and *Acer serrulatum* (BR1) and *Liquidambar formosana* (BR2). The BR1 stand was established from a previous Japanese cedar stand that had been damaged by stand-replacing landslide deposition (Cheng et al. 2016a). The BR2 stand was established after the clearcut harvest of a previous Chinese fir stand. Notably, the BR1 stand had the highest rock content but the lowest soil fertility owing to landslide deposition (Cheng et al. 2016a).

The present study initially conducted an inventory to assess stand characteristics determined on the basis of randomly selected 20 m × 20 m sampling plots (n = 2–6) at each stand (Cheng et al. 2013). Generally, the oldest stand, CP1, had the highest mean diameter at breast height (DBH), canopy height, and basal area (BA) but the lowest tree density among the selected stands (Table 1). Two BR stands had considerably lower DBH, canopy height, and BA results compared with the CP stands.

Litterfall mass

We collected litterfall by using a 1 × 1 m^2 nylon mesh litter trap erected 1 m above ground. Two litter traps were randomly installed in each sampling plot, and 4 to 12 litter traps were measured in each stand. Litterfall was collected monthly from January 2012 to January 2019. We defined litterfall as leaves, branches <2.5 cm in diameter, reproductive tissue, and miscellaneous material collected on the litter trap. Large branches or large pieces of tree bark were not sampled. The collected litterfall was oven dried at 65°C to constant mass and weighed.

The annual litterfall mass was calculated as the summation of monthly litterfall from January to December in each year. However, the annual litterfall mass was slightly adjusted to be calculated from February to January in the BR stands till to the end of litterfall season.

Meteorological data

The monthly mean temperature and precipitation over the study period in Xitou are shown in Figure 1. The mean monthly temperature ranged from 11.7°C in January to 20.6°C in July. The annual precipitation ranged from 1,254 to 3,008 mm, with most rainfall occurring between May and September.

Data concerning typhoon events were provided by the Central Weather Bureau of Taiwan and are detailed in Table 2. The typhoon disturbances varied in terms of track, intensity, and interaction between wind circulation and mountainous terrain. A severe typhoon disturbance in this study was defined as a significant mechanical disturbance of the forest canopy that resulted in prominent ground coverage with the defoliated litter. In each of 2012, 2013, 2015, and 2016, at least one severe typhoon was recorded; therefore, these years were considered the years with typhoon disturbances in this study. By contrast, only minor or even no typhoon disturbances occurred in 2014, 2017, and 2018; therefore, these years were considered the years without typhoon disturbances in this study (Table 2).

Seasonal and interannual litterfall variation

The degree of litterfall seasonality was examined through two methods (Lawrence 2005; Zhang et al. 2014). First, the difference between the maximum and minimum monthly litterfall mass (kg ha^{-1} $month^{-1}$) was calculated. A higher ratio indicated higher seasonality. Second, the seasonal coefficient

Table 1. Stand characteristics of the analyzed coniferous and broadleaf plantation stands in Xitou, central Taiwan.

Site	Species	Year planted	Altitude (m)	Tree density (no. ha^{-a})	Mean DBH[a] (cm)	BA[b] (m^b ha^{-a})	Canopy height (m)	Litter traps (no.)
CP1	*Cryptomeria japonica*	1920	1050	408	48.6	77.9	30.9	6
CP2	*Cryptomeria japonica*	1960	1170	658	33.9	64.0	27.6	6
CP3	*Cryptomeria japonica*	1973	1370	1358	23.1	59.7	20.8	6
CP4	*Cryptomeria japonica*	1971	1300	806	34.9	80.1	23.5	8
CP5	*Cunninghamia lanceolata*	1979	1100	762	29.5	53.7	24.1	8
CP6	*Taiwania cryptomerioides; Cunninghamia lanceolata*	1981	1100	654	29.4	47.2	24.3	12
CP7	*Taiwania cryptomerioides*	1988	1270	1068	23.9	49.3	18.7	8
BR1	*Cerasus campanulate; Acer serrulatum*	1988	1200	616	12.6	11.5	7.2	6
BR2	*Liquidambar formosana*	1998	950	988	13.2	13.9	11.1	4

[a]DBH: diameter at breast height.
[b]BA: basal area.

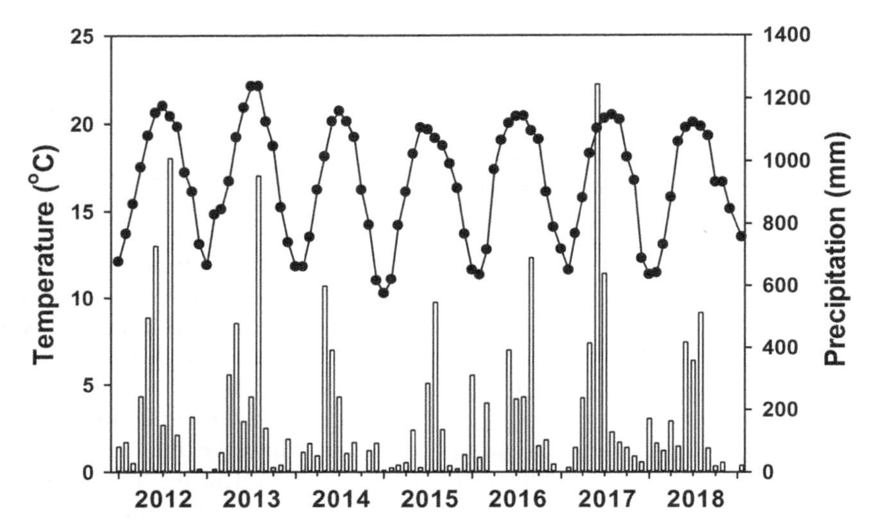

Figure 1. Monthly mean temperature and precipitation between 2012 and 2018 in Xitou, central Taiwan.

Table 2. List of typhoon events between 2012 and 2018 in Xitou, central Taiwan.

	Typhoon	Period	Pressure (h Pa)	Wind speed (m s^{-a})	Category	Disturbances in Xitou[a]
2012	Talim	June 19–21	985	25	Mild	Significant[a]
2012	Saola	July 30–Aug 3	960	38	Moderate	Significant
2013	Soulik	July 11–13	925	51	Strong	Significant
2013	Usagi	Sep 19–22	910	55	Strong	Significant
2014	Matmo	July 21–23	960	38	Moderate	
2015	Soudelor	Aug 6–9	930	48	Moderate	Significant
2015	Dujuan	Sep 27–29	925	51	Strong	Significant
2016	Meranti	Sep 12–15	900	60	Strong	
2016	Megi	Sep 25–28	940	45	Moderate	Significant
2017	Haitang	July 29–31	990	20	Mild	
2018	Maria	July 9–11	915	55	Strong	

[a]Significant mechanical canopy disturbances in Xitou.

of variation (CV, the ratio of the standard deviation to the mean) for monthly litterfall was determined; a higher CV indicated higher seasonality.

Furthermore, interannual litterfall variation was examined according to the difference between the highest and lowest annual litterfall mass results and the CV for annual litterfall mass throughout the study period. A higher ratio of the highest to lowest annual litterfall mass and a higher CV indicated greater interannual litterfall variation.

Statistics

A one-way analysis of variance (ANOVA) table was employed to evaluate the differences in annual litterfall mass between the study years, and the means among years at each stand were subsequently compared using the least significant difference test at a 5% probability level ($P < 0.05$). A repeated-measures ANOVA was conducted to measure differences in litterfall mass among the stands; the amount of annual litterfall mass served as the repeated measure, and the stand served as the fixed factor. The means among stands were compared using the least significant difference test at a 5% probability level ($P < 0.05$). A linear regression analysis between stand age and litterfall amount was tested. The annual litterfall mass were also linearly tested with annual or growing season mean temperature and precipitation. Statistics were run using SAS software (version 9.4).

Results

Litterfall seasonality

The monthly litterfall pattern for the nine stands between 2012 and 2018 is depicted in Figure 2. Extremely high peaks driven by typhoon disturbances were distinct, especially for the CP stands, for which the amounts of monthly litterfall exceeded 4,000 kg ha^{-1} in months with typhoon disturbances and contributed to 70% of the annual litterfall mass. In the years without typhoon disturbances, namely 2014, 2017, and 2018, the monthly litterfall was relatively constant throughout the year and exhibited relatively low seasonality. The ratio of maximum to minimum monthly litterfall varied considerably among the study years. In the years with typhoon disturbances, namely 2012, 2013, 2015, and 2016, the ratios of maximum to minimum monthly litterfall were all over 150, whereas they were below 100 in all the years without typhoon disturbances (Table 3). Higher seasonal CVs for monthly litterfall were observed in the years with typhoon disturbances. The average seasonal CVs for the years with and without typhoon disturbances were 170% and only 100%, respectively; this finding indicated that strong seasonality had been induced by typhoon disturbances (Table 4).

The patterns of monthly litterfall varied considerably between the CP and BR stands. The litterfall pattern of the BR stands was a bimodal-timing pattern, namely a pattern of one major peak in the deciduous season from October to January and a smaller peak in the

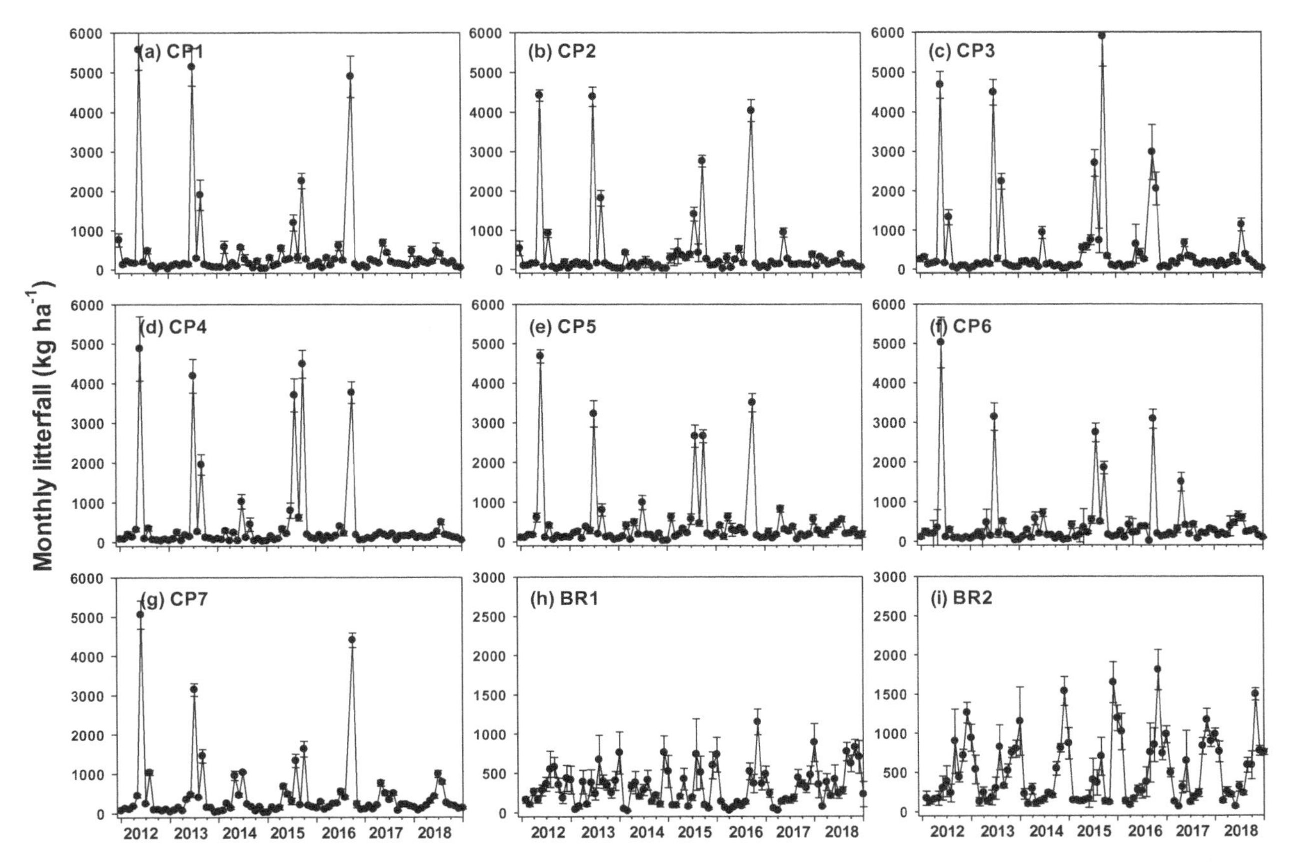

Figure 2. Monthly litterfall patterns on the coniferous and broadleaf plantation stands between 2012 and 2018 in Xitou, central Taiwan. In the year of 2012, 2013, 2015, and 2016, at least one severe typhoon was recorded and only minor or even no typhoon disturbances occurred in 2014, 2017, and 2018. Each symbol is the mean of the monthly litterfall mass, and the standard deviation is plotted as error bars.

Table 3. Ranges of monthly litterfall mass (kg ha^{-a} $month^{-a}$) and seasonality for each year from 2012 to 2018 for coniferous and broadleaf plantation stands in Xitou, central Taiwan.

		2012*[a]	2013*	2014	2015*	2016*	2017	2018
CP1	Range	24–5572	19–5136	20–572	25–2254	41–4895	50–688	63–471
	Max./Min.[b]	232	264	28	92	118	14	8
	CV (%)[c]	236	218	106	137	228	82	54
CP2	Litterfall	19–4420	25–4391	18–427	23–2755	17–4306	38–939	62–381
	Max./Min.	233	174	23	122	236	25	6
	CV (%)	222	213	101	130	223	122	54
CP3	Litterfall	17–4680	21–4491	15–934	24–5891	38–2976	39–666	52–1134
	Max./Min.	279	214	64	243	79	17	22
	CV (%)	216	207	137	173	159	77	107
CP4	Litterfall	33–4876	35–4184	17–1021	21–4483	36–3762	44–235	97–501
	Max./Min.	149	120	61	219	105	5	5
	CV (%)	262	203	144	170	229	43	64
CP5	Litterfall	47–4675	45–3222	20–989	25–2653	47–3505	52–828	87–557
	Max./Min.	100	72	49	107	84	5	6
	CV (%)	233	184	112	139	175	87	47
CP6	Litterfall	45–3850	19–2617	28–598	34–2282	68–2571	51–1247	112–528
	Max./Min.	85	137	21	66	38	24	5
	CV (%)	243	197	103	140	177	113	55
CP7	Litterfall	63–5055	27–3146	18–1032	22–1621	48–4398	65–763	75–987
	Max./Min.	81	116	57	73	92	12	13
	CV (%)	224	169	117	115	204	74	87
BR1	Litterfall	38–578	42–755	18–756	49–736	26–1150	26–884	71–822
	Max./Min.	15	18	42	15	45	34	12
	CV (%)	55	65	73	83	106	80	56
BR2	Litterfall	135–1261	126–1150	95–1535	116–1645	81–1806	66–1165	63–1495
	Max./Min.	9	9	16	14	22	19	24
	CV (%)	71	73	104	101	86	76	79

[a]*Years with significant typhoon disturbances
[b]Max./Min.: ratio of maximum to minimum monthly litterfall
[c]CV: coefficient of variation for monthly litterfall
Note: Broadleaf plantation: BR; coniferous plantation: CP

typhoon and rainy season from June to September (Figure 2). Seasonal variation at the BR stands was less strong than that at the CP stands, especially in the years with typhoon disturbances. The ratios of maximum to minimum monthly litterfall at the BR stands were generally lower than 30. In addition, the average CV of monthly litterfall at the BR stands, namely 80%, was lower than that at the CP stands.

Table 4. Annual litterfall mass (mean ± standard deviation) and variation between 2012 and 2018 for coniferous and broadleaf stands in Xitou, central Taiwan.

	CP1	CP2	CP3	CP4	CP5	CP6	CP7	BR1	BR2
2012*[a]	7701 ± 1556 a[b]	6409 ± 480 ab	7374 ± 847 b	6262 ± 2446 b	6739 ± 742 b	6741 ± 2027 a	7563 ± 1032 a	3712 ± 476 a	6171 ± 1362 a
2013*	8212 ± 1441 a	7308 ± 1250 a	7869 ± 1131 b	7386 ± 2015 b	5747 ± 1625 b	5233 ± 1376 b	6469 ± 918 b	4032 ± 1138 a	5559 ± 1402 a
2014	2185 ± 556 c	1385 ± 357 c	2152 ± 659 c	2406 ± 850 c	2919 ± 1209 c	2453 ± 1333 d	3553 ± 568 d	3439 ± 541 a	5112 ± 1226 a
2015*	5639 ± 1121 b	7031 ± 1013 a	11,877 ± 2813 a	10,692 ± 1398 a	8128 ± 1213 a	7128 ± 835 a	5360 ± 660 c	3817 ± 912 a	6139 ± 2293 a
2016*	6872 ± 1284 ab	5780 ± 1007 b	6758 ± 2383 b	5262 ± 1003 b	6196 ± 1224 b	5395 ± 750 b	6799 ± 645 b	3610 ± 708 a	6888 ± 2080 a
2017	2580 ± 324 c	2360 ± 398 c	2516 ± 477 c	1625 ± 450 c	2862 ± 1122 c	4030 ± 1343 c	3368 ± 586 d	3535 ± 1098 a	6245 ± 1802 a
2018	2566 ± 527 c	2084 ± 250 c	2894 ± 721 c	1870 ± 595 c	3273 ± 1255 c	3688 ± 1639 cd	3485 ± 617 d	5003 ± 923 a	6318 ± 842 a
Mean	5106 ± 2577 AB[c]	4622 ± 2535 AB	5920 ± 3557 A	5071 ± 3325 A	5177 ± 2054 A	4953 ± 1678 A	5228 ± 1725 A	3878 ± 533 B	6062 ± 571 A
Max./Min.[d]	3.75	5.28	5.52	6.58	2.84	2.91	2.25	1.45	1.34
CV (%)[e]	50.1	54.5	59.8	65.2	39.7	33.9	32.7	13.7	9.4

[a]*Years with significant typhoon disturbances
[b]Different small letters indicate differences among years at each stand ($P < 0.05$)
[c]Different capital letters indicate differences among stands ($P < 0.05$)
[d]Max./Min.: ratio of maximum to minimum annual litterfall
[e]CV: coefficient of variation for annual litterfall
Note: Broadleaf plantation: BR; coniferous plantation: CP

Annual litterfall

The annual litterfall mass results summed from the monthly litterfall mass results are shown in Table 3. At the CP stands, the amount of litterfall peaked in the months with typhoon disturbances; also, the annual litterfall mass was more than twice as high in the years with typhoon disturbances than in the years without typhoon disturbances, namely 6,000 kg ha^{-1} yr^{-1} versus 2,500 kg ha^{-1} yr^{-1} (Table 4). However, the annual litterfall mass at the BR stands was less closely related to typhoon disturbances than was that at the CP stands, and no significant difference in annual litterfall mass among the study years was observed ($P > 0.05$). Owing to the considerable yearly variation at the CP stands, the ratio of maximum to minimum annual litterfall ranged from 2.25 to 6.58, and the CVs for annual litterfall ranged from 33% to 65% (Table 4). Because no significant differences in annual litterfall mass were observed among the study years at the BR stands ($P > 0.05$), the ratios of maximum to minimum annual litterfall (<1.5) and the CVs for annual litterfall (9%–14%) at the BR stands were lower than those at the CP stands.

The 7-year mean annual litterfall mass for all stands ranged from 3,878 to 6,062 kg ha^{-1} yr^{-1} (Table 4). The mean annual litterfall mass demonstrated no age-related trends among the stands ($R^2 = 0.01$ for linear regression, $P > 0.05$, Figure S1); however, the relatively low annual litterfall mass at the BR1 stand, which had been established in the area with landslide deposition. Moreover, except some limited stands, annual litterfall mass in the present study was not significantly related to annual or growing season mean temperatures and annual precipitation ($P > 0.05$, Table S1).

Discussion

Litterfall seasonality

Similar to the results of previous studies (Lin et al. 2003; Wang et al. 2013; Liu et al. 2018), our results revealed a distinct peak with a clear seasonal litterfall pattern due to typhoon disturbances. However, the pattern of litterfall seasonality in Xitou varied substantially between the CP and BR stands; this finding refuted our first hypothesis that typhoon disturbances have a similar influence to all forest types. The CP stands, including Japanese cedar, Chinese fir, and *T. cryptomerioides*, all exhibited a substantial litterfall pulse due to typhoon disturbances. However, the typhoon disturbances had only minor impacts on the BR stands, and their litterfall seasonality was lower than that at the CP stands.

High litterfall seasonality has been reported extensively in deciduous (Zhang et al. 2014) and dry (Lawrence 2005; Parsons et al. 2014) forests. Litterfall pulse in such forests is subject to physiological responses to seasonal changes in temperature, precipitation, and photoperiods. Zhang et al. (2014) reported that temperate deciduous forest had the highest seasonality compared with those of other forest types, with a ratio of maximum to minimum monthly litterfall of 34.8 and a CV of 135%. Lawrence (2005) reported a CV for monthly litterfall of 82% for a tropical dry forest in southern Mexico. Based on our observations, litterfall seasonality at the CP stands in Xitou is somewhat higher than those forest types, especially in years with typhoon disturbances (Table 3). The following environmental and physiological factors may explain such high litterfall seasonality induced by typhoon disturbances.

Short disturbance time

Strong winds and heavy rain from typhoon disturbances usually last a few days and induce an extreme litterfall pulse immediately after each disturbance. Thus, a single high peak caused by a typhoon disturbance can result in significantly high seasonality. By contrast, litterfall peaks in temperate deciduous or dry forests are not concentrated in such a short period and may extend over several months (Bray and Gorham 1964; Hughes and Fahey 1994). The more extended litterfall season could lead to lower seasonality compared with that after typhoon disturbances.

Retention of dead leaves and branches on trees

Although most deaths of leaves and branches on CP trees reportedly occur from August to October (Miyaura and Hozumi 1993), dead leaves and branches remain attached on trees for a certain period (Yoshida and Hijii 2006; Matsushita et al. 2017). Canopy photos in the Japanese cedar plantations (at CP1 and CP4, Figure S2) taken in December 2018 displayed the retained dead leaves and branches on trees. The retained litter on the tree after physiological death can be cleared after typhoon disturbance, thus accumulating litterfall mass in the month of the typhoon disturbance and increasing seasonality.

Monoculture plantation stands

Diverse tree species reportedly exhibit unsynchronized litterfall, meaning that some litter overlaps from month to month and litterfall seasonality is reduced (Zalamea and Gonzalez 2008; Zhang et al. 2014). However, the plantation stands in Xitou typically consist of only one or two tree species. Litterfall at these plantation stands tends to exhibit synchronous responses to environmental fluctuations and contributes to higher seasonality.

Typhoon disturbances exerted only a minor influence at the BR stands compared with the CP stands. The results of this study partially refuted our second hypothesis, namely that litterfall patterns varied between years with and without typhoon disturbances. The relatively minor influence of typhoon disturbances at the BR stands may have been because of the smaller trees at these stands (Table 1; Walker 1991). The surrounding taller CP plantations provide a windshield to reduce physical disturbance. In addition, BR trees reportedly have higher wind resistance than do CP trees (Fujimori 2001). The major litterfall peaks in fall and winter observed in the present study suggest that physiological factors are more influential than environmental disturbance to litterfall patterns at the BR stands. Lu et al. (2003) and Lin et al. (1997) reported similar results, namely that major litterfall peaks occur in periods of physiological leaf senescence in other BR forests in Taiwan, except for in years when severe canopy damage is caused by typhoon disturbances (Wang et al. 2013).

Interannual litterfall variation

Variation in annual litterfall mass was high at the CP stands. The ratios of the highest to lowest annual litterfall mass and the CVs were higher than those recorded in many studies that have conducted long-term litterfall monitoring (Kouki and Hokkanen 1992; Hennessey et al. 1992; Enright 1999; Starr et al. 2005; Yanai et al. 2012; Yang et al. 2017). Generally, interannual litterfall variation is related to weather conditions such as the variability of annual temperature and precipitation that differ from year to year. For example, Kouki and Hokkanen (1992) reported that variation in the interannual litterfall mass of Scots pine in Finland had been driven by the temperature conditions in the current and preceding years. Hennessey et al. (1992) proposed that annual litterfall mass varied alongside rainfall conditions in a loblolly pine stand in Oklahoma, United States. However, the annual litterfall mass in the present study was not substantially related to the annual or growing season mean temperatures and precipitation ($P > 0.05$, Table S1); suggesting typhoon disturbances best explained the variability of litterfall mass. Notably, the annual litterfall mass in the years with typhoon disturbances was more than twice as high as that in the years without typhoon disturbances.

The amount of annual litterfall mass was relatively uniform at the BR stands (Table 4) where the low interannual litterfall variation may have been attributable to the relatively minor influence of typhoon disturbances. In addition, the BR species shed all their litter in winter and did not retain dead litter on trees to enhance the annual litterfall mass in the years with typhoon disturbances. The CVs for interannual litterfall variation at the BR stands at 10% in Table 4 were similar to or even lower than those for BR forests in New Zealand (CV = 20%, Alley et al. 1998), the United States (CV = 14%–21%; Adam 2008; Yanai et al. 2012; Yang et al. 2017), and southern Taiwan (CV = 15%; Chin 2008). The relatively low litterfall variation and uniform annual litterfall mass at the BR stands may indicate that evident growth limitations are absent in Xitou. The constant foliage growth at the BR stands may provide additional evidence to support that typhoon disturbance rather than temperature or precipitation was the primary driving force for high interannual litterfall variability at the CP stands.

Annual litterfall mass

The mean annual litterfall mass of 5,100 kg ha^{-1} yr^{-1} for the nine analyzed stands in this study was comparable with that of other plantation stands with similar tree stand characteristics (Nakane 1995; Yoshida and Hijii 2006; Liu et al. 2018). In the present study, annual litterfall did not exhibit a clear trend with respect to stand age (Figure S1); this finding refuted our third hypothesis, namely that litterfall is related to tree stocking (Hennessey et al. 1992; Matala et al. 2008). However, our results corresponded to those of studies that have suggested that litterfall mass increases until canopy closure and remains relatively constant thereafter (Bray and Gorham 1964; Adu-Bredu et al. 1997; Starr et al. 2005). Notably, the youngest stand age among the CP stands in the present study (> 24 years) was more than a decade older than the age observed for canopy closure in another study (Chiang and Liu 1989).

Regarding the BR plantations, the annual litterfall mass of BR2 stand did not differ from the CP stands (Table 4), regardless of its lower tree stocking; this finding was likely attributable to the higher litter production in the BR trees than in the CP trees (Liu et al. 2004). However, the relatively low annual litterfall mass at BR1 compared to BR2 and the CP stands may have been due to this stand containing gaps and having low soil fertility (Cheng et al. 2016a).

Environmental implications

The high interannual variation at the CP stands suggested that long-term sampling is essential for accurate estimation of annual litterfall. In this study, our long-term litterfall collection may have been more reliable than that conducted in other studies based on short-term records representing average annual litterfall mass (Chiang and Liu 1989; Huang et al. 2017). For the BR plantations, interannual litterfall variation seems to be less critical; however, spatial variability should be considered because these plantations are generally established with higher variability in terms of site conditions (Table 4) (Cheng et al. 2016b). Because litter production can serve as an indicator of stand production, the relationship between annual litterfall mass and tree growth must be understood from both spatial and temporal perspectives to enable future research (Enoki et al. 2011).

Furthermore and notably, the typhoon disturbances that occurred during the study period were insufficiently severe to influence stand structure; we noticed no apparent tree damage or mortality inside any stand. The return times of devastating typhoon events can be longer than those observed in our study period, as demonstrated through an observation of a long-term experimental plot in Xitou (Cheng et al. 2017). Otherwise, litterfall mass and patterns can differ once a devastating typhoon disturbance that greatly influences stand structure has occurred (Lin et al. 2017).

Conclusion

The pattern of litterfall varied substantially between CP and BR plantation stands in Xitou. The deciduous BR stands had peak litterfall in fall and winter, whereas the CP stands exhibited high litterfall pulse results due to typhoon disturbances. This difference was illustrated by the higher seasonal variation at the CP stands than at the BR stands. Three mechanisms could explain this higher variation at the CP stands, namely (i) a short disturbance time, (ii) the retention of dead leaves and branches on trees, and (iii) monocultural tree species. In addition, the yearly variation driven by typhoon disturbances was different at the CP stands compared to that at the BR stands, which revealed constant interannual litterfall throughout the study period. Because of the high interannual variation observed in this study, it was concluded that long-term sampling is essential for accurate estimation of annual litterfall at CP stands. By contrast, for BR plantations, interannual litterfall variation seems less critical, and spatial variability should be considered because these plantations are generally established with higher variability in terms of site conditions. Because litter production can serve as an indicator of stand production, the relationship between annual litterfall mass and tree growth must be understood from both spatial and temporal perspectives to enable future research.

Acknowledgments

This study was supported by the Ministry of Science and Technology of Taiwan and a cooperative grant from the Ministry of Science and Technology of Taiwan and the Russian Foundation for Basic Research (RFBR). We gratefully acknowledge H.J. Ruan and C.Y. Chen for their assistance with field and lab work.

Disclosure statement

No potential conflict of interest was reported by the authors.

Funding

This work was supported by the RFBR and MOST [18-54-52005]; Ministry of Science and Technology, Taiwan (TW) [107-2923-B-002-002-MY3].

References

Adam MB. 2008. Long-term leaf fall mass from three watersheds on the fernow experimental forest, West Virginia. In: Jacobs DF, Michler CH, editors. Proceedings, 16th central hardwood forest conference; April 8–9; West Lafayette, IN. Newtown Square (PA): USDA Forest Service. p. 179–186. General Technical Report NRS P-24.

Adu-Bredu S, Yokota T, Ogawa K, Hagihara A. 1997. Tree size dependence of litter production, and above-ground net production in a young Hinoki (*Chamaecyparis obtusa*) stand. J For Res. 2:31–37. doi:10.1007/BF02348260.

Alley JC, Fitzgerald BM, Berben PH, Haslett SJ. 1998. Annual and seasonal patterns of litter-fall of hard beech (*Nothofagus truncata*) and silver beech (*Nothofagus menziesii*) in relation to reproduction. New Zeal J Bot. 36:453–464. doi:10.1080/0028825X.1998.9512583.

Bray JR, Gorham E. 1964. Litter production in forests of the world. Adv Ecol Res. 2:101–157.

Brown S, Lugo AE. 1982. The storage and production of organic matter in tropical forests and their role in the global carbo cycle. Biotropica. 14:161–187. doi:10.2307/2388024.

Chave J, Navarrete D, Almeida S, Alvarez E, Aragao LEOC, Bonal D, Chatelet P, Silva-Espejo JE, Goret J-Y, von Hilderbrand P, et al. 2010. Regional and seasonal patterns of litterfall in tropical South America. Biogeosciences. 7:43–55. doi:10.5194/bg-7-43-2010.

Cheng CH, Hsiao SC, Huang YS, Hung CY, Pai CW, Chen CP, Menyailo OV. 2016a. Landslide-induced changes of soil physicochemical properties in Xitou, Central Taiwan. Geoderma. 265:187–195. doi:10.1016/j.geoderma.2015.11.028.

Cheng CH, Huang YS, Menyailo OV, Chen CT. 2016b. Stand development and aboveground biomass accumulation in cropland afforestation in Taiwan. Taiwan J For Sci. 31:105–118.

Cheng CH, Hung CY, Chen CP, Pei CW. 2013. Biomass carbon accumulation in aging Japanese cedar plantations in Xitou, central Taiwan. Bot Stud. 54:60. doi:10.1186/1999-3110-54-60.

Cheng CP, Wei C, Tsai MJ, Tsao TM. 2017. A Weibull model of the impact of thinning and a typhoon event on the stand structure of *Cryptomeria japonica* in central Taiwan over 100 years. J For Res. 22:22–29. doi:10.1080/13416979.2016.1256550.

Chiang CH, Liu SW. 1989. Age and seasonal variation of litter fall and nutrient contents of *Cryptomeria Japonica*. J Exp For Nat Taiwan Univ. 3:1–20. (in Chinese with English summary).

Chin CC 2008. Study on the spatial and temporal change of litterfall in Nanjenshan lowland rain forest [Master Thesis]. National Pingtung University of Science and Technology, Pingtung (Taiwan). (in Chinese with English summary).

Enoki T, Inoue T, Tashiro N, Ishii H. 2011. Aboveground productivity of an unsuccessful 140-year-old cryptomeria japonica plantation in northern Kyushu, Japan. J For Res, 16:268, 274.

Enright NJ. 1999. Litterfall dynamics in a mixed conifer-angiosperm forest in northern New Zealand. J Biogeogr. 26:149–157. doi:10.1046/j.1365-2699.1999.00257.x.

Feng C, Wang Z, Ma Y, Fu S, Chen HYH. 2019. Increased litterfall contributes to carbon and nitrogen accumulation following cessation of anthropogenic disturbances in degraded forests. For Ecol Manag. 432:832–839. doi:10.1016/j.foreco.2018.10.025.

Fujimori T. 2001. Ecological and silvicultural strategies for sustainable forest management. Amsterdam (The Netherlands): Elsevier Science B.V.

Hennessey TC, Dougherty PM, Cregg BM, Wittwer RF. 1992. Annual variation in needle fall of a loblolly pine stand in relation to climate and stand density. For Ecol Manag. 51:329–338. doi:10.1016/0378-1127(92)90332-4.

Holdridge LR. 1967. Life zone ecology. Sen Jose (Costa Rica): Tropical Science Center.

Huang YH, Hung CY, Lin IR, Kume T, Menyailo OV, Cheng CH. 2017. Soil respiration patterns and rates at three Taiwanese forest plantations: dependence on elevation, temperature, precipitation, and litterfall. Bot Stud. 58:49. doi:10.1186/s40529-017-0205-7.

Hughes JW, Fahey TJ. 1994. Litterfall dynamics and ecosystem recovery during forest development. For Ecol Manag. 63:181–198. doi:10.1016/0378-1127(94)90110-4.

Kouki J, Hokkanen T. 1992. Long-term needle litterfall of a Scots pine *Pinus sylvestris* stand: relation to temperature factors. Oecologia. 89:176–181. doi:10.1007/BF00317216.

Lawrence D. 2005. Regional-scale variation in litter production and seasonality in tropical dry forests of southern Mexico. Biotropica. 37:561–570. doi:10.1111/j.1744-7429.2005.00073.x.

Lin KC, Hamburg SP, Tang SI, Hsia YJ, Lin TC. 2003. Typhoon effects on litterfall in a subtropical forest. Can J For Res. 33:2184–2192. doi:10.1139/x03-154.

Lin KC, Hamburg SP, Wang L, Duh CT, Huang CM, Chang CT, Lin TC. 2017. Impacts of increasing typhoons on the structure and function of a subtropical forest: reflections of a changing climate. Sci Rep. 7:4911. doi:10.1038/s41598-017-05288-y.

Lin KC, Hwanwu CB, Liu CC. 1997. Phenology of broadleaf tree species in the Fushan Experimental Forest of northeastern Taiwan. Taiwan J For Sci. 12:247–353. (in Chinese with English summary).

Liu C, Westman CJ, Berg B, Kutsch W, Wang GZ, Man R, Ilvesniemi H. 2004. Variation in litterfall-climate relationships between coniferous and broadleaf forests in Eurasia. Global Ecol Biogeogr. 13:105–114. doi:10.1111/j.1466-882X.2004.00072.x.

Liu WL, Yu JC, Wang YN, Cheng CP, Chen CP, Cheng CH. 2018. Temporal and spatial variation of litterfall in the plantations of Xitou Natural Education Area: differences in seasons and vegetation types. Quart J Chin For. 51:231–250. (in Chinese with English summary).

Lodge DT, Scatena FN, Asbury CE, Sanchez MJ. 1991. Fine litterfall and related nutrient inputs resulting from Hurricane Hugo in subtropical wet and lower montane rain forests of Puerto Rico. Biotropica. 23:336–342. doi:10.2307/2388249.

Lu EY, Leong CM, Jhou RL, Peng JY, Liou SL. 2003. Litterfall study on adjacent plantations of *Schima suberba, Cunninghamia lanceolate*, and *Phyllostachys pubescens*: litterfall dynamics. J Exp For Nat Taiwan Univ. 17:171–185. (in Chinese with English summary).

Matala J, Kellomaki S, Nuutinen T. 2008. Litterfall in relation to volume growth of trees: analysis based on literature. Scand J For Res. 23:194–202. doi:10.1080/02827580802036176.

Matsushita A, Yoshida T, Hijii N, Takenaka C. 2017. Changes in the chemical compositions of leaf litter in the canopy of a Japanese cedar plantation. J For Res. 22:256–260.

Miyaura T, Hozumi K. 1993. A growth model of a single sugi (*Cryptomeria japonica*) tree based on the dry matter budget of its aboveground parts. Tree Physiol. 13:263–274. doi:10.1093/treephys/13.3.263.

Nakane K. 1995. Soil carbon cycling in a Japanese cedar (*Cryptomeria japonica*) plantation. For Ecol Manag. 72:185–197. doi:10.1016/0378-1127(94)03465-9.

Parsons SA, Valdez-Ramirez V, Congdon RA, Williams SE. 2014. Contrasting patterns of litterfall seasonality and seasonal changes in litter decomposability in a tropical rainforest region. Biogeosciences. 11:5047–5056. doi:10.5194/bg-11-5047-2014.

Starr M, Saarsalmi A, Hokkanen T, Merila P, Helmisaari HS. 2005. Models of litterfall production for Scots pine (*Pinus Sylvestris L.*) in Finland using stand, site and climate factors. For Ecol Manag. 205:215–225. doi:10.1016/j.foreco.2004.10.047.

Vitousek PM. 1984. Litterfall, nutrient cycling, and nutrient limitation in tropical forests. Ecology. 65:285–298. doi:10.2307/1939481.

Walker LR. 1991. Tree damage and recovery from Hurricane Hugo in Luquillo Experimental Forest, Puerto Rico. Biotropica. 23:379–385. doi:10.2307/2388255.

Wang HC, Lin KC, Huang CY. 2016. Temporal and spatial patterns of remotely sensed litterfall in tropical and subtropical forests of Taiwan. J Geophys Res Biogeosci. 121:509–522. doi:10.1002/2015JG003113.

Wang HC, Wang SF, Lin KC, Lee Shaner PJ, Lin TC. 2013. Litterfall and element fluxes in a natural hardwood forest and a Chinese-fir plantation experiencing frequent typhoon disturbance in central Taiwan. Biotropica. 45:541–548. doi:10.1111/btp.12048.

Yanai RD, Arthur MA, Acker M, Levine CR, Park BB. 2012. Variation in mass and nutrient concentration of leaf litter across years and sites in a northern hardwood forest. Can J For Res. 42:1597–1610. doi:10.1139/x2012-084.

Yang Y, Yanai RD, See CR, Arthur MA. 2017. Sampling effort and uncertainty in leaf litterfall mass and nutrient flux in northern hardwood forest. Ecosphere. 8:e01999. doi:10.1002/ecs2.1999.

Yoshida T, Hijii N. 2006. Spatiotemporal distribution of aboveground litter in a *Cryptomeria japonica* plantation. J For Res. 11:419–426. doi:10.1007/s10310-006-0235-6.

Zalamea M, Gonzalez G. 2008. Leaffall phenology in a subtropical wet forest in Puerto Rico: from species to community patterns. Biotropica. 40:295–304. doi:10.1111/j.1744-7429.2007.00389.x.

Zhang H, Yuan W, Dong W, Liu S. 2014. Seasonal patterns of litterfall in forest ecosystem worldwide. Ecol Complex. 20:240–247. doi:10.1016/j.ecocom.2014.01.003.

Differences in climate and drought response of the exotic plantation species *Abies firma, Cryptomeria japonica,* and *Chamaecyparis obtusa* in southern Korea

Jong Bin Jung, Hyun Jung Kim, Ji Sun Jung, Jong Woo Kim and Pil Sun Park

ABSTRACT

Exotic species plantations are increasing for timber production and other economic benefits. However, evaluation of species adaptation to local climates requires long-term research and the information is still limited. This study was conducted to understand the growth response of three exotic tree species, *Abies firma, Cryptomeria japonica*, and *Chamaecyparis obtusa*, to regional moisture conditions during the dry spring and wet summer in plantations located in south-central Korea. We examined the growth response of *A. firma, C. japonica*, and *C. obtusa* to monthly precipitation and drought indices from 1950 to 1998 using tree-ring analysis. The radial growth of *A. firma* showed a significantly positive relationship with precipitation and drought indices in spring ($p < 0.05$). Water stress in spring was the main limitation to radial growth in *A. firma*. In contrast, *C. japonica* and *C. obtusa*, with indeterminate growth, had negative correlations with precipitation and drought indices in summer ($p < 0.05$). Abnormally high summer precipitation may interrupt photosynthesis by reducing sunshine duration and evaporation, negatively affecting the growth of *C. japonica* and *C. obtusa*. The different responses of these species to monthly precipitation and drought indices imply that regional precipitation patterns should be carefully considered in species selection for the establishment of exotic species plantations.

Introduction

Exotic species with fast growth, straight form, and high commercial value are often favored over native species in forestry (Zobel et al. 1987; Haysom and Murphy 2003). Plantations of *Picea sitchensis* (Bong.) Carr. in Nordic countries, *Pinus radiata* D. Don in New Zealand, and *Eucalyptus* spp. in Africa are well-known examples of exotic species plantations (Pohjonen and Pukkala 1990; Kjær et al. 2014). However, careful consideration is required to establish exotic species plantations because environmental conditions in the introduced range may not be a good fit for the chosen species.

Precipitation and soil moisture play an important role in the success of exotic species plantations (Zobel et al. 1987) and drought adaptability to the introduced sites often determines their survival and growth (Colangelo et al. 2018; Vejpustková and Čihák 2019). Exotic species plantations with high water use could be more vulnerable to extreme drought events than natural forests (Fernández et al. 2009). *Pseudotsuga menziesii* (Mirb.) Franco, which had been widely planted in Europe, exhibited a decline in radial growth during increasing summer temperatures and drought due to global warming in Europe (Sergent et al. 2014; Vejpustková and Čihák 2019). Exotic *Robinia pseudoacacia* L. was negatively affected by drought stress, resulting in lower basal area increments than native species in Spanish riparian forests (González-Muñoz et al. 2015). Adaptability to regional moisture conditions should be an important consideration in the establishment of exotic species plantations (Meason and Mason 2014).

Exotic species have been actively used for rehabilitation and timber production in Korea since the 1960s. *Pinus rigida* Mill. and *R. pseudoacacia* are representative exotic species used for rehabilitation and *Larix kaempferi* (Lamb.) Carrière is used for timber production in Korea (Lee et al. 2017). Around 400 exotic species were tested for introduction to Korea in the 1950s to the 1980s, and over 90% failed due to misfit to climate, poor growth, or poor timber quality (Korea Forest Research Institute 2013).

Cryptomeria japonica (Thunb. ex L.f.) D. Don and *Chamaecyparis obtusa* (Siebold & Zucc.) Endl. are two exotic species with high potential as major timber species in southern Korea since their introduction from Japan in 1905 (Joseon Forest Society 1926; Kang 2003; Korea Forest Research Institute 2014). *Abies firma* Siebold & Zucc. was introduced in 1906 from Japan and planted mostly in arboretums and experimental forests in southern Korea (Kim 1975; Kwon et al. 1978). Despite over 100 years of plantation management of these species, information on their moisture adaptation to introduced sites and drought tolerance in the Korean climate is still limited (Kim 1978; Park et al. 2015a).

The normal precipitation of southern Korea ranges from 1,100 to 2,000 mm, with a mean annual precipitation of 1,450 mm between 1981 and 2010, which is higher than the mean annual precipitation of 1,162 mm in the Korean peninsula (Korea Meteorological Administration 2012). However, a high frequency of short-term droughts (less than 200 days) was witnessed, resulting in higher drought severity in the southern region than in other areas of Korea (Kim and Yoo 2006; Oh et al. 2014). Increasing consecutive dry days in spring and high precipitation in summer contributed to spring drought and summer floods (Choi 2004; Kim et al.

2005), which are expected to increase due to climate change (Boo et al. 2004; Nam et al. 2015). Understanding the responses of exotic species to regional moisture conditions during the growing season is essential for the management of exotic species plantations, especially with the increase in alternating dry-wet conditions in the southern region of Korea.

This study aimed to understand the growth responses of the exotic species *A. firma, C. japonica*, and *C. obtusa* to regional moisture conditions in spring and summer in plantations in southern Korea. We hypothesized that these species would be sensitive to drought in Korea since their plantations there have lower precipitation than their natural habitats in Japan (Tsukada 1982; Hoshino et al. 2001; Kubota 2006). To accomplish our purpose, we investigated 1) radial growth response to monthly precipitation, 2) growth response to drought indices at different timescales, and 3) the spatial scale of drought response.

Materials and methods

Study sites and species

The study was conducted at three non-native conifer plantations of *A. firma, C. japonica*, and *C. obtusa* in Nambu University Forest (35°01′N, 127°36′E) of Seoul National University in Gwangyang, Korea. Nambu University Forest is located in the south-central part of the Korean peninsula (Figure 1). The three plantations were established in 1921. They are located on lower mountain slopes between 105 and 308 m a.s.l. and have similar environmental conditions except the timing of thinning events (Table 1). The *C. obtusa* stand was thinned in 1999, the *C. japonica* stand in 2000, and the *A. firma* stand in 2001, 2005, and 2009. Salvage logging of typhoon-damaged trees was conducted in the *C. obtusa* plantation in 1987.

According to the meteorological data measured between 1996 and 2017 at the Chusan office of Nambu University Forest at 98 m a.s.l., the mean annual temperature of the area is 13.7°C. The coldest and hottest months are January and August, with mean temperatures of 1.6°C and 26.5°C, respectively. Mean annual precipitation is 1,610 mm and more than 50% of the precipitation is concentrated in the summer. Gneiss is the dominant rock type (Korea Institute of Geoscience and Mineral Resources 2019). The soil type is loam and sandy loam and belongs to the Inceptisols and Entisols (National Institute of Agricultural Sciences 2019). This area is warm-temperate forest dominated by *Pinus densiflora* Siebold & Zucc., *Quercus serrata* Murray, *Quercus variabilis* Blume, *Carpinus tschonoskii* Maxim., *Lindera erythrocarpa* Makino, and *Zelkova serrata* (Thunb.) Makino.

A. firma, C. japonica, and *C. obtusa* are representative coniferous species in warm-temperate and temperate forests in Japan and are important timber species (Japan Forestry Agency 2018; Iwaizumi et al. 2019). Their natural habitats are from 30° to 40° north latitude from Kyushu to northern Honshu (Kimura et al. 2014; Iwaizumi et al. 2019). The three species differ in physiological characteristics. *A. firma* has determinate growth, whereas *C. japonica* and *C. obtusa* have an indeterminate growth habit (Nagai et al. 2012; Shiraki et al. 2016). *A. firma* is known to be more shade-tolerant than *C. japonica* (Suzuki and Tsukahara 1987; Ozaki and Ohsawa 1995) and *C. obtusa* is known to be more drought-tolerant than *C. japonica* (Tsukada 1982; Nagakura et al. 2004).

A. firma, C. japonica, and *C. obtusa* were introduced to Korea in early 1900s (Joseon Forest Society 1926; Kim 1975) and plantation areas are 6,296 ha for *C. japonica* and 52,423 ha for *C. obtusa* (Korea Forest Research Institute 2014; Korea Forest Service 2019). *C. obtusa* plantations are increasing by 3,800–5,700 ha annually in the southern part of Korea with increasing demand, whereas *A. firma* and *C. japonica* plantations remain within small areas (Kang 2003; Korea Forest Service 2019).

Core sampling and tree-ring chronology

Twenty dominant or co-dominant trees were selected at each plantation for core sampling from 2016 to 2018. Two cores per tree were extracted perpendicular to the slope using a 5.15 mm increment borer at 0.2 m above the ground. A height of 0.2 m was used for core sampling to measure radial growth from the earliest stage possible. A total of 120

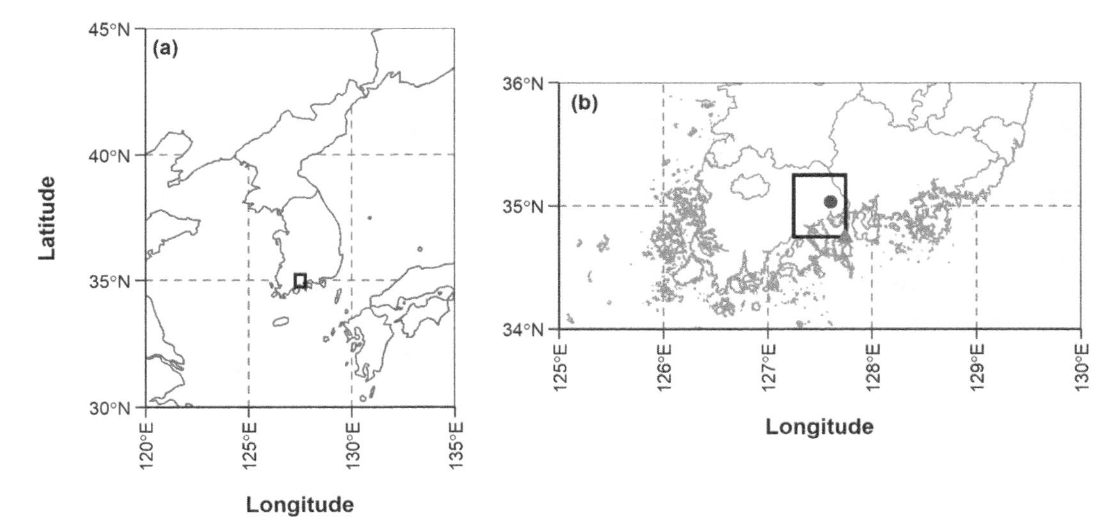

Figure 1. (a) Location of the Nambu University Forest of Seoul National University in Korea. (b) A closed circle indicates the Nambu University Forest where the study was conducted. A closed triangle indicates Yeosu weather station where data on evaporation and sunshine duration were collected. Climate variables of temperature and precipitation were downloaded from CRU TS v4.01 in a square area (34°75′–35°25′N, 127°25′–127°75′E).

Table 1. Stand information of *Abies firma, Cryptomeria japonica,* and *Chamaecyparis obtusa* plantations used for study sites in Nambu University Forest of Seoul National University, Gwangyang, Korea.

Species	*Abies firma*	*Cryptomeria japonica*	*Chamaecyparis obtusa*
Establishment year	1921	1921	1921
Area (ha)	0.5	1.1	2.4
Elevation (m)	105–129	143–152	233–308
Aspect (°)	330–22	358–14	325–30
Slope (°)	18–21	26–31	10–20
Thinning year	2001, 2005, 2009	2000	1999

cores were sampled from the three plantations. The cores were stored in plastic straws and moved to the laboratory.

Cores were air-dried, glued on wooden mounts, and sanded until the cells of the cross-section looked clear (Stokes and Smiley 1968). Then, cross-dating between cores was carried out under a stereomicroscope using the list-method (Yamaguchi 1991). After visual cross-dating, cores were scanned with an Epson Expression 1000XL scanner (Seiko Epson Corp., Suwa, Japan) at 1,200 dpi resolution and tree-ring widths were measured using the WinDENDRO^{TM} program (Regent Instruments Inc., Québec, Canada) in 0.001 mm units. Cross-dating quality of measured tree-ring series was checked using the COFECHA program (Holmes 1983). Three tree-ring series of *A. firma* that had low correlations with a master chronology were excluded from further analysis. Measured tree-ring series were standardized using a spline curve that had a frequency response of 50% at a wavelength of 0.67 to remove non-climatic noises (Cook and Peters 1981). The residual chronologies were produced by removing the variances caused by autocorrelation from detrended series using autoregressive model (AR model) and averaged using the bi-weight robust mean for each species to exclude the influence of outliers (Cook and Kairiukstis 1990). First-order autocorrelations were 0.055 for *A. firma*, 0.068 for *C. japonica* and −0.029 for *C. obtusa* after the application of the AR model. In this study, we used residual chronologies truncated at 1950–1998 in order to remove the noise caused by thinning after 1999.

Mean ring width (MRW), expressed population signal (EPS), subsample signal strength (SSS), mean sensitivity (MS), Rbar (within/between trees), and mean series inter-correlation (SI) were calculated for the three species' chronologies. EPS represents the variance of an infinite perfect population chronology explained by a finite sample chronology and gives a confidence to the sample chronology that represents the common signal (Briffa and Jones 1990). As Buras (2017) suggested, we also showed SSS to evaluate the strength of common signal between our samples. MS signifies inter-annual variability within a series and Rbar is an average pairwise correlation coefficient among tree-ring series within/between trees (Fritts 1976; Briffa and Jones 1990). SI represents the average correlation between one tree-ring series and a master chronology made by the other series for each species (Cook and Kairiukstis 1990).

Climate variables

The Climatic Research Unit (CRU) TS v4.01 dataset was used for the monthly time-series of minimum, mean, and maximum temperature and precipitation of the study area (Figure 2, Harris et al. 2014). The Gwangyang weather station was the nearest weather station to the study sites. However, the Gwangyang weather station started collecting data on evaporation and sunshine duration from 2011 to 2016, respectively, thus we used monthly evaporation and sunshine duration collected from the Yeosu weather station (65 m a.s.l.), which is 35 km away from the study sites (Korea Meteorological Administration 2018). The correlation coefficients between data from the Yeosu weather station and the Gwangyang weather station were over 0.92 ($p < 0.01$).

Monthly evaporation was calculated based on free-water evaporation measured using a small pan with a size of 20 cm in diameter and 10 cm in height at 24 h intervals (Lee and Kim 1985). The sunshine duration was the time in which the sunlight directly hit the surface of the earth and was measured by a rotating-type sunshine duration sensor (Korea Meteorological Administration 2018). We used climate data for 50 years, from 1949 to 1998. Data on evaporation and sunshine duration for 5 months from July to November 1950 were lost, so the monthly mean data from 1945 to 1955 were used for the missing period.

Drought indices

Drought severity can be described by using a specific drought index at a specific timescale, and each drought index has its own advantages and disadvantages. Three drought indices, the self-calibrating Palmer Drought Severity Index (scPDSI, Wells et al. 2004), the Standardized Precipitation Index (SPI, McKee et al. 1993), and the Standardized Precipitation Evapotranspiration Index (SPEI, Vicente-Serrano et al. 2010) were employed in this study for comparing and evaluating the growth response of each species to drought in multiple timescales and for identifying the most influential climate variable related with drought index to radial growth.

The scPDSI was provided by Dai (2017), which is calculated based on the difference between actual precipitation and potential precipitation under normal conditions at a specific location (details in Wells et al. (2004)). The scPDSI takes into account temperature and soil moisture conditions; however, it has a fixed timescale (Palmer 1965; Vicente-Serrano et al. 2012). In contrast, SPI and SPEI can be calculated with multiple timescales; thus, they can be used to analyze drought effects in hydrological, agricultural, and ecological aspects (Vicente-Serrano et al. 2012). SPI converts the precipitation deficit to probabilities based on long-term precipitation records and is relatively simple because it relies upon precipitation only (McKee et al. 1993; Tsakiris and Vangelis 2004). SPEI is similar to SPI; however, it uses water balance, considering temperature and evapotranspiration (Vicente-Serrano et al. 2010).

Both SPI and SPEI were calculated based on the CRU TS v4.01 dataset at the timescale of 1, 3, and 6 months using the SPEI package in the R program (Beguería et al. 2014). The period of the drought indices was from 1950 to 1998, the same as the period of the residual chronologies. The values of scPDSI, SPI and SPEI increase as drought severity decreases.

Statistical analysis

Bootstrapped Pearson's correlation was applied to assess the relationship between climate variables and the residual chronologies of *A. firma, C. japonica,* and *C. obtusa* (Zang

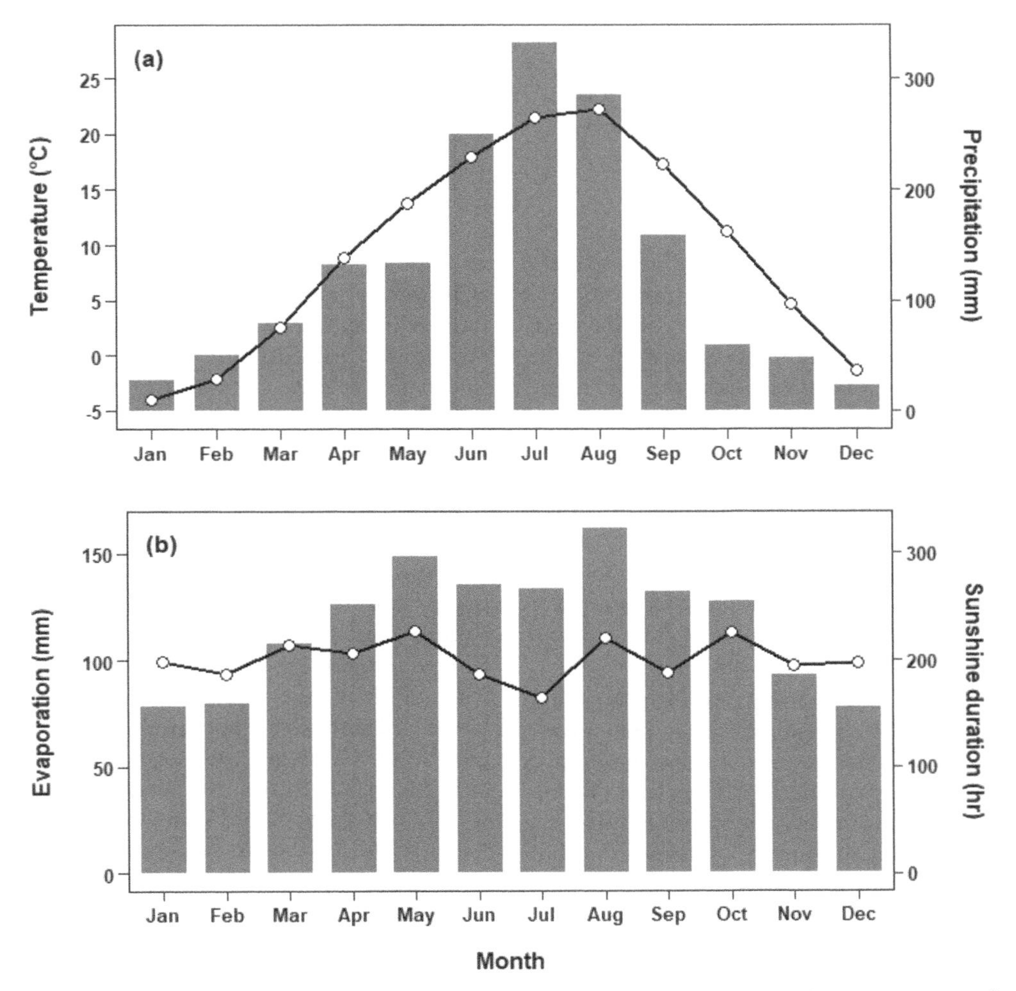

Figure 2. Climate variables of the Nambu University Forest of Seoul National University from 1949 to 1998. (a) Monthly mean temperature (line) and precipitation (bar), (b) evaporation (line) and sunshine duration (bar). Temperature and precipitation data were downloaded from the CRU TS v4.01 dataset. Evaporation and sunshine duration were obtained from the Yeosu weather station.

and Biondi 2015). Twelve consecutive months from November of the previous year to October of the current year were used for climate variables in the correlation analysis. We also compared the drought response of the three species using bootstrapped Pearson's correlations of three drought indices (scPDSI, SPI, and SPEI) and the residual chronologies. Growing season drought indices from April to October of the current year were used in the correlation analysis (Park et al. 2015b; Seo et al. 2017).

Spatial correlation analysis was conducted to investigate drought responses over spatial scales, using 0.5-degree gridded SPEI data from 1950 to 1998 at a timescale of 6 months (Beguería et al. 2010). This timescale was chosen because drought indices at 6-month time-scales reflect seasonal moisture conditions and plant growth better than other timescales (Tsakiris and Vangelis 2004; Barbeta et al. 2013). Pearson's correlation coefficients between drought indices and residual chronologies in spring (April–May) and summer (June–August) seasons were calculated. The drought pattern of southern Korea is similar to the southern part of the Yangtze River in China and central/southern Japan (Oh et al. 2014); thus, we conducted spatial analysis over the East Asian region. All statistical analyses were conducted using dplR (Bunn 2008), treeclim (Zang and Biondi 2015) and raster (Hijmans 2019) packages in R.3.6.1 (R Core Team 2019).

Results

Species chronologies

Over the common period of 1950–1998, *A. firma* showed the highest MRW at 2.27 mm, followed by *C. obtusa* at 1.96 mm and *C. japonica* at 1.65 mm (Table 2). All three species' chronologies met a criterion (EPS > 0.85) during the period. SSS and SI values also showed high coherence among cores from each species. The three species' chronologies had MS values of 0.21–0.30. Rbar values, which represent common signal within and between trees, ranged from 0.47 to 0.70 and 0.25–0.45, respectively. The *A. firma* chronology had the highest Rbar values in both within and between trees.

Table 2. Descriptive statistics for species chronologies from 1950 to 1998.

Species	*Abies firma*	*Cryptomeria japonica*	*Chamaecyparis obtusa*
No. trees/cores	20/37	20/40	20/40
MRW/STD (mm)	2.27/1.31	1.65/0.65	1.96/1.28
EPS	0.96	0.94	0.91
SSS	0.99	0.99	0.99
MS	0.29	0.21	0.30
Rbar.wt	0.70	0.47	0.50
Rbar.bt	0.45	0.32	0.25
SI	0.61	0.53	0.44

MRW: mean ring width; STD: standard deviation; EPS: expressed population signal; SSS: subsample signal strength; MS: mean sensitivity; Rbar.wt: average pairwise correlation coefficients within trees; Rbar.bt: average pairwise correlation coefficients between trees; SI: mean series intercorrelation.

C. obtusa had the lowest average correlation between trees at 0.25. SI values were similar to Rbar values, which were the highest in *A. firma* at 0.61, followed by *C. japonica* at 0.53 and *C. obtusa* at 0.44.

Climate-growth relationship

A. firma showed a negative relationship with the mean and maximum temperature of November in the previous year, with all temperature variables of June and with the maximum temperature of May in the current year ($p < 0.05$, Figure 3). On the other hand, the correlation coefficients between temperature variables and radial growth of *C. japonica* and *C. obtusa* were not significant.

Radial growth of *A. firma* showed a significantly positive correlation with May precipitation of the current year ($r = 0.45$, $p < 0.05$). In contrast, *C. japonica* and *C. obtusa* showed a negative relationship with the June precipitation of the current year. A negative correlation with June precipitation of the current year was also observed in *A. firma*, although it was not significant ($r = -0.20$).

The radial growth of *C. obtusa* had a positive relationship with July evaporation of the current year. The radial growth of *A. firma* decreased with increasing sunshine duration in December of the previous year and September and October of the current year ($p < 0.05$). The relationship between the radial growth of *C. japonica* and summer sunshine duration of the current year was positive.

Growth response to drought

All drought indices (scPDSI, SPI, and SPEI) showed similar relationships to the radial growth of the same species for short-term drought (Figure 4). At the 1-month timescale, the growth of *A. firma* was positively correlated with SPI and SPEI in May and *C. japonica* and *C. obtusa* showed negative correlations with SPI and SPEI in June. In 3- and 6-month timescales, *A. firma* showed significantly positive relationships with all drought indices in spring ($p < 0.05$). *C. japonica* had a negative relationship with drought indices in summer and autumn ($p < 0.05$), whereas the negative relationships between the growth of *C. obtusa* and drought indices were not significant at 3- and 6-month timescales.

Spatial correlations showed regional patterns of drought responses for the three species (Figure 5). The significant positive correlation between the radial growth of *A. firma* and spring (April–May) SPEI at the 6-month timescale mainly occurred in the southern to central parts of the Korean peninsula ($p < 0.05$). The radial growth of *C. japonica* also showed a significantly negative correlation with SPEI in the summer (June–August) in southern Korea. Meanwhile, the correlation between the radial growth of *C. obtusa* and summer SPEI was significant only in central Korea. No species' radial growth showed a clear pattern with the spring and summer SPEI in East Asian regions except in the southern region of the Korean peninsula.

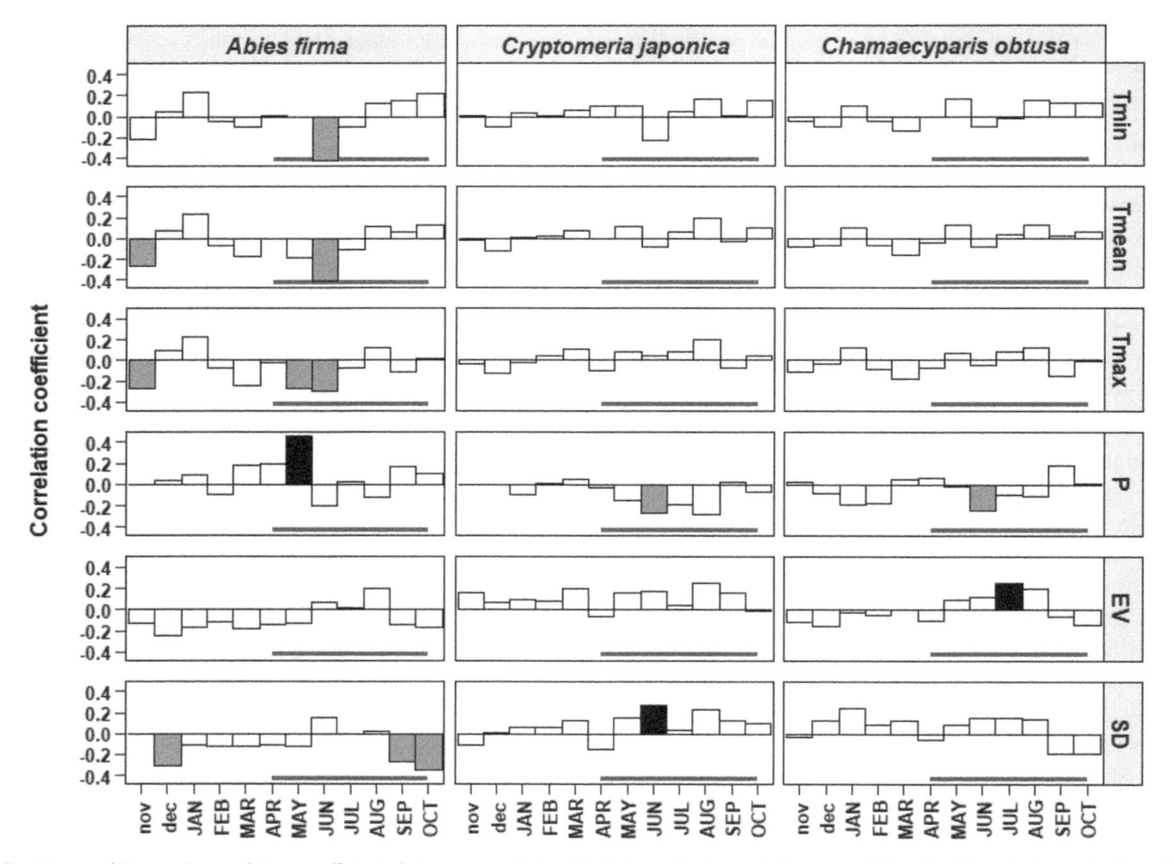

Figure 3. Bootstrapped Pearson's correlation coefficients between species' residual chronologies and climate variables. Black bars indicate significantly positive correlations and gray bars indicate significantly negative correlations ($p < 0.05$) between residual chronology and climate variables between 1949 and 1998. Grey lines represent the growing season of the current year. Climate variables represent Tmin: Minimum temperature; Tmean: Mean temperature; Tmax: Maximum temperature; P: Precipitation; EV: evaporation; and SD: Sunshine duration. Lowercase characters indicate months of previous year and uppercase characters indicate months of current year.

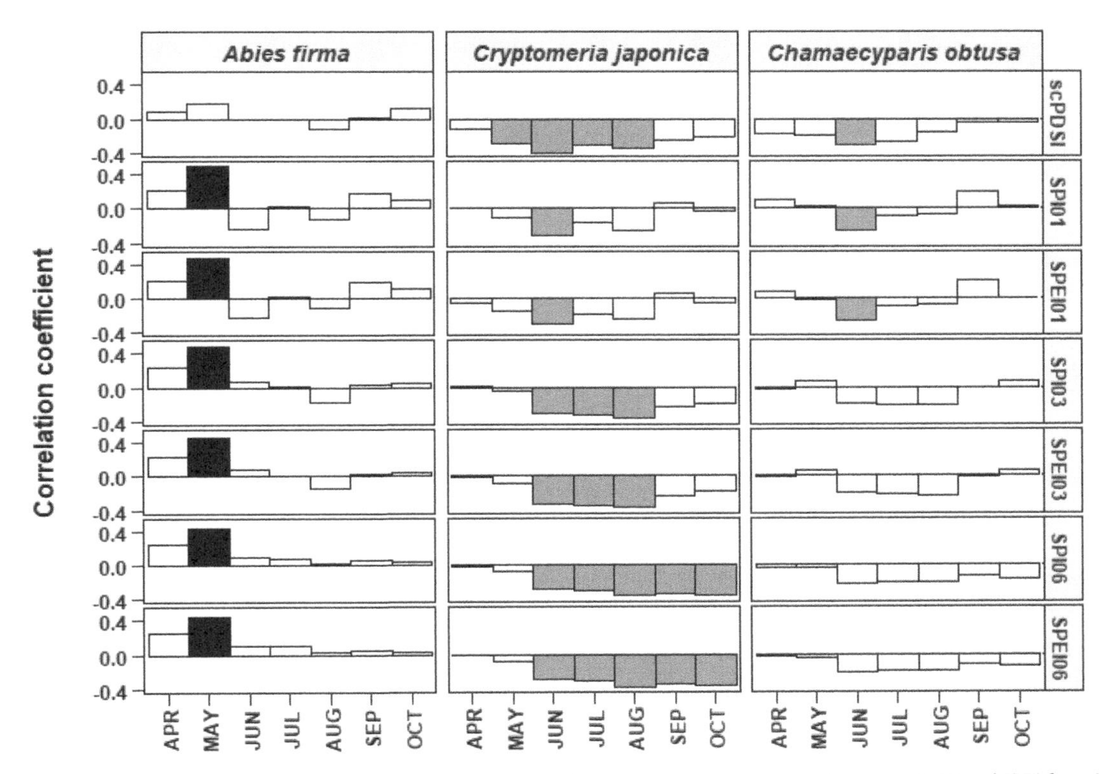

Figure 4. Bootstrapped Pearson's correlation coefficients between residual chronologies and monthly drought indices (scPDSI, SPI and SPEI) from April to October of the current year from 1950 to 1998. Numbers after drought indices represent time scales of 1 3, and 6 months. Black bars indicate significantly positive correlations and grey bars indicate significantly negative correlations ($p < 0.05$).

Discussion

Species-specific response to climate variables

The growth response to precipitation differed between *A. firma* and the two other species. The radial growth of *A. firma* showed a positive relationship with May precipitation of the current year and negative relationships with all temperature variables of June of the current year. Hot and dry conditions during the late spring and early summer reduce the radial growth of conifer species in Korea (Kim 1978; Park and Yadav 1998b; Park et al. 2001; Seo and Park 2002). The late spring drought usually occurs in mid-May (Lee and Byun 2009). Low precipitation in spring is likely to cause spring drought, and high temperatures may intensify water deficits by increasing evaporation (Trenberth et al. 2014). Trees close their stomata under water deficits to reduce transpiration, thereby reducing water loss, with a consequent reduction in carbon assimilation (Chaves 1991). Consequently, the low precipitation in May and high temperature in June caused water stress, which negatively affected the radial growth of *A. firma*.

A. firma, C. japonica, and *C. obtusa* are distributed in humid or moist regions with high summer precipitation in their native habitats (Hoshino et al. 2001; Kubota 2006; Kimura et al. 2014). Thus, these species were planted in southern Korea where precipitation is over 1,200 mm (Korea Forest Research Institute 2012). Kim (1978) reported that the growth of *A. firma* and *C. japonica* has a positive relationship with summer precipitation in the current year, which is in contrast to our result showing a negative relationship between June precipitation in the current year and radial growth. The negative relationship between June precipitation and radial growth might be explained by the decrease in solar radiation due to the monsoon rainfall. From mid-June to early July, the development of rain bands across East Asia provides a large portion of annual precipitation in this region (Lee and Kim 1983; Byun and Lee 2002). High precipitation results in a decrease in sunshine duration, leading to a decrease in solar radiation for photosynthesis and tree growth in June–July (Park and Yadav 1998a; Ahn et al. 2016). As a result, the significant positive correlation between June sunshine duration and growth of *C. japonica* indicates the complicated relationships among growth, sunshine duration, and precipitation under moist conditions (Stahle et al. 1991).

The negative relationship of current summer precipitation with radial growth of *C. japonica* and *C. obtusa* might be related to the indeterminate growth of these species (Nagai et al. 2012; Shiraki et al. 2016). In multiple-flush species, the pre-formed leaves and shoots flush out, then recurrent flushes follow within the same growing season (Pallardy 2008). The recurrent flush of *C. japonica* occurs in June–July (Nagai et al. 2012), and high precipitation in this period might interfere with radial growth by a recurrent flush, which seems to negatively affect the radial growth of this species.

Drought response and species' physiological traits

The drought indices in this study were calculated by different climate variables. However, scPDSI and SPEI showed a similar growth response as SPI, which was calculated based on simple precipitation data, indicating that precipitation excess or shortage affects radial growth more than temperature, soil moisture, or evapotranspiration. Temperature variables did not show a significant relationship with radial growth except for in *A. firma*, also implying

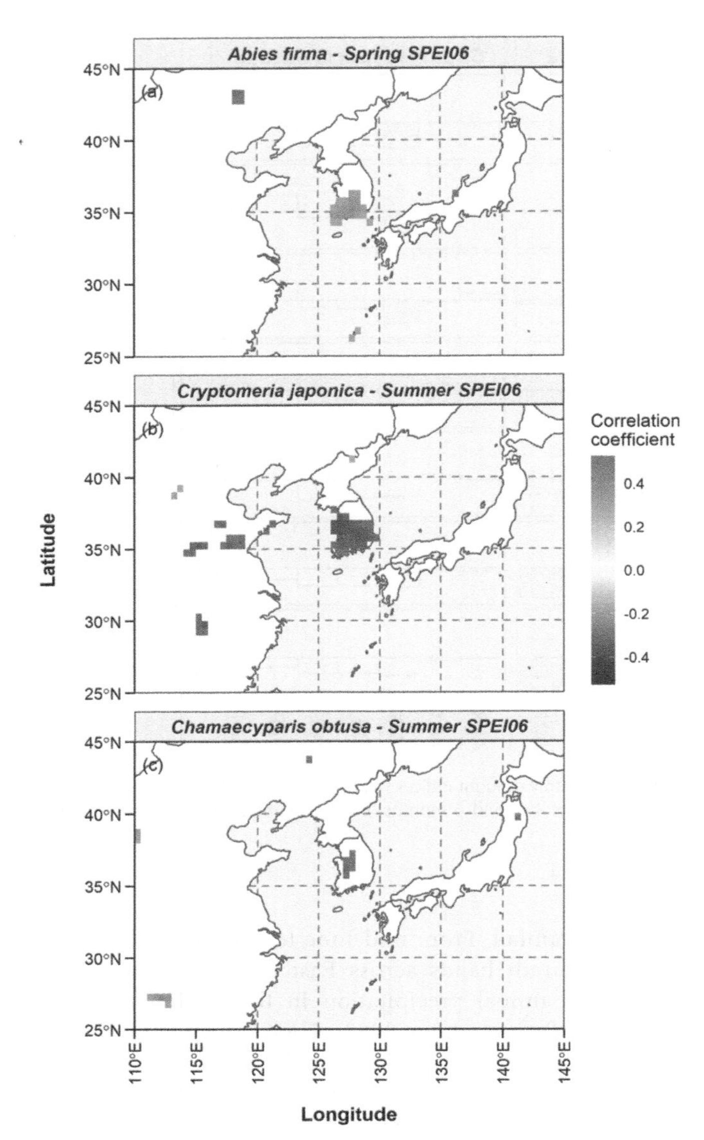

Figure 5. Spatial correlation between species' residual chronology and seasonal 6-month SPEI from 1950 to 1998. (a) *Abies firma* and April-May SPEI, (b) *Cryptomeria japonica* and June-August SPEI and (c) *Chamaecyparis obtusa* and June-August SPEI. Red indicates a significantly positive relationship and purple indicates a significantly negative relationship ($p < 0.05$).

that radial growth is affected by precipitation more than the temperature in this region.

Species-specific response to drought depends on the physiological characteristics that determine species behavior under water deficit (Yin and Bauerle 2017). Hydraulic traits of xylem and stomata control influence the drought response of each species (Brodribb et al. 2014; Anderegg et al. 2018). Conifers have two main pathways to cope with drought: isohydric and anisohydric (Brodribb et al. 2014). Isohydric species maintain a constant leaf water potential through stomata control, independent of soil water status. In contrast, the leaf water potential of anisohydric species changes with soil water status and evaporative demand (Tardieu and Simonneau 1998). Under water stress, isohydric Pinaceae species close stomata immediately through a high concentration of foliar abscisic acid (ABA), resulting in reduced carbon assimilation. In contrast, Cupressaceae species are anisohydric; thus, the xylem has high cavitation resistance and water potential is used to regulate stomata closure, maintaining photosynthetic capacity, which enables Cupressaceae species to recover rapidly after drought (Brodribb and Mcadam 2013). The anisohydric behavior of the two Cupressaceae species, *C. japonica* and *C. obtusa*, could maintain a net assimilation rate under dry conditions, which makes them more tolerant to spring drought compared to *A. firma* (Nagakura et al. 2004).

The shade tolerance of the species might also affect drought response (Markesteijn and Poorter 2009). Drought tolerance has a negative relationship with shade tolerance in temperate forests (Niinemets and Valladares 2006). Higher leaf longevity and lower leaf dry mass per area (LMA) are associated with shade tolerance, whereas drought-tolerant evergreen conifers tend to have low leaf longevity and high LMA, implying a trade-off between shade tolerance and drought tolerance (Hallik et al. 2009). Shade-tolerant species may invest more biomass in leaves to capture sufficient light than in roots to absorb water, resulting in less drought tolerance (Shipley and Meziane 2002). *A. firma* is the most shade-tolerant species among the three species, with higher LMA and a longer leaf longevity of ~10 years (Suzuki and Tsukahara 1987; Miyashita and Tateno 2014; Ito et al. 2017). The trade-off between shade tolerance and drought tolerance discussed above made *A. firma* the most vulnerable to drought among the three species.

In conclusion, we found that precipitation was the prevailing climatic factor for the radial growth of *A. firma, C. japonica*, and *C. obtusa*. In particular, spring drought and high summer precipitation negatively affected the radial growth of these species. We also found that drought response was species specific and limited in terms of spatial and temporal scales. This suggests that more careful management of water resources in each exotic species plantation is needed in the southern regions of Korea under climate change. Also, seasonal precipitation patterns should be carefully considered in species selection for the establishment of exotic species plantations. However, our study only showed the growth response of exotic species during twentieth century, and further dendroclimatological research will cover more recent climatic conditions and growth response.

Acknowledgments

Support was provided by R&D Program for Forest Science Technology (Project No. 2014109C10-2020-AA01) of the Korea Forestry Promotion Institute, Korea Forest Service, and research funding (500-20170206) of Seoul National University. We would like to thank all of those who participated in the field survey and data processing. We thank the Nambu University Forest, Seoul National University for permitting access and data collection. We acknowledge the Research Institute of Agriculture and Life Sciences, Seoul National University, for language assistance and the anonymous reviewers for their valuable comments.

Disclosure statement

No potential conflict of interest was reported by the authors.

Funding

This work was supported by the Korea Forest Service (Korea Forestry Promotion Institute) [2014109C10-2020-AA01]; Seoul National

University [500-20170206].

References

Ahn SH, Zo IS, Jee JB, Kim BY, Lee DG, Lee KT. 2016. The estimation of monthly average solar radiation using sunshine duration and precipitation observation data in Gangneung region. J Korean Earth Sci Soc. 37(1):29–39. doi:10.5467/JKESS.2016.37.1.29.

Anderegg WRL, Konings AG, Trugman AT, Yu K, Bowling DR, Gabbitas R, Karp DS, Pacala S, Sperry JS, Sulman BN, et al. 2018. Hydraulic diversity of forests regulates ecosystem resilience during drought. Nature. 561(7724):538–541. doi:10.1038/s41586-018-0539-7

Barbeta A, Ogaya R, Peñuelas J. 2013. Dampening effects of long-term experimental drought on growth and mortality rates of a holm oak forest. Global Change Biol. 19(10):3133–3144. doi:10.1111/gcb.12269.

Beguería S, Vicente-Serrano SM, Angulo-Martínez M. 2010. A multiscalar global drought dataset: the SPEIbase: a new gridded product for the analysis of drought variability and impacts. Bull Am Meteorol Soc. 91(10):1351–1356. doi:10.1175/2010BAMS2988.1.

Beguería S, Vicente-Serrano SM, Reig F, Latorre B. 2014. Standardized precipitation evapotranspiration index (SPEI) revisited: parameter fitting, evapotranspiration models, tools, datasets and drought monitoring. Int J Climatol. 34(10):3001–3023. doi:10.1002/joc.3887.

Boo KO, Kwon WT, Oh JH, Baek HJ. 2004. Response of global warming on regional climate change over Korea: an experiment with the MM5 model. Geophys Res. 31:L21206.

Briffa K, Jones P. 1990. Basic chronology statistics and assessment. In: Cook ER, Kairiukstis LA, editors. Methods of dendrochronology: applications in the environmental sciences. Dordrecht (NL): Kluwer Academic Publishers; p. 137–152.

Brodribb TJ, Mcadam SAM. 2013. Abscisic acid mediates a divergence in the drought response of two conifers. Plant Physiol. 162 (3):1370–1377. doi:10.1104/pp.113.217877.

Brodribb TJ, Mcadam SAM, Jordan GJ, Martins SCV. 2014. Conifer species adapt to low-rainfall climates by following one of two divergent pathways. Proc Natl Acad Sci U S A. 111(40):14489–14493. doi:10.1073/pnas.1407930111.

Bunn AG. 2008. A dendrochronology program library in R (dplR). Dendrochronologia. 26(2):115–124. doi:10.1016/j.dendro.2008.01.002.

Buras A. 2017. A comment on the expressed population signal. Dendrochronologia. 44:130–132. doi:10.1016/j.dendro.2017.03.005.

Byun HR, Lee DK. 2002. Defining three rainy seasons and the hydrological summer monsoon in Korea using available water resources index. J Meteorolog Soc Jpn. 80(1):33–44. doi:10.2151/jmsj.80.33.

Chaves MM. 1991. Effects of water deficits on carbon assimilation. J Exp Bot. 42(1):1–16. doi:10.1093/jxb/42.1.1.

Choi Y. 2004. Trends on temperature and precipitation extreme events in Korea. J Korean Geog Soc. 39(5):711–721.

Colangelo M, Camarero J, Ripullone F, Gazol A, Sanchez-Salguero R, Oliva J, Redondo M. 2018. Drought decreases growth and increases mortality of coexisting native and introduced tree species in a temperate floodplain forest. Forests. 9(4):205. doi:10.3390/f9040205.

Cook ER, Kairiukstis LA. editors. 1990. Methods of dendrochronology: applications in the environmental sciences. Dordrecht (NL): Kluwer Academic Publishers.

Cook ER, Peters K. 1981. The smoothing spline: a new approach to standardizing forest interior tree-ring width series for dendroclimatic studies. Tree-Ring Bull. 41:45–53.

Dai A. 2017. Data from: dai global Palmer drought severity index (PDSI) [dataset]. Research Data Archive at the National Center for Atmospheric Research, Computational and Information Systems Laboratory. [accessed. 2019(Feb):8]. doi:10.5065/D6QF8R93.

Fernández ME, Gyenge J, Schlichter T. 2009. Water flux and canopy conductance of natural versus planted forests in Patagonia, South America. Trees-structure and Function. 23(2):415–427. doi:10.1007/s00468-008-0291-y.

Fritts HC. 1976. Tree rings and climate. Caldwell (NJ): Blackburn Press.

González-Muñoz N, Linares J, Castro-Díez P, Sass-Klaassen U. 2015. Contrasting secondary growth and water-use efficiency patterns in native and exotic trees co-occurring in inner Spain riparian forests. Forest Syst. 24(1):e017. doi:10.5424/fs/2015241-06586.

Hallik L, Niinemets Ü, Wright IJ. 2009. Are species shade and drought tolerance reflected in leaf-level structural and functional differentiation in Northern Hemisphere temperate woody flora? New Phytol. 184(1):257–274. doi:10.1111/j.1469-8137.2009.02918.x.

Harris I, Jones PD, Osborn TJ, Lister DH. 2014. Updated high-resolution grids of monthly climatic observations – the CRU TS3.10 Dataset. Int J Climatol. 34(3):623–642. doi:10.1002/joc.3711.

Haysom KA, Murphy ST. 2003. The status of invasiveness of forest tree species outside their natural habitat: a global review and discussion paper. Rome: FAO. Forest Health and Biosecurity Working Paper FBS/3E.

Hijmans RJ 2019. Raster: geographic data analysis and modeling. R package version 3.0-7; [accessed 2019 Oct 18]. https://cran.r-project.org/web/packages/raster/raster.pdf.

Holmes RL. 1983. Computer assisted quality control in tree-ring dating and measurement. Tree-Ring Bull. 43:69–78.

Hoshino D, Nishimura N, Yamamoto S. 2001. Age, size structure and spatial pattern of major tree species in an old-growth *Chamaecyparis obtusa* forest, central Japan. For Ecol Manage. 152(1):31–43. doi:10.1016/S0378-1127(00)00614-9.

Ito K, Ota T, Mizoue N, Yoshida S, Sakuta K, Inoue A, Ito S, Okada H. 2017. Differences in growth responses between *Cryptomeria japonica* and *Chamaecyparis obtusa* planted in group selection openings in Kyushu, southern Japan. J For Res. 22(2):126–130. doi:10.1080/13416979.2017.1283978.

Iwaizumi MG, Ohtani M, Nasu J, Takahashi M. 2019. Development of highly polymorphic genomic microsatellite markers and their application to gene flow in a natural population of *Abies firma*. J For Res. 24(5):330–334. doi:10.1080/13416979.2019.1663579.

Japan Forestry Agency. 2018. Annual report on forest and Forestry in Japan – fiscal year 2017 (summary). Tokyo:Ministry of Agriculture, Forestry and Fisheries. English.

Joseon Forest Society. 1926. Green of the peninsula. Seoul: Joseon Forest Society. (Japanese)

Kang YH. 2003. Historical documents on proper tree selection system during the periods of Chosun dynasty and under the Japanese rule. Korean J Ecol. 26(6):341–347. doi:10.5141/JEFB.2003.26.6.341.

Kim DH, Yoo C. 2006. Analysis of spatial distribution of droughts in Korea through drought severity-duration-frequency analysis. J Korea Water Resour Assoc. 39(9):745–754.

Kim EH, Kim MK, Lee WS. 2005. The regional characteristics of daily precipitation intensity in Korea for recent 30 years. J Korean Earth Sci Soc. 26(5):404–416.

Kim SK. 1978. Correlation between the diameter growth of momi fir and Japanese cedar and the meteorological factors. Jour Jinju A & F Jr coll. 16:25–29.

Kim SS. 1975. A study on the woody plants introduced to the southern part of Korea. J Korean For Soc. 26:31–41.

Kimura MK, Uchiyama K, Nakao K, Moriguchi Y, San Jose-Maldia L, Tsumura Y. 2014. Evidence for cryptic northern refugia in the last glacial period in *Cryptomeria japonica*. Ann Bot. 114(8):1687–1700. doi:10.1093/aob/mcu197.

Kjær ED, Lobo A, Myking T. 2014. The role of exotic tree species in Nordic forestry. Scand J For Res. 29(4):323–332. doi:10.1080/02827581.2014.926098.

Korea Forest Research Institute. 2012. Gyeongje sujong 5: pyeonbaek [Economical tree species 5: *chamaecyparis obtusa*]. Seoul: Korea Forest Research Institute. (Korean)

Korea Forest Research Institute. 2013. Growth performance of exotic trees in Korea. Seoul: Korea Forest Research Institute. (Korean)

Korea Forest Research Institute. 2014. Nambujiyeog juyo sujongbyeol jawonteugseong mich pyeong-ga [Resource characteristics and evaluation of major tree species in the southern region of Korea]. Seoul: Korea Forest Research Institute. Korean.

Korea Forest Service. 2019. Statistical yearbook of forestry 2019. Daejeon:Korean Forest Service. No. 11-1400000-000001-10.

Korea Institute of Geoscience and Mineral Resources. 2019. MGEO, multiplatform geoscience information system. Daejeon: korea Institute of Geoscience and Mineral Resources; [accessed 2019 Sep 5]. https://mgeo.kigam.re.kr. Registration required.

Korea Meteorological Administration. 2012. The climate atlas of Korea. Seoul:Korea meteorological Administration.

Korea Meteorological Administration. 2018. Annual climatological report. Seoul:Korea meteorological Administration.

Kubota Y. 2006. Spatial pattern and regeneration dynamics in a temperate *Abies–Tsuga* forest in southwestern Japan. J For Res. 11(3):191–201. doi:10.1007/s10310-006-0205-z.

Kwon YC, Kim OR, Kim JK, Kang DC, Park MA. 1978. Study on silvicultural characteristics of momi-fir (*Abies firma* Siebold et Zuccarini) on southern part of Korea. Jour Jinju A & F Jr coll. 16:1–8.

Lee BS, Kim SS. 1983. Climatological characteristics of the Changma season. J Korean Met Soc. 19(1):1–11.

Lee DK, Kwon KC, Kang KS. 2017. Contribution of tree plantation, tree breeding and soil erosion control techniques developed during Saemaul Undong periods to the successful forest rehabilitation in the Republic of Korea. J Korean For Soc. 106(4):371–379.

Lee KH, Kim MI. 1985. Seasonal variations of the evaporation in Korea. J Korean Assoc Hydrol Sci. 18(3):243–251.

Lee SM, Byun HR. 2009. Some causes of the May drought over Korea. Asia-Pac J Atmos Sci. 45(3):247–264.

Markesteijn L, Poorter L. 2009. Seedling root morphology and biomass allocation of 62 tropical tree species in relation to drought- and shade-tolerance. J Ecol. 97:311–325. doi:10.1111/j.1365-2745.2008.01466.x.

McKee TB, Doesken NJ, Kleist J 1993. The relationship of drought frequency and duration to time scales. In: Proceedings of the 8th Conference on Applied Climatology; Jan 17-22; Anaheim (CA): American Meteorological Society. p. 179–184.

Meason DF, Mason WL. 2014. Evaluating the deployment of alternative species in planted conifer forests as a means of adaptation to climate change – case studies in New Zealand and Scotland. Ann For Sci. 71 (2):239–253. doi:10.1007/s13595-013-0300-1.

Miyashita A, Tateno M. 2014. A novel index of leaf RGR predicts tree shade tolerance. Funct Ecol. 28(6):1321–1329. doi:10.1111/1365-2435.12290.

Nagai S, Saitoh TM, Kobayashi H, Ishihara M, Suzuki R, Motohka T, Nasahara KN, Muraoka H. 2012. In situ examination of the relationship between various vegetation indices and canopy phenology in an evergreen coniferous forest, Japan. Int J Remote Sens. 33 (19):6202–6214. doi:10.1080/01431161.2012.682660.

Nagakura J, Shigenaga H, Akama A, Takahashi M. 2004. Growth and transpiration of Japanese cedar (*Cryptomeria japonica*) and hinoki cypress (*Chamaecyparis obtusa*) seedlings in response to soil water content. Tree Physiol. 24(11):1203–1208. doi:10.1093/treephys/24.11.1203.

Nam WH, Hayes MJ, Svoboda MD, Tadesse T, Wilhite DA. 2015. Drought hazard assessment in the context of climate change for South Korea. Agric Water Manag. 160:106–117. doi:10.1016/j.agwat.2015.06.029.

National Institute of Agricultural Sciences. 2019. Korea soil information system. Wanju: National Institute of Agricultural Sciences. [accessed 2019May10https://soil.rda.go.kr/soil/soilmap/characteristic.jsp

Niinemets Ü, Valladares F. 2006. Tolerance to shade, drought, and waterlogging of temperate Northern Hemisphere trees and shrubs. Ecol Monogr. 76(4):521–547. doi:10.1890/0012-9615(2006)076[0521:TTSDAW]2.0.CO;2.

Oh SB, Byun HR, Kim DW. 2014. Spatiotemporal characteristics of regional drought occurrence in East Asia. Theor Appl Climatol. 117 (1–2):89–101. doi:10.1007/s00704-013-0980-3.

Ozaki K, Ohsawa M. 1995. Successional change of forest pattern along topographical gradients in warm-temperate mixed forests in Mt Kiyosumi, central Japan. Ecol Res. 10(3):223–234.

Pallardy SG. 2008. Physiology of woody plants. 3rded. San Diego (CA): Academic Press. Chapter 3, Vegetative growth. p.39–86.

Palmer WC 1965. Meteorological drought. Washington (DC): Weather Bureau, U.S. Department of Commerce. Research Paper No. 45.

Park SG, You HC, Oh CJ, Choi WK. 2015a. Analysis of the correlation between site environmental factors and tree ring growth in *Chamaecyparis obtusa* stands in Jeonnam province. Korean J Environ Ecol. 29(5):777–784. doi:10.13047/KJEE.2015.29.5.777.

Park S-Y, Eom C-D, Seo J-W. 2015b. Seasonal change of cambium activity of pine trees at different growth sites. J Korean Wood Sci Technol. 43(4):411–420. doi:10.5658/WOOD.2015.43.4.411.

Park WK, Koo KA, Kong WS, Pumijumnong N. 2001. Effects of El Nino-Southern Oscillation (ENSO) on tree growths in central Korea. Korean J Quat Res. 15(1):53–61.

Park WK, Yadav RR. 1998a. A dendroclimatic analysis of *Pinus densiflora* from Mt. Chiri in Southern Korea. Ann Sci For. 55:451–459.

Park WK, Yadav RR. 1998b. Reconstruction of May precipitation (AD 1731-1995) in west-central Korea from tree rings of Korean red pine. Asia-Pac J Atmos Sci. 34(3):459–465.

Pohjonen V, Pukkala T. 1990. *Eucalyptus globulus* in Ethiopian forestry. For Ecol Manage. 36(1):19–31. doi:10.1016/0378-1127(90)90061-F.

R Core Team. 2019. R: A language and environment for statistical computing. Vienna (AU): R Foundation for Statistical Computing. [accessed 2019Sep5https://www.R-project.org/

Seo JW, Choi EB, Ju JD, Shin CS. 2017. The association of intra-annual cambial activities of *Pinus koraiensis* and *Chamaecyparis pisifera* planted in Mt. Worak with climatic factors. J Korean Wood Sci Technol. 45(1):43–52. doi:10.5658/WOOD.2017.45.1.43.

Seo JW, Park WK. 2002. Reconstruction of May precipitation (317 Years: AD. 1682~1998) using tree rings of *Pinus densiflora* S. et. Z. in western Sorak Mt. Korean J Quat Res. 16(1):29–36.

Sergent AS, Rozenberg P, Bréda N. 2014. Douglas-fir is vulnerable to exceptional and recurrent drought episodes and recovers less well on less fertile sites. Ann For Sci. 71(6):697–708. doi:10.1007/s13595-012-0220-5.

Shipley B, Meziane D. 2002. The balanced-growth hypothesis and the allometry of leaf and root biomass allocation. Funct Ecol. 16:326–331. doi:10.1046/j.1365-2435.2002.00626.x.

Shiraki A, Azuma W, Kuroda K, Ishii HR. 2016. Physiological and morphological acclimation to height in cupressoid leaves of 100-year-old *Chamaecyparis obtusa*. Tree Physiol. 37 (10):1327–1336.

Stahle DW, Cleaveland MK, Cerveny RS. 1991. Tree-ring reconstructed sunshine duration over central USA. Int J Climatol. 11(3):285–295. doi:10.1002/joc.3370110305.

Stokes M, Smiley T. 1968. An introduction to tree-ring dating. Chicago (IL): University of Chicago Press.

Suzuki E, Tsukahara J. 1987. Age structure and regeneration of old growth *Cryptomeria japonica* forests on Yakushima Island. Bot Mag Tokyo. 100(3):223–241. doi:10.1007/BF02492832.

Tardieu F, Simonneau T. 1998. Variability among species of stomatal control under fluctuating soil water status and evaporative demand: modelling isohydric and anisohydric behaviours. J Exp Bot. 49:419–432. doi:10.1093/jxb/49.Special_Issue.419.

Trenberth KE, Dai A, van der Schrier G, Jones PD, Barichivich J, Briffa KR, Sheffield J. 2014. Global warming and changes in drought. Nat Clim Change. 4:17–22. doi:10.1038/nclimate2067.

Tsakiris G, Vangelis H. 2004. Towards a drought watch system based on spatial SPI. Water Resour Manag. 18(1):1–12. doi:10.1023/B:WARM.0000015410.47014.a4.

Tsukada M. 1982. *Cryptomeria japonica*: glacial refugia and late-glacial and postglacial migration. Ecology. 63(4):1091–1105. doi:10.2307/1937247.

Vejpustková M, Čihák T. 2019. Climate response of Douglas fir reveals recently increased sensitivity to drought stress in central Europe. Forests. 10(2):97. doi:10.3390/f10020097.

Vicente-Serrano SM, Beguería S, López-Moreno JI. 2010. A multiscalar drought index sensitive to global warming: the standardized precipitation evapotranspiration index. J Clim. 23(7):1696–1718. doi:10.1175/2009JCLI2909.1.

Vicente-Serrano SM, Beguería S, Lorenzo-Lacruz J, Camarero JJ, López-Moreno JI, Azorin-Molina C, Revuelto J, Morán-Tejeda E, Sanchez-Lorenzo A. 2012. Performance of drought indices for ecological, agricultural, and hydrological applications. Earth Interact. 16 (10):1–27. doi:10.1175/2012EI000434.1.

Wells N, Goddard S, Hayes MJ. 2004. A self-calibrating Palmer drought severity index. J Clim. 17(12):2335–2351. doi:10.1175/1520-0442-(2004)017<2335:ASPDSI>2.0.CO;2.

Yamaguchi DK. 1991. A simple method for cross-dating increment cores from living trees. Can J For Res. 21(3):414–416. doi:10.1139/x91-053.

Yin J, Bauerle TL. 2017. A global analysis of plant recovery performance from water stress. Oikos. 126(10):1377–1388. doi:10.1111/oik.04534.

Zang C, Biondi F. 2015. treeclim: an R package for the numerical calibration of proxy-climate relationships. Ecography. 38 (4):431–436. doi:10.1111/ecog.01335.

Zobel BJ, van Wyk G, Stahl P. 1987. Growing exotic forests. New York (NY): John Wiley & Sons.

Investigating the factors influencing trap capture of bark and ambrosia beetles using long-term trapping data in a cool temperate forest in central Japan

Naoto Kamata, Sunisa Sanguansub, Roger A. Beaver, Toshihiro Saito and Toshihide Hirao

ABSTRACT

From 1994 to 2003, bark and ambrosia beetles were captured from April to November at 12 sites in the University of Tokyo Chichibu Forest, central Japan, using flight-barrier traps with alpha-pinene and ethanol as a lure. Additional trapping was conducted between July 2013 and November 2014 at the same sites using Lindgren's funnel traps with ethanol. Factors influencing trap captures were investigated, accounting especially for the indirect influence of sika deer on beetle populations due to induced tree mortality. Owing to incomplete data collection in 2013, trap captures of August and after August ("AUG" for 12 years) were analyzed separately from those of the whole season ("ALL" for 11 years). Trap captures in 2013–2014 were greater than those in 1994–2003. There was also an increase in the number of species across both periods, which was more conspicuous in "AUG". Seventeen indicator species were found in 2013–2014, and only two in 1994–2003. This could be partially explained by the difference in the lure used. A sudden population increase in 25 species was observed between the average over 1994–2003 and 2013–2014. Increasing trends during the 1994–2003 were also recognized in 13 species, with a sudden increase in 6 species in the last few years of the period. These coincided with increases in sika deer populations across both periods. An increase in tree mortality caused by increases in the deer population is likely the cause of the increase in bark and ambrosia beetles.

Introduction

Problems caused by bark and ambrosia beetles have been increasing in the world. Although outbreaks of bark beetles were well known to cause devastating damage to conifer stands by transmitting blue stain fungi, ambrosia beetles were believed to be pests for logs, not living trees (Coulson and Witter 1984). However, the situation has changed since the late 1980s. Epidemics of the Japanese oak wilt caused by the fungus *Raffaelea quercivora* Kubono & Shin. Ito carried by the native ambrosia beetle *Platypus quercivorus* (Murayama) have been prevalent in Japan since the early 1990s (Kamata et al. 2002). Meanwhile, in the Southeastern USA, laurel wilt has done devastating damage to avocado trees (Fraedrich et al. 2007). The laurel wilt kills trees belonging to the family Lauraceae. The pathogen is a *R. lauricola* complex carried by the ambrosia beetle *Xyleborus glabratus* Eichhoff. *Xyleborus glabratus* is native to Asia but was first found in the US in 2002 (Haack and Rabaglia 2013). In California, *Euwallacea fornicatus* complex (*Euwallacea fornicatus* (Eichhoff), *Euwallacea kuroshio* (Gomez and Hulcr), and *Euwallacea perbrevis* (Schedl)) began to kill a wide range of host plants including avocado trees in 2012 (Eskalen et al. 2012; Smith et al. 2019). The three species are also invasive to the US, originating in Asia (Stouthamer et al. 2017; Smith et al. 2019). They attack tea, cocoa, citrus, rambutan, macadamia, and castor as well as avocado in their native areas (Smith et al. 2019). Monitoring invasive bark and ambrosia beetles is, therefore, important not only in forest science but also in agriculture.

In Japan, the sika deer *Cervus nippon* Temminck population has increased greatly, which has caused a great impact on the ecosystem (Takatsuki 2009). They directly cause tree death by bark stripping. Alongside that, due to their intensive browsing on understory vegetation, topsoil is washed away by rain directly hitting the ground. Root systems become exposed and lose the ability to support the tree. These trees are then easily downed by typhoons that bring both a great amount of rainfall and strong winds. Tree death and injuries caused by deer overpopulation have likely produced food resources (weakened trees, dying trees, decaying wood) for bark and ambrosia beetles, both directly and indirectly.

Long-term monitoring of bark and ambrosia beetles was carried out in the University of Tokyo Chichibu Forest (UTCF) using flight-barrier traps with bait for 10 years, from 1994 and 2003 (Saito et al. 2005, 2013). We expected to see the indirect influence of the increase in sika deer population on the population of bark and ambrosia beetles in this long-term data. We also conducted additional monitoring late in the flight season in 2013 and a whole flight season of 2014. Many species that were not found during the 1994–2003 period were found in 2013 and 2014. In this study, we reanalyzed the 10-year data (1994–2003) by comparing it to the 2013–2014 data to determine whether environmental effects influence trap captures, and if there was an indirect influence of deer overpopulation on bark and ambrosia beetle populations.

Materials and Methods

Study sites for insect trapping

Insect trapping was conducted at the same 12 sites as Saito et al. (2005) in the UTCF, located approximately 100 km west of Tokyo (35° 55′ N, 138° 49′ E) (Table 1). There were 6 trapping sites along a road in both the Irikawa and Takikawa catchments, with elevations ranging from 850 m a.s.l. to 1150 m a.s.l. All 6 sites in the Takikawa catchment were located in natural deciduous hardwood forests (850–1060 m a.s.l.). However, four lower-elevation sites in the Irikawa catchment were located in plantations (900–1040 m a.s.l.). These are conifer plantations except for I-3 (*Zelkova serrata* plantation). The highest and the second-highest sites in Irikawa catchment were natural forests dominated by deciduous hardwood trees. Four site attributes: CATCHMENT (Irikawa vs. Takikawa), ELEVATION, STAND (plantation vs. natural forest), and TREE (conifers vs. hardwoods) are shown in Table 1.

Deer density and tree mortality

Table 2 shows data sources of deer population density, which were obtained near our research sites and used in this study. Deer censuses were conducted between 1986 and 2016 by the UTCF (Ishida et al. 1993, 2003), the Japanese Agency for Cultural Affairs (Gunma Prefecture et al. 1988, 1994, 2002, 2010, 2018), or Saitama Prefecture (Wildlife Management Office 1997) by the driving method or using helicopter overflight. Data obtained at Irikawa and Takikawa catchments and areas around the confluence of the two rivers were used for the analysis. Five tree censuses were conducted between 1994 and 2014 by the UTCF (Sawada et al. 2006; Yoshida et al. 2012; Haraguchi et al. 2019). The data of 74 quadrats (25 m × 25 m each), which were surveyed during all five censuses, were used for the analysis. Data regarding damage caused by deer were available at the tree census 2004 and after.

Insect collection

In 2013–2014, a wet type of Lindgren's 12-multi-funnel trap (Lindgren 1983) (PHEROTECH, VC, BC, Canada) was used for trapping at each site. Ethanol was put into a 50-ml conical tube as an attractant. A hole, 7 mm in diameter, was made in the cap, through which a cotton rope (8 mm in diameter) was put into the tube to control the emission rate. About 100 ml of propylene glycol was put into the bucket at the bottom of the trap to kill and preserve captured insects. One trap was set in each site from July 20 to October 8 in 2013 and from April 3 to November 4 in 2014. Captured insects were collected at irregular intervals ranging from 2 weeks to 1 month, because temperature affects the flight, and were sorted into morphospecies. Among these, individuals belonging to the subfamilies Scolytinae and Platypodinae (Coleoptera, Curculionidae) were identified and used for further analysis.

In 1994–2003, a black flight-barrier trap (Sankei Kagaku Co. Ltd., Kagoshima, Japan) was set in each site. The attractant was a commercial lure, MADARAKOURU (Sankei Kagaku Co. Ltd., Kagoshima, Japan), which is a combination of alpha-

Table 1. Profile of trapping sites at the University of Tokyo Chichibu Forest (after Saito et al. 2005).

Site	Latitude	Longitude	Elevation (m a.s.l.)	Forest type
Takikawa catchment				
T-1	35° 55 31″ N	138° 49 46″ E	850	Deciduous hardwood forest (old-growth natural forest)
T-2	35° 55 28″ N	138° 49 40″ E	870	Deciduous hardwood forest (secondary natural forest)
T-3	35° 55 10″ N	138° 49 51″ E	930	Deciduous hardwood forest (old-growth natural forest)
T-4	35° 54 46″ N	138° 49 05″ E	1,050	Deciduous hardwood forest (secondary natural forest)
T-5	35° 54 41″ N	138° 49 05″ E	1,050	Deciduous hardwood forest (secondary natural forest)
T-6	35° 54 39″ N	138° 49 24″ E	1,060	Deciduous hardwood forest (secondary natural forest)
Irikawa catchment				
I-1	35° 56 36″ N	138° 49 11″ E	900	*Chamaecyparis obtusa* plantation
I-2	35° 56 30″ N	138° 49 06″ E	960	*Abies firma* plantation
I-3	35° 56 36″ N	138° 49 03″ E	1,010	*Zelkova serrata* plantaition
I-4	35° 56 32″ N	138° 49 00″ E	1,040	*Pinus* spp. plantation
I-5	35° 56 27″ N	138° 48 35″ E	1,130	Deciduous hardwood forest (secondary natural forest)
I-6	35° 56 25″ N	138° 48 27″ E	1,150	Deciduous hardwood forest (secondary natural forest)

Table 2. Data source of sika deer population density surveyed inside Tochimoto Tract of the University of Tokyo Chichibu Forest and used in this study. Tochimoto Tract consists of three catchments: Irikawa, Takikawa, and Nakatsugawa. Yaktakezawa and Kudonosawa are branch streams of the Irikawa River and the Takikawa River, respectively. Kawamata is located near the confluence of the two rivers.

Projector*	Year	Location (Area)	Method**	Reference
ACA	1986	Kudonosawa (107.3 ha)	D	Gunma Prefecture et al. (1988)
UTCF	1987	Tochimoto (2,664.7 ha)	H	Ishida et al. (1993)
UTCF	1988	Tochimoto (2,664.7 ha)	H	*ditto*
UTCF	1989	Tochimoto (2,664.7 ha)	H	*ditto*
ACA	1992	Yatakezawa (61.3 ha), Kawamata (66.1 ha), Kudonosawa (110.6 ha)	D	Gunma Prefecture et al. (1994)
SP	1996	Irikawa (649 ha), Takikawa (688 ha)	H	Wildlife Management Office (1997)
SP	1997	Yatakezawa (64.5 ha)	D	*ditto*
ACA	2000	Yatakezawa (100.8 ha), Kawamata (66.1 ha), Kudonosawa (110.6 ha)	D	Gunma Prefecture et al. (2002)
UTCF	2001	Tochimoto (2,448.9 ha by 11 flights, each covered 29.94–415.56 ha)	H	Ishida et al. (2003)
ACA	2008	Yatakezawa (100.8 ha), Kawamata (114.9 ha), Kudonosawa (104.1 ha)	D	Gunma Prefecture et al. (2010)
ACA	2016	Yatakezawa (100.8 ha), Kawamata (114.9 ha), Kudonosawa (104.1 ha)	D	Gunma Prefecture et al. (2018)

* ACA, Japanese Agency for Cultural Affairs; UTCF, The University of Tokyo Chichibu Forest; SP, Saitama Prefecture.
** D, driving method; H, helicopter survey.

pinene and ethanol, both placed in individual plastic containers (6 x 2.5 cm) so that there were 2 containers placed at each trap. See Saito et al. (2005) for details of the methodology for the 1994–2003 monitoring.

Data analysis

The time series of deer population density was fitted with an exponential curve after removing the data from 2016. Deer population densities in 2016 were much lower than the trend set by the other years, so data from 2016 were removed, which allowed the use of an exponential curve.

The numbers of standing live and dead trees larger than 5 cm in diameter at breast height (DBH) were separately calculated for each tree census. The number of trees with damage caused by deer (debarking or injury by antler) was calculated, but this was only possible for the census 2004 and after.

Beetle data collected in this study (2013–2014: the "NEW period" in this paper) were analyzed together with those obtained during the 1994–2003 period and published in Saito et al. (2013) (the "OLD period" in this paper). The factors used in the data analysis were YEAR (numeric), CATCHMENT (Irikawa vs. Takikawa), ELEVATION (numeric), STAND (plantation vs. natural forest), TREE (conifers vs. hardwoods), and PERIOD ("OLD period" (-1994–2003) vs. "NEW period" (2013–2014)). All the data analyses were conducted using the free statistical computing software R (ver. 3.6.1) (R Development Core Team 2019).

Because the 2013 data did not include the entire flight period, this data could not be analysed together with the other years. So, when the data of the "OLD period" and "NEW period" were analysed together ("BOTH period"), analyses using whole season ("ALL") datasets excluded 2013 (Table A1), while analyses using data from August and after ("AUG") included all 12 years (Table A2). The effects of PERIOD on trap capture (species richness and abundance) per site each year were analyzed using a generalized linear model with a Poisson distribution function.

A PERmutational Multivariate ANalysis Of VAriance (PERMANOVA) was employed to determine the influence of the six factors on the bark and ambrosia beetle assemblage per trap each year. Packages "vegan" (Ver 2.5-5) (Oksanen et al. 2019) and "permute" (Ver 0.9-5) (Simpson 2019) were used for this analysis.

INdicator SPecies ANalysis (INSPAN) was employed to identify the indicator species for each of the four factors (CATCHMENT, STAND, TREE, and PERIOD). Species with an indicator value greater than 25% ($p < 0.05$) were recognized as indicator species, as per Dufrêne and Legendre (1997). Packages "vegan" (Ver 2.5-5) (Oksanen et al. 2019) and "labdsv" (Ver 2.0-1) (Roberts 2019) were used for this analysis.

Time-series clustering using dynamic time warping as distance was employed to cluster insect species by patterns of annual change in the trap captures (increase/decrease or no trend). To remove an effect of abundance, the number of trap captures was standardized for each species before the clustering. A package "TSclust" (Montero and Vilar 2014) was used for this analysis.

Results

The density of the deer population exponentially increased from 1986 to 2007: the population density was low before

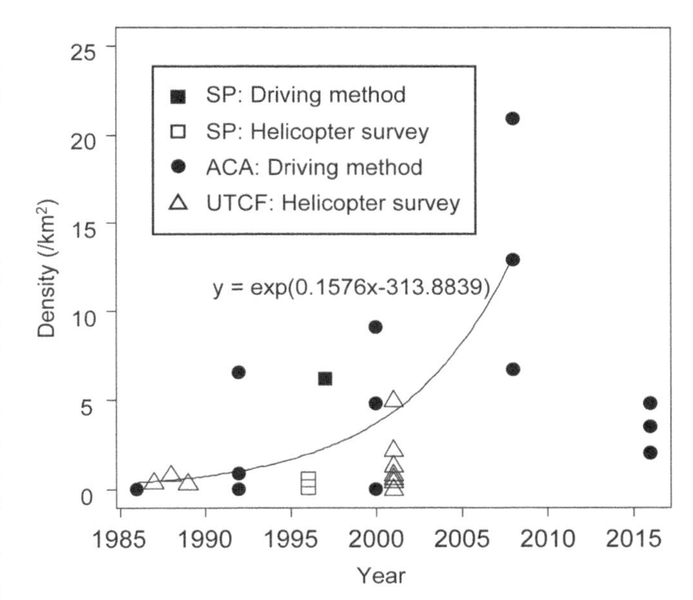

Figure 1. Population density of sika deer around the trap sites in watersheds of the Irikawa River and the Takikawa River, the University of Tokyo Chichibu Forest. Deer densities were estimated by helicopter survey (open) and driving method (solid). Data sources are Gunma Pref. et al. (1988, 1994, 2002, 2010, 2018) (Ishida et al. (1993), Ishida et al. 2003) (triangle), Wildlife Management Office (1997) (square).

1990, then increased greatly after the mid-1990 s through 2007 (Figure 1). However, at some point between 2007 and 2016, the population density decreased greatly.

The number of standing trees larger than 5 cm in DBH, living and dead, was stable for the 20 years covered by the five tree censuses, ranging between 6,376 and 6,742 with a peak at 2004 (Figure 2(a)). However, the number of standing dead trees continued to increase from 240 to 1,540, whereas that of

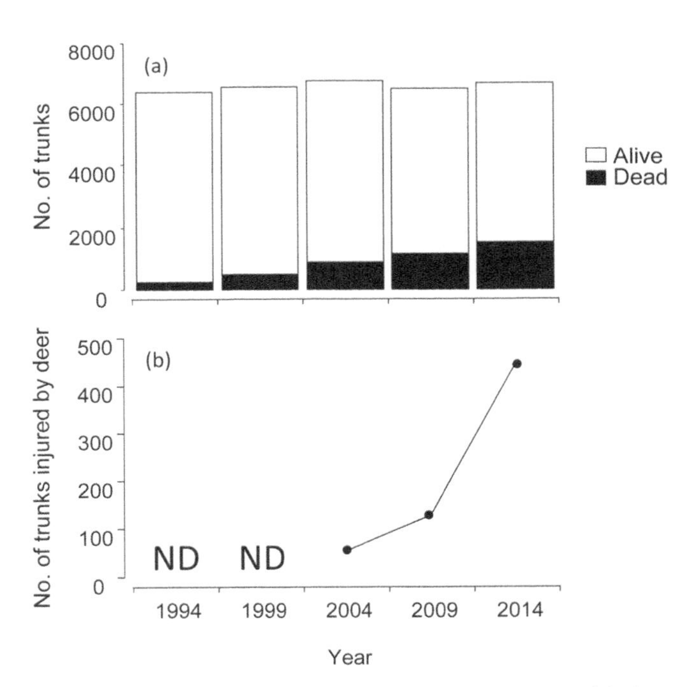

Figure 2. Results of five tree censuses at 74 quadrats (25 m × 25 m) of the long-term ecological research plot on the Irikawa catchment in the University of Tokyo Chichibu Forest (1994–2014).

(a) The number of live and dead standing trees, (b) the number of live trees injured by deer. Tree trunks larger than 5 cm in DBH were included in the results. Regarding the first three times of tree censuses out of the five, each time of census was conducted for 3 years (1994–1996, 1999–2001, and 2004–2006). (Sawada et al. 2006). In this paper, they are indicated by the first year of each census. ND = no data. Data sources are Sawada et al. (2006), Yoshida et al. (2012), and Haraguchi et al. (2019).

Table 3. Abundance of Scolytinae and Platypodinae captured at the University of Tokyo Chichibu Forest in 2013 and 2014. The number of captures during 1994–2003 (Saito et al. 2013) is also shown.

ID	Species		2013	2014	1994–2003*
Scolytinae					
S09	*Cryphalus laricis* Niisima				10
S10	*Cryphalus piceae* (Ratzeburg)			1	6
S23	*Eidophelus imitans* Eichhoff				2
S24	*Eidophelus minutus* Blandford				1
S38	*Hypothenemus tristis* (Eichhoff)	*1		17	36
S56	*Scolytogenes candidus* (Nobuchi)				4
S06	*Coccotrypes fagi* (Nobuchi)				2
S07	*Coccotrypes nubilus* (Blandford)			2	15
S13	*Cyrtogenius luteus* (Blandford)		1	16	17
S15	*Dryocoetes affinis* Blandford		1	3	8
S16	*Dryocoetes autographus* (Ratzeburg)				2,823
S17	*Dryocoetes hectographus* Reitter			21	4
S18	*Dryocoetes niijimai* Nobuchi				18
S19	*Dryocoetes pilosus* Blandford	*2		1	7
S20	*Dryocoetes rugicollis* Eggers				6
S21	*Dryocoetes* sp.				8
S22	*Dryocoetiops moestus* (Blandford)		8	11	47
S62	*Taphrorychus pilosus* (Murayama)		2	19	
S30	*Hylastes parallelus* Chapuis			6	24
S31	*Hylastes plumbeus* Blandford			1	23
S35	*Hylurgops inouyei* Nobuchi				87
S36	*Hylurgops interstitialis* (Chapuis)				30
S37	*Hylurgops palliatus* (Gyllenhal)			10	14
S32	*Hylesinus eos* Spessivtseff			2	4
S33	*Hylesinus laticollis* Blandford			2	
S34	*Hylesinus tristis* Blandford				1
S44	*Neopteleobius scutulatus* Blandford			4	58
S55	*Pseudohyorrhynchus wadai* Murayama				1
S61	*Sueus niisimai* (Eggers)		33	42	58
S45	*Orthotomicus suturalis* (Gyllenhal)				1
S60	*Scolytus frontalis* Blandford		1		1
S46	*Phloeosinus gifuensis* Murayama		1	2	
S47	*Phloeosinus lewisi* Chapuis				54
S48	*Phloeosinus perlatus* Chapuis				13
S49	*Phloeosinus rudis* Blandford				1
S50	*Phloeosinus seriatus* Blandford				1
S53	*Polygraphus kisoensis* Niijima				13
S54	*Polygraphus proximus* Blandford			1	137
S25	*Ernoporicus insularum* (Krivolutskaya)			1	
S65	*Trypodendron lineatum* (Olivier)			202	435
S66	*Trypodendron proximum* (Niisima)			54	5
S67	*Trypodendron signatum* (Olivier)			1	2
S57	*Scolytoplatypus daimio* Blandford		235	540	49
S58	*Scolytoplatypus mikado* Blandford		831	1,918	16,116
S59	*Scolytoplatypus tycon* Blandford		27	642	338
S63	*Tomicus brevipilosus* (Eggers)				1
S64	*Tomicus piniperda* (Linnaeus)				32
S01	*Ambrosiodmus lewisi* (Blandford)				6
S02	*Ambrosiodmus rubricollis* (Eichhoff)				16
S03	*Ambrosiophilus atratus* (Eichhoff)	*3	2	92	53
S04	*Anisandrus maiche* (Stark)		1		
S05	*Cnestus mutilatus* (Blandford)	*4			52
S11	*Cyclorhipidion japonicum* (Nobuchi)	*5			1
S12	*Cyclorhipidion misatoensis* (Nobuchi)	*6			1
S14	*Debus emarginatus* (Eichhoff)	*7			1
S26	*Euwallacea interjectus* (Blandford)			1	
S27	*Euwallacea minutus* (Blandford)		20	17	14
S28	*Euwallacea validus* (Eichhoff)		9	787	2,372
S29	*Heteroborips seriatus* (Blandford)			171	2,272
S39	*Indocryphalus aceris* (Niisima)			2	2
S40	*Indocryphalus majus* (Eggers)				1
S41	*Indocryphalus pubipennis* (Blandford)		3	158	408
S42	*Indocryphalus sordidus* (Blandford)				1
S43	*Microperus kirishimanus* (Murayama)		11		
S68	*Xyleborinus attenuatus* (Blandford)		43	297	217
S69	*Xyleborinus saxesenii* (Ratzeburg)				154
S70	*Xyleborinus schaufussi* (Blandford)		6	32	16
S71	*Xyleborus muticus* Blandford		1	2	
S72	*Xyleborus ohtoensis* Nobuchi			2	
S73	*Xylosandrus brevis* (Eichhoff)		18	617	821
S74	*Xylosandrus crassiusculus* (Motschulsky)		9	29	80
S75	*Xylosandrus germanus* (Blandford)		116	1,408	1,355
	Subtotal		1,379	7,134	28,356
Platypodinae					
S08	*Crossotarsus niponicus* Blandford		1		1

(*Continued*)

Table 3. (Continued).

ID	Species	2013	2014	1994–2003*
S51	*Platypus modestus* Blandford	3	1	7
S52	*Platypus severini* Blandford			3
	Subtotal	4	1	11
	TOTAL	1,383	7,135	28,367

*: After Saito et al. (2013).
*1: *Hypothenemus expers* Blandford in Saito et al. (2013) was misidentified. That species belongs in Scolytogenes (Wood 1966). For the taxonomy of *Hypothenemus tristis* see Beaver (2012).
*2: *Dryocoetiops coffeae* (Eggers) is given as a synonym of *D. moestus* (Blandford) in Beaver et al. (2019).
*3: *Ambrosiophilus atratus* (Eichhoff) was transferred from *Xyleborus* by Hulcr and Cognato (2009).
*4: *Cnestus mutilatus* (Blandford) was transferred from *Xyleborus* by Dole and Cognato (2010).
*5: *Cyclorhipidion japonicum* (Nobuchi) was transferred from *Xyleborus* by Smith et al. (2018).
*6: *Cyclorhipidion misatoensis* (Nobuchi) was transferred from *Xyleborus* by Smith et al. (2018).
*7: *Xyleborus exesus* Blandford is given as a synonym of *Debus emarginatus* (Eichhoff) by Hulcr (2010).

standing live trees continued to decrease from 6,136 to 5,145. The number of trees damaged by deer increased by about 8 times from 2004 to 2014 (Figure 2(b)).

Twenty-two and 41 species belonging to the subfamily Scolytinae were captured in 2013 and 2014, respectively (Table 3, Tables A3, A4). Two and one species belonging to the subfamily Platypodinae were captured in 2013 and 2014, respectively. Among these, *Taphrorychus pilosus* (Murayama), *Hylesinus laticollis* Blandford, *Phloeosinus gifuensis* Murayama, *Ernoporicus insularum* (Krivolutskaya), *Anisandrus maiche* (Stark), *Euwallacea interjectus* (Blandford), *Microperus kirishimanus* (Murayama), *Xyleborus muticus* Blandford, *Xyleborus ohtoensis* Nobuchi were not collected during the "OLD period". *Anisandrus maiche* was the first recorded occurrence of the species in Japan.

Table 4 shows the number of trap captures and the number of species for each year. The number of species and abundance collected per site each year was significantly greater in the "NEW period" than the "OLD period", both for "ALL" and "AUG" data, because the effect of PERIOD was significant in the four models and because the coefficients for the "NEW period" were all positive (Table 5).

The effects of the factors on the assemblage collected by each trap in each year are shown in Tables 6 and 7 for both "ALL" and "AUG", respectively. Effects of YEAR, CATCHMENT, TREE, and PERIOD were significant for all the analyses (PERMANOVA, $p < 0.05$), although that of STAND was marginal in some cases (PERMANOVA, $p < 0.1$). Among the factors, excluding YEAR and PERIOD, the effects of ELEVATION and CATCHMENT were the greatest. The contribution of STAND was the smallest followed by TREE. The contribution of PERIOD was smaller than that of YEAR but was still significant. The contribution of YEAR was smaller when the "NEW period" and "OLD period" were analyzed separately. The contribution of YEAR as shown in the R^2 value was 0.138 when both 2013 and 2014 were included in the analysis but decreased to 0.062 and 0.085 when 2013 and 2014 were excluded, respectively. On the contrary, the contribution of PERIOD increased when either 2013 or 2014 was included. The contribution of YEAR was greater than that of PERIOD in all of the analyses, indicating that at a community level effect of PERIOD was smaller than that of YEAR.

Table 8 shows the results of INSPAN. Analysis using "ALL" data detected more indicator species than those using "AUG", with the exception of *Xylosandrus germanus* (Blandford) in the Takikawa catchment. The results obtained

Table 4. The number of species and abundance of Scolytinae and Platypodinae captured at the University of Tokyo Chichibu Forests in each year from 1994 to 2003, and from 2013 to 2014.

		OLD period										NEW period	
PERIOD	YEAR	1994	1995	1996	1997	1998	1999	2000	2001	2002	2003	2013	2014
ALL	No. of Species	33	30	37	40	39	35	33	49	37	37		40
	Abundance	3,916	2,270	1,218	2,375	2,592	4,898	5,201	3,119	1,636	1,142		7,135
AUG	No. of Species	9	13	10	13	12	16	13	13	13	13	24	24
	Abundance	81	248	105	288	532	235	116	95	73	146	1,383	1,811

ALL: April–November
AUG: August–November
Data in the OLD period were after Saito et al. (2013).

Table 5. Effects of PERIOD on the number of species and abundance of trap captures analyzed by a generalized linear model with a Poisson distribution function. OLD period (1994–2003) was used in the base model.

Data	Response Var.	Explanatory Var.	Estimate	Std. Error	*z*-value	*p*-value
ALL	No. of species	(Intercept)	2.66	0.02	110.7	<0.001
		NEW period	0.28	0.07	3.9	<0.001
	Abundance	(Intercept)	5.47	0.01	920.5	<0.001
		NEW period	0.92	0.01	69.6	<0.001
AUG	No. of species	(Intercept)	1.31	0.05	27.4	<0.001
		NEW period	0.88	0.08	10.6	<0.001
	Abundance	(Intercept)	2.78	0.02	121.8	<0.001
		NEW period	2.11	0.03	73.1	< 0.001

ALL: April–November
AUG: August–November
Data in the OLD period were after Saito et al. (2013).

Table 6. Effects of each factor on the community structure of bark and ambrosia beetles captured by bait traps at the University of Tokyo Chichibu Forest during the whole season (ALL) of 1994–2003, 2014, and both (permutational multivariate analysis of variance). R-square values with a significant level of each factor are shown.

	1994–2003 & 2014 all variables	1994–2003 OLD period wo PERIOD	2014 NEW period wo PERIOD
YEAR	0.074***	0.036***	
CATCHMENT (Irikawa vs. Takikawa)	0.056***	0.072***	0.075
ELEVATION	0.082***	0.099***	0.095
STAND (plantation vs. natural forest)	0.012.	0.015*	0.046
TREE (conifers vs. hardwoods)	0.025***	0.030**	0.076
PERIOD (1994–2003 vs. 2014)	0.065***		
Residuals	0.685	0.749	0.708
Total	1.000	1.000	1.000

0 "***" 0.001 "**" 0.01 "*" 0.05 "." 0.1 " " 1

Table 7. Effects of each factor on the community structure of bark and ambrosia beetles captured by bait traps at the University of Tokyo Chichibu Forest in August and after (AUG) of 1994–2003 and 2013–2014 (permutational multivariate analysis of variance). R-squared values with a significant level of each factor are shown.

	1994–2003 & 2013–2014 all variables	1994–2003 & 2013–2014 wo YEAR	1994–2003 & 2014 all variables	1994–2003 & 2013 all variables	1994–2003 OLD period wo PERIOD	2013–2014 NEW period wo PERIOD
YEAR	0.138***		0.085***	0.062***	0.030***	0.095.
CATCHMENT (Irikawa vs. Takikawa)	0.043***	0.043***	0.053***	0.054***	0.070***	0.045
ELEVATION	0.028***	0.028***	0.033***	0.034***	0.043***	0.109*
STAND (plantation vs. natural forest)	0.010.	0.010.	0.012.	0.012.	0.015.	0.024
TREE (conifers vs. hardwoods)	0.011*	0.011*	0.015*	0.014*	0.020**	0.050
PERIOD (1994–2003 vs. 2014)	0.069***	0.186***	0.075***	0.066***		
Residuals	0.700	0.722	0.727	0.758	0.823	0.677
Total	1.000	1.000	1.000	1.000	1.000	1.000

0 "***" 0.001 "**" 0.01 "*" 0.05 "." 0.1 " " 1

Table 8. Indicator species detected by indicator species analysis for bark and ambrosia beetle captured at the University of Tokyo Chichibu forest. The indicator value for each indicator species is shown in parentheses.

	ALL				AUG			
Species	CAT	STAND	TREE	PERIOD	CAT	STAND	TREE	PERIOD
Ambrosiophilus atratus (Eichhoff)				N (0.87)				
Dryocoetes autographus (Ratzeburg)	I (0.83)	P (0.80)	C (0.80)	O (0.93)	I (0.66)	P (0.67)	C (0.62)	O (0.54)
Dryocoetes hectographus Reitter				N (0.49)				
Euwallacea minutus (Blandford)				N (0.54)				N (0.42)
Euwallacea validus (Eichhoff)		P (0.76)	C (0.81)	N (0.77)			C (0.26)	N (0.30)
Heteroborips seriatus (Blandford)			C (0.59)					
Hylastes parallelus Chapuis		P (0.26)	C (0.32)					
Hypothenemus tristis (Eichhoff)				N (0.41)				
Indocryphalus pubipennis (Blandford)				N (0.80)				
Phloeosinus lewisi Chapuis			C (0.34)					
Polygraphus proximus Blandford	I (0.42)	P (0.45)	C (0.52)					
Scolytoplatypus daimio Blandford				N (0.99)				N (1.00)
Scolytoplatypus mikado Blandford								N (0.91)
Scolytoplatypus tycon Blandford				N (0.95)				N (0.67)
Sueus niisimai (Eggers)				N (0.73)				N (0.78)
Tomicus piniperda (Linnaeus)		P (0.26)	C (0.32)					
Trypodendron lineatum (Olivier)				N (0.75)				
Trypodendron proximum (Niisima)				N (0.74)				
Xyleborinus attenuatus (Blandford)	T (0.57)	N (0.65)	H (0.64)	N (0.93)				N (0.62)
Xyleborinus saxesenii (Ratzeburg)				O (0.58)				O (0.26)
Xyleborinus schaufussi (Blandford)				N (0.64)				N (0.28)
Xylosandrus brevis (Eichhoff)				N (0.88)				N (0.63)
Xylosandrus crassiusculus (Motschulsky)				N (0.72)				N (0.49)
Xylosandrus germanus (Blandford)				N (0.91)	T (0.52)			N (0.85)

According to Dufrêne and Legendre (1997), species with the indicator value is equal to or larger than 0.25 ($p < 0.05$) are judged as indicator species.
CAT: I, Irikawa Catchment; T, Takikawa Catchment.
STAND: P, plantation; N, natural forest.
TREE: C, conifers; H, hardwoods.
PERIOD: O, OLD (1994–2003); N, NEW (2013–2014).

for "ALL" were as follows: *Dryocoetes autographus* (Ratzeburg) was detected as an indicator species for Irikawa catchment, plantation, conifers, and "OLD period" (1994–-2003). *Polygraphus proximus* Blandford was an indicator for Irikawa catchment, plantation, and conifers. *Euwallacea validus* (Eichhoff) was an indicator for plantation, conifer, and "NEW period" (2013–2014). Many species were recognized as indicators of plantation and conifers. However, only *Xyleborinus attenuatus* (Blandford) acted as an indicator for natural forest and hardwoods. *Xyleborinus attenuatus* was also an indicator of the "NEW period" (2013–2014). Many indicator species (16 in "ALL" and 11 in "AUG",

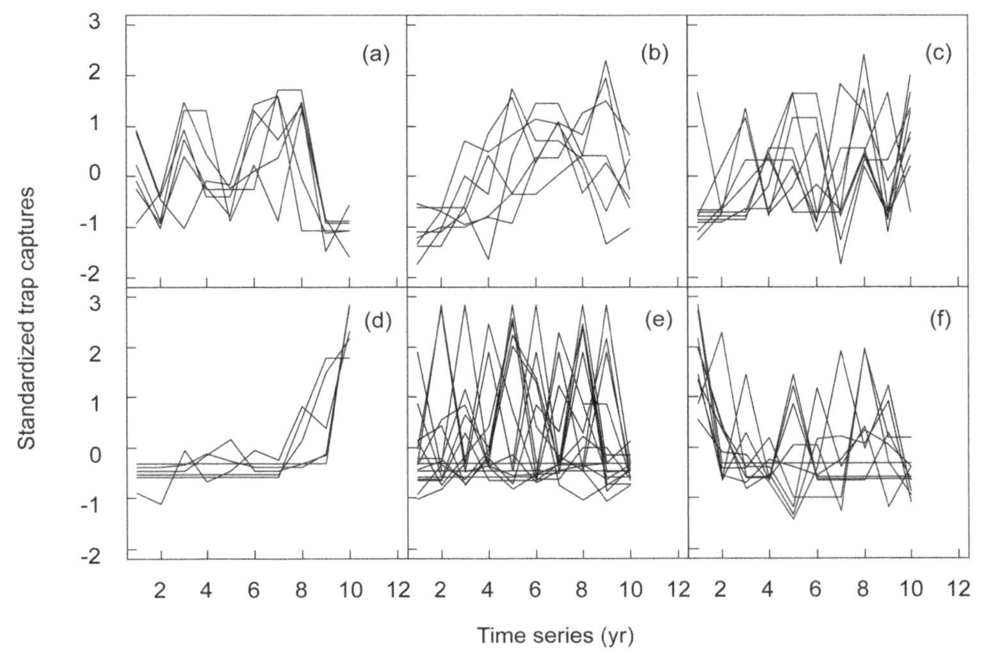

Figure 3. Result of a time-series clustering using dynamic time warping as distance for "ALL" data in the "OLD period" (1994–2003). Time-series line graphs of each cluster corresponding to Figure A1 are shown (a–f).

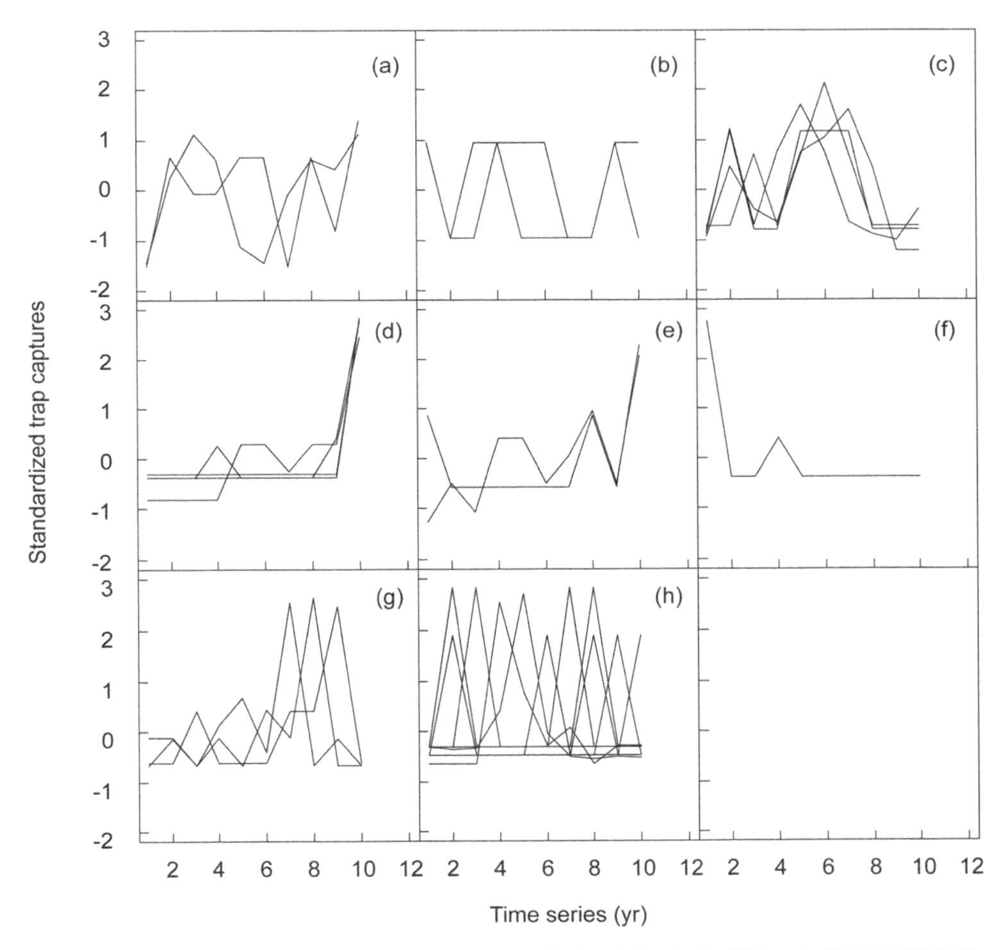

Figure 4. Result of a time-series clustering using dynamic time warping as distance for "AUG" data in the "OLD period" (1994–2003). Time-series line graphs of each cluster corresponding to Figure A2 are shown (a–h).

respectively) were found for the "NEW period", but only *Xyleborinus saxesenii* (Ratzeburg) and *D. autographus* were indicator species for the "OLD period".

In the "OLD period" (1994–2003), a time-series clustering detected increasing trends for 13 species in "ALL" (clusters B and D) (Figure 3(b,c), Figure A1) and 9

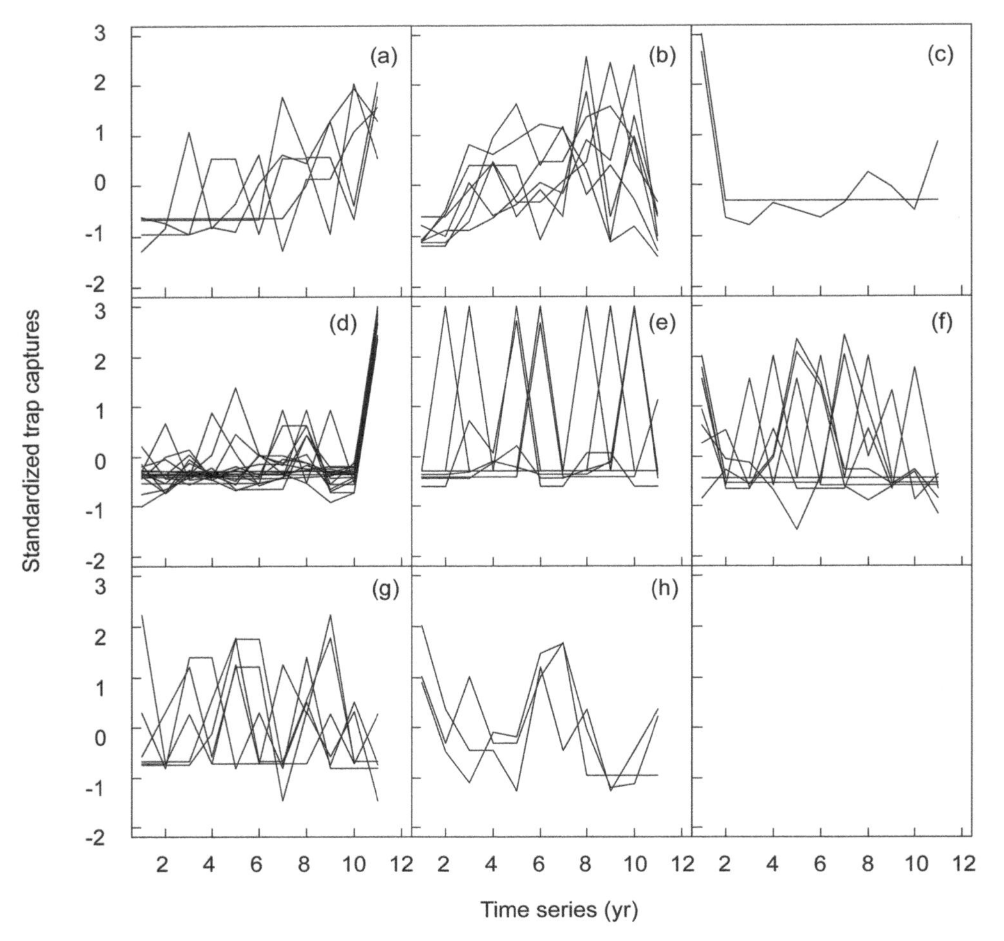

Figure 5. Result of a time-series clustering using dynamic time warping as distance for "ALL" data for 11 years in the "OLD period" (1994–2003) and the "NEW period" (2014). Time-series line graphs of each cluster corresponding to Figure A3 are shown (a–h).

species in "AUG" datasets (clusters D, E, and G) (Figure 4(d,e,g), Figure A2). In "ALL", a sudden increase in the last few years of the period was recognized in cluster D (6 spp.) (Figure 3(d)), while a continuous increase was found in the cluster B (7 spp.) (Figure 3(b)). When data of the "NEW period" (2013–2014) were included, increasing trends were detected for 37 species in "ALL" (clusters A, B, and D) (Figure 5(a,b,d), Figure A3) and 15 species in "AUG" (clusters C, D, and E) (Figure 6(c-e), Figure A4). Sudden increases in the "NEW period" were found in cluster D (25 spp.) of "ALL" (Figure 5(d)), and in clusters C (4 species), D (6 species), and E (5 species) of "AUG" (Figure 6(c-e)). On the other hand, decreasing trends were detected in cluster F of the "OLD period" of "AUG" dataset (1 sp.; *Dryocoetiops moestus* (Blandford)) (Figure 4(f), Figure A2), and cluster C for whole periods in "ALL" datasets (2 spp.; *D. moestus* and *Phloeosinus rudis* Blandford) (Figure 5(c), Figure A3). The decreasing trends of the three species were based on the largest capture rate in the first year (1994). For *D. moestus*, an increasing trend was recognized after a large decrease in the second year, and there were no captures of *P. rudis* after one capture in 1994. Two indicator species of the "OLD period" (Table 8), *D. autographus* and *X. saxesenii*, were clustered into clusters E (no trend) and B (increasing trend) in the "OLD period" of "ALL" (Figure 3(b,e), Figure A1), and clusters H and C (both had no trend) of "AUG" dataset (Figure 4(c,h), Figure A2).

Discussion

The latest list of bark and ambrosia beetles in Japan (Goto 2009) did not include *A. maiche* in a checklist of bark and ambrosia beetles in Japan. As the *A. maiche* captured in 2013 was a first for Japan, distributions of Scolytinae and Platypodinae species have likely been changing due to globalization and potentially climate change (Haack and Rabaglia 2013). The results of PERMANOVA indicated that the contribution of YEAR to the community structure was greater than that of PERIOD. In the analyses using data from "AUG," the difference was greater when both 2013 and 2014 were included than when only one of these years was included. The results suggest that the difference in the community structure varied greatly between individual years in the "OLD period" and between the "OLD period" and the "NEW period".

In addition to an increasing trend in the "OLD period," a sudden increase between the average over the "OLD" period and the "NEW period" was also found in many species. However, care should be taken when addressing this increase, due to differences in traps and attractants.

Some studies have been carried out comparing trap captures of bark and ambrosia beetles using Lindgren's funnel traps and flight-barrier traps. Galko et al. (2016) reported that 1.5 times more *Ips typographus* (L.) were collected in flight-barrier traps as compared to Lindgren's traps. Flechtmann et al. (2001) found that the trap capture of major species per surface area was significantly greater in flight-barrier traps, although results depended on insect

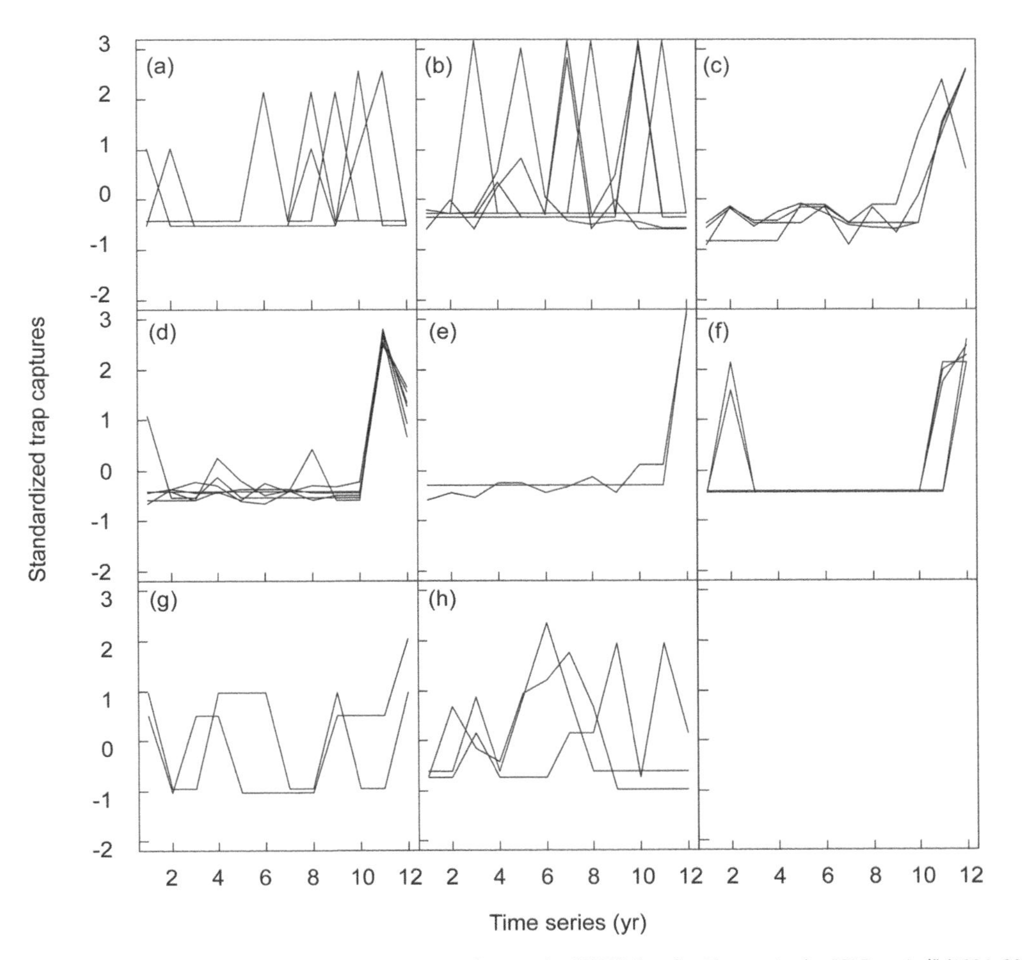

Figure 6. Result of a time-series clustering using dynamic time warping as distance for "AUG" data for 12 years in the "OLD period" (1994–2003) and the "NEW period" (2013 and 2014). Time-series line graphs of each cluster corresponding to Figure A4 are shown (a–h).

species. According to these results, any increase in "NEW period" cannot be attributed to the difference in trap type.

The number of species and individuals captured in each site each year was greater in the "NEW period" than in the "OLD period". During the 2 years of the "NEW period", many species were captured that were not found in the "OLD period". However, the population density of these species was likely low, because the number of captures was one to two individuals.

The INSPAN also detected 16 species as indicators for the "NEW period", whereas only two species were indicators for the "OLD period". The two indicator species of the "OLD period" were *D. autographus* and *X. saxesenii*. Both of these were not collected during the "NEW period". One likely cause of no trap captures of *D. autographus* during the "NEW period" is the attractant used. Alpha-pinene is a semiochemical, which is emitted from conifers when these trees are stressed (Schroeder and Lindelow 1989; Huber et al. 2000). *Dryocoetes autographus* was attracted to alpha-pinene. According to the results of the INSPAN, *D. autographus* is also an indicator of Irikawa catchment, plantation, conifers, and the "OLD period". Plantations were located only in the Irikawa catchment. The plantations were populated by conifer species, with one exception of *Z. serrata*. Therefore, the results obtained by INSPAN for *D. autographus* appear reasonable. However, the reason why *X. saxesenii* was not collected in the "NEW period" is unclear because the host range of *X. saxesenii* is known to include almost all conifers and hardwoods (Walker 2008). *Xyleborinus saxesenii* was a major species in an ambrosia beetle assemblage that was collected in the same combination of traps (Lindgren's funnel trap) and lure (ethanol) in Tennessee, USA (Oliver and Mannion 2001). *Tomicus piniperda* (Linnaeus) is known to attack fresh materials of conifers soon after tree weakening, breakage, or felling, so it is reasonable that *T. piniperda* was detected as an indicator for plantations and conifers. However, it seems strange that *T. piniperda* was not an indicator for the "OLD period", in which alpha-pinene was used as an attractant together with ethanol, because fresh conifer materials emit higher levels of terpenes than ethanol from resin. Schroeder and Lindelow (1989) measured the attraction of beetles to alpha-pinene, ethanol, and combinations of the two compounds using baited flight-barrier traps. They reported that *T. piniperda* was the species most strongly attracted by only alpha-pinene. Ethanol also attracted this species, but to a lesser extent than alpha-pinene. This species was synergistically attracted to combinations of alpha-pinene and ethanol at low release rates of alpha-pinene. However, at the highest release rate of alpha-pinene, smaller numbers of *T. piniperda* were captured. During the "OLD period" of our study, the antagonistic effect of ethanol on *T. piniperda* likely decreased the trap capture rate, probably due to the high emission rate of alpha-pinene.

The 16 indicator species of the "NEW period" can be classified into 3 groups according to their host range: conifers, hardwoods, and both. *Eidophelus minutus* Blandford, *Hypothenemus tristis* (Eichhoff), *X. attenuatus, Scolytoplatypus tycon* Blandford, *Scolytoplatypus daimio* Blandford, *Xylosandrus brevis* (Eichhoff), *Xyleborinus schaufussi* (Blandford),

Indocryphalus pubipennis (Blandford), and *Sueus niisimai* (Eggers) attack only hardwoods (Kabe 1960; Atkinson 2019). It is reasonable that greater numbers of individuals were captured of these species during the "NEW period" when only ethanol was used as bait. Unlike *D. autographus, X. attenuatus* was detected as an indicator species for Takikawa catchment, natural forest, hardwoods, and the "NEW period". All six sites in the Takikawa catchment were located in natural forest dominated by hardwoods, so the results are reasonable. However, species that attack conifers need more careful consideration. Schroeder and Lindelow (1989) also found that *Trypodendron lineatum* (Olivier) was not attracted at all by alpha-pinene but was strongly attracted by ethanol even though its host plants include conifers as well as hardwoods. Even for conifers, *T. lineatum* tends to prefer older logs cut the previous year over newly cut logs. These old logs potentially release relatively high amounts of ethanol that are produced in deteriorating tree tissue, while alpha-pinene is probably released in lower amounts when compared with newly cut or fallen trees. This is a likely cause for *T. lineatum* being an indicator species for the "NEW period" even though *T. lineatum* attacks conifers. Other indicator species of the "NEW period" included conifer specialists (*Dryocoetes hectographus* Reitter and *Trypodendron proximum* (Niisima)), and generalists that attack both conifers and hardwoods (*Ambrosiophilus atratus* (Eichhoff), *E. validus, Xylosandrus crassiusculus* (Motschulsky), and *X. germanus*). The reason why they increased in the "NEW period" is unclear. *Euwallacea validus* was detected as indicators of plantation and conifers, but also an indicator of the "NEW period". However, *X. crassiusculus* and *X. germanus* attack relatively older material (Sanguansub S, personal observation) so the same mechanism affecting *T. lineatum* was likely affecting these two species.

According to the results of the time-series clustering, increasing trends during the "OLD period" were detected in many species (13 out of 66 species in "ALL"; 9 out of 30 species in "AUG"). Although decreasing trends were recognized in *D. moestus* and *P. rudis* (cluster F of "ALL" and cluster C of "AUG"), it is not appropriate to judge that these decreased during the "OLD period", because the decrease was relative to the highest capture rate in the first year (1994). Regarding *P. rudis*, no individuals were captured after 1994. An increasing trend was recognized in *D. moestus* after the greatest capture rate in 1994. Therefore, many species showed increasing trends during the 1994–2003 period, but none showed decreasing trends.

Sika deer density increased exponentially by the census of 2008 but decreased greatly at the census of 2016. According to Ministry of the Environment of Japan, sika deer population density in Saitama Prefecture continued to increase (MOE 2015a) and reached 20–30/km^2 around the UTCF by 2014 (MOE 2015b). In Chichibu, extraordinary snowfall was observed in February 2014. Snow accumulation at the Chichibu Weather Station located in downtown Chichibu was 98 cm in depth (JMA 2014). Many sika deer killed by avalanches were found after the extraordinary snow accumulation (Kamata N, personal observation), which was a likely cause of the lower density in 2016. Forest decline caused by sika deer overpopulation has been reported in many locations in Japan (e.g. Takatsuki 2009). In this study site, the number of standing dead trees increased by 6.4 times over 20 years, although it is expected to be stable under a stationary system. The number of live trees damaged by sika deer has increased greatly since 2004. The sika deer population started to increase greatly after the mid-1990 s. These results indicate that increases in the population of sika deer were the likely cause of the increased tree mortality since 1994.

These results support our hypothesis about the importance of indirect effects of deer population increase on the sizes of bark and ambrosia beetle populations. Dead trees and live trees but damaged by deer could be resources for the bark and ambrosia beetles. The increase of these food resources was likely the direct cause of the increase of bark and ambrosia beetle populations. During the "OLD period", trap captures increased gradually in seven species and suddenly in the last few years in nine species in "ALL" (Figure 3(b,d), Figure A1). A sudden increase in trap captures in the "NEW period" was recognized in 25 spp. in "ALL" (Figure 5(d), Figure A2) and 15 spp. in "AUG" (Figure 6(c-e), Figure A3). The difference in attractants can explain some of these increases, but not all of them. An increase in tree mortality due to an increase in deer population was likely the cause of the increases in beetle species that could not be explained by differences in the attractant used, and partially contributed to those that could be explained by the difference.

Acknowledgments

This study was supported by Grant-in-Aid for Scientific Research (A) (23255011 and 16H02760) and JSPS Core-to-Core Project (FY2016–FY2018 and FY2019–2021) to NK. We also express our sincere thanks to the two anonymous reviewers for their valuable comments to the earlier versions of this manuscript. Masanori Fujii helped setting the traps and insect collection. Former students of Kasetsart University helped sorting insects. William E Wright helped English editing and provided helpful comments. We thank all of them.

Disclosure statement

No potential conflict of interest was reported by the authors.

Funding

This work was supported by the Japan Society for the Promotion of Science [Grant-in-Aid for Scientific Research 23255011]; Japan Society for the Promotion of Science [JSPS Core-to-Core Project (FY2019—FY2021)]; Japan Society for the Promotion of Science [JSPS Core-to-Core Project (FY2016—FY2018)]; Japan Society for the Promotion of Science [Grant-in-Aid for Scientific Research 16H02760].

References

Atkinson TH. 2019. Bark and ambrosia beetles of North and Central America. [accessed 2020 Mar 14]. https://www.barkbeetles.info/index.php.

Beaver RA. 2012. The taxonomy of two Asian bark beetles, *Stephanoderes tristis* Eichhoff and *Dryocoetes apatoides* Eichhoff (Coleoptera: curculionidae, Scolytinae). Entomologist's Mon Mag. 147:223–229.

Beaver RA, Smith SM, Sanguansub S. 2019. A review of the genus *Dryocoetiops* Schedl, with new species, new synonymy and a key to species (Coleoptera: curculionidae: scolytinae). Zootaxa. 4712:236–250. doi:10.11646/zootaxa.4712.2.4.

Coulson RN, Witter JA. 1984. Forest entomology: ecology and management. New York (NY): Wiley.

Dole SA, Cognato AI. 2010. Phylogenetic revision of *Xylosandrus* Reitter (Coleoptera: curculionidae: scolytinae: xyleborina). Proc Calif Acad Sci. 61:451–545.

Dufrêne M, Legendre P. 1997. Species assemblages and indicator species: the need for a flexible asymmetrical approach. Ecol Monogr. 67:345–366.

Eskalen A, Gonzalez A, Wang DH, Twizeyimana M, Mayorquin JS, Lynch SC. 2012. First report of a *Fusarium* sp. and its vector tea shot hole borer (*Euwallacea fornicatus*) causing Fusarium dieback on avocado in California. Plant Dis. 96:1070. doi:10.1094/PDIS-03-12-0276-PDN.

Flechtmann C, Ottati ALT, Berisford CW. 2001. Ambrosia and bark beetles (Scolytidae: coleoptera) in pine and eucalypt stands in southern Brazil. For Ecol Manag. 142(1–3):183–191. doi:10.1016/S0378-1127(00)00349-2.

Fraedrich SW, Harrington TC, Rabaglia RJ. 2007. Laurel wilt: a new and devastating disease of redbay caused by a fungal symbiont of the exotic redbay ambrosia beetle. Newslett Mich Entomol Soc. 51 (1&2):15–16.

Galko J, Nikolov C, Kunca A, Vakula J, Gubka A, Zúbrik M, Rell S, Konôpkal B. 2016. Effectiveness of pheromone traps for the European spruce bark beetle: a comparative study of four commercial products and two new models. Lesnicky Casopis. 62(4):207–215.

Goto H. 2009. Taxonomic history of Japanese bark and ambrosia beetles with a check list of them. J Jap For Soc. 91(6):479–485. Japanese. doi:10.4005/jjfs.91.479

Gunma Prefecture, Saitama Prefecture, Tokyo Metropolis, Yamanashi Prefecture, Nagano Prefecture Education Committees. 1988. Report on Japanese serow in Kanto Mountains (Fiscal years 1986-1987). Tokyo: Japanese Agency for Cultural Affairs. Japanese.

Gunma Prefecture, Saitama Prefecture, Tokyo Metropolis, Yamanashi Prefecture, Nagano Prefecture Education Committees. 1994. Report on Japanese serow in Kanto Mountains (Fiscal years 1992-1993). Tokyo: Japanese Agency for Cultural Affairs. Japanese.

Gunma Prefecture, Saitama Prefecture, Tokyo Metropolis, Yamanashi Prefecture, Nagano Prefecture Education Committees. 2002. Report on Japanese serow in Kanto Mountains (Fiscal years 2000-2001). Tokyo: Japanese Agency for Cultural Affairs. Japanese.

Gunma Prefecture, Saitama Prefecture, Tokyo Metropolis, Yamanashi Prefecture, Nagano Prefecture Education Committees. 2010. Report on Japanese serow in Kanto Mountains (Fiscal years 2008-2009). Tokyo: Japanese Agency for Cultural Affairs. Japanese.

Gunma Prefecture, Saitama Prefecture, Tokyo Metropolis, Yamanashi Prefecture, Nagano Prefecture Education Committees. 2018. Report on Japanese serow in Kanto Mountains (Fiscal years 2016-2017). Tokyo: Japanese Agency for Cultural Affairs. Japanese.

Haack R, Rabaglia RJ. 2013. Exotic bark and ambrosia beetles in the USA: potential and current invaders. In: Peña JE, editor. Potential invasive pests of agricultural crops. Wallingford: CABI; p. 48–74.

Haraguchi R, Saito T, Yoshida Y, Takatoku K, Niwa Y, Igarashi Y. 2019. Enumeration data (2014) for a long-term ecological research plot in The University of Tokyo Chichibu Forest [a revised edition]. Misc Info Univ Tokyo For. 61:75–81. Japanese.

Huber DPW, Gries R, Borden JH, Pierce HD Jr. 2000. A survey of antennal responses by five species of coniferophagous bark beetles (Coleoptera: scolytidae) to bark volatiles of six species of angiosperm trees. Chemoecology. 10(3):103–113. doi:10.1007/PL00001811.

Hulcr J. 2010. Taxonomic changes in palaeotropical Xyleborini (Coleoptera, Curculionidae, Scolytinae). ZooKeys. 56:105–119. doi:10.3897/zookeys.56.520.

Hulcr J, Cognato AI. 2009. Three new genera of oriental Xyleborina (Coleoptera: curculionidae: scolytinae). Zootaxa. 2204. 19–36.

Ishida K, Igarashi Y, Sawada H, Sakai H. 2003. An aerial survey of large mammals in Chichibu Mountains, Central Japan. Bull Univ Tokyo For. 109:65–371.

Ishida K, Yamane A, Akaiwa T, Igarashi Y. 1993. Distribution of Japanese serow *Capricornis crispus* and sika deer *Cervus nippon* in Chichibu Mountains. Bull Univ Tokyo For. 89:99–111. Japanese.

Japan Meteorology Agency. 2014. Extraordinary snow accumulation and blizzard during February 14–19, 2014. p. 10. [accessed 2020 Mar 14]. http://www.data.jma.go.jp/obd/stats/data/bosai/report/2014/20140214/jyun_sokuji20140214-0219.pdf. Japanese.

Kabe M. 1960. On the hosts and habitats of the Scolytid and Platypodid-beetles in Japan. Maebashi: Maebashi Regional Forest Office. Japanese.

Kamata N, Esaki K, Kato K, Igeta Y, Wada K. 2002. Potential impact of global warming on deciduous oak dieback caused by ambrosia fungus carried by ambrosia beetle in Japan. B Entomol Res. 92 (2):119–126. doi:10.1079/BER2002158.

Lindgren BS. 1983. A multiple funnel trap for Scolytid beetles (Coleoptera). Can Ent. 115(3):299–302. doi:10.4039/Ent115299-3.

Ministry of the Environment. 2015a. Population density of sika deer and other wildlife at each Japanese prefecture estimated by Bayesian method. p. 41. [accessed 2020 Mar 14]. http://www.env.go.jp/press/files/jp/26912.pdf. Japanese.

Ministry of the Environment. 2015b. Population density of sika deer in Japan in early 2014 (regional scale maps). [accessed 2020 Mar 14:6 p. http://www.env.go.jp/press/files/jp/28231.pdf. Japanese.

Montero P, Vilar JA. 2014. TSclust: an R package for time series clustering. J Stat Softw. 62(1):1–43. doi:10.18637/jss.v062.i01.

Oksanen J, Blanchet FG, Friendly M, Kindt F, Legendre P, McGlinn D, Minchin PR, O'Hara RB, Simpson GL, Solymos P, et al. 2019. Package 'vegan': community ecology package. R package version 2.5-6. p. 296. [accessed 2020 Mar 14]. https://cran.r-project.org/web/packages/vegan/vegan.pdf.

Oliver JB, Mannion CM. 2001. Ambrosia beetle (Coleoptera: scolytidae) species attacking chestnut and captured in ethanol-baited traps in middle Tennessee. Environ Entomol. 30(5):909–918. doi:10.1603/0046-225X-30.5.909.

R Development Core Team. 2019. R: A language and environment for statistical computing. Vienna (Austria): R Foundation for Statistical Computing; ISBN 3-900051-07-0, [accessed 2020 Mar 14]. http://www.R-project.org.

Roberts DW 2019. Labdsv: ordination and multivariate analysis for ecology. R package version 2.0-1. p. 68. [accessed 2020 Mar 14]. https://cran.r-project.org/web/packages/labdsv/labdsv.pdf.

Saito T, Goto H, Hirao T, Kamata N. 2013. Revision of a list of subfamily Scolytinae and Platypodinae captured by bait traps at the University of Tokyo Chichibu Forest in 1994-2003. Misc Info Univ Tokyo For. 53:169–193. Japanese.

Saito T, Ishida K, Yamane A, Sasaki K. 2005. Long term monitoring record of Scolytid Beetle populations at the Tokyo University Forest in Chichibu, Central Japan. Misc Info Univ Tokyo For. 44:251–275. Japanese.

Sawada H, Omura K, Shibano S, Fujiwara A, Kaji M. 2006. Enumeration data (1994-2005) for a long-term ecological research plot at Tokyo University Forest in Chichibu. Misc Info Univ Tokyo For. 45:71–218. Japanese.

Schroeder LM, Lindelow A. 1989. Attraction of scolytids and associated beetles by different absolute amounts and proportions of alpha-pinene and ethanol. J Chem Ecol. 15(3):807–818. doi:10.1007/BF01015179.

Simpson GL 2019. Package 'permute': functions for generating restricted permutations of data. R package version 0.9-5. p. 29. [accessed 2020 Mar 14]. https://cran.r-project.org/web/packages/per mute/permute.pdf

Smith SM, Beaver RA, Cognato AI. 2018. New synonymy, new combinations and other taxonomic changes in Japanese xyleborine ambrosia beetles (Coleoptera: curculionidae: scolytinae). Zootaxa. 4521 (3):391–403. doi:10.11646/zootaxa.4521.3.5.

Smith SM, Gomez DF, Beaver RA, Hulcr J, Cognato AI. 2019. Reassessment of the species in the *Euwallacea fornicatus* (Coleoptera: curculionidae: scolytinae) complex after the rediscovery of the "lost" type specimen. Insects. 10(9):E261. doi:10.3390/insects10090261.

Stouthamer R, Rugman-Jones P, Thu PQ, Eskalen A, Thibault T, Hulcr J, Wang L-J, Jordal BH, Chen C-Y, Cooperband M, et al. 2017. Tracing the origin of a cryptic invader: phylogeography of the *Euwallacea fornicatus* (Coleoptera: curculionidae: scolytinae) species complex. Agr For Ent. 19(4):366–375. doi:10.1111/afe.12215

Takatsuki S. 2009. Effects of sika deer on vegetation in Japan: A review. Biol Conserv. 142(9):1922–1929. doi:10.1016/j.biocon.2009.02.011.

Walker K. 2008. Fruit-tree pinhole borer (*Xyleborinus saxeseni*). [accessed 2011 Nov 27] http://www.padil.gov.au http://www.padil.gov.au/pests-and-diseases/pest/main/135733.

Wildlife Management Office. 1997. Report on population and distribution of the deer in Saitama Prefecture. Kawasaki: Wildlife Management Office. Japanese.

Wood SL. 1966. New synonymy in the Platypodidae and Scolytidae (Coleoptera). Great Basin Nat. 26:17–33.

Yoshida Y, Niwa Y, Igarashi Y, Chishima T, Haraguchi R, Omura K. 2012. Enumeration data (2009) for a long-term ecological research plot in The University of Tokyo Chichibu Forest. Misc Info Univ Tokyo For. 52:187–305. Japanese.

Influence of seasonality and climate on captures of wood-boring Coleoptera (Bostrichidae and Curculionidae (Scolytinae and Platypodinae)) using ethanol-baited traps in a seasonal tropical forest of northern Thailand

Sunisa Sanguansub, Sawai Buranapanichpan, Roger A Beaver, Teerapong Saowaphak, Nobuaki Tanaka and Naoto Kamata

ABSTRACT

Insects in the tropics usually have continuous generations throughout the year. We reanalyzed published data of wood-boring beetles, belonging to three taxonomic groups (Bostrichidae; Curculionidae: Scolytinae, Platypodinae), that were captured by ethanol-baited traps continuously set for three years and collected every two weeks in the lowland montane forest in northern Thailand. Because trap captures seemed to have 1-yr cycle, we hypothesized that 1-yr cycle of climate had caused 1-yr cycle in the trap captures. To test this hypothesis, cycles of both total trap captures (TTC) and of each species, synchrony in time-series trap captures, and causality of temperature and rainfall to the TTC were determined. Eighty-nine species were captured over the three years. Among 55 species (>2 individuals), 30 species showed the greatest peak of spectral density at 1-yr, but only three were significant. Some species had (a) cycle(s) shorter than one year. However, 20 species making up 69.7% of TTC and 38 species making up 91.1% of TTC showed significant synchrony with TTC diagnosed by the Phillips-Ouliaris cointegration test and Pearson's correlation function, respectively. Temperature, rainfall, and season (solar elevation angle) showed significant causalities, the effect of season being the strongest. Both temperature and rainfall positively influenced TTC with lags. These results indicate that seasonality in temperature and rainfall caused a 1-yr cycle in flying beetles of a majority of the more abundant species, and synchrony among species, which resulted in the 1-yr cycle of TTC. The revolution and tilt of the earth was a likely driving force.

Introduction

This study deals with bark- and wood-boring beetles belonging to the families Curculionidae: Scolytinae and Platypodinae (bark and ambrosia beetles) and Bostrichidae (powder-post beetles). The bark beetles (some Scolytinae) live primarily in the inner bark and feed directly on plant tissues, including bark and phloem (Wood 1982). The ambrosia beetles (some Scolytinae and all Platypodinae) live in the wood and feed only on ambrosia fungi growing in the xylem (Beaver 1989). The Bostrichidae are also wood borers, but feed directly on plant tissues, often using endosymbiotic bacteria to aid digestion (Crowson 1981). All three ecological groups include pest species of considerable economic importance (Liu et al. 2008; Vega and Hofstetter 2015). Therefore, the determination of the influence of seasonality and climate on their biology and life cycles is of importance. Many studies monitoring the seasonal occurrence of bark and/or ambrosia beetles using traps in temperate forests or cooler regions have been reported; however, in seasonal tropical forests, there have been few long-term studies monitoring xylobiotic beetles. Beaver and Löyttyniemi (1991) carried out 1-year monitoring in two separate years in a seasonal tropical forest in Zambia. Macedo-Reis et al. (2016) took 5-day samples in 10 months over three years in a tropical dry forest in Brazil. Most studies have been carried out over a period shorter than two years (e.g. Sandoval et al. 2017), including Hulcr et al. (2008), in which monitoring was conducted at each of two different forest types in northern Thailand over 17 months in total.

To understand the underlying patterns of the seasonal fluctuations of flying xylobiotic beetles across different climate zones, a comparison of long-term data that has been collected using the same (or similar) methodology is needed. We have started to monitor bark and ambrosia beetles in many locations, using soda-bottle traps baited with ethanol, from a tropical rainforest in Sabah, Malaysia to a hemiboreal forest in Hokkaido, Japan. Sanguansub et al. (2020) published 3 years of data of wood-boring beetles, belonging to the family Bostrichidae and subfamilies Scolytinae and Platypodinae of the family Curculionidae, collected in a seasonal tropical forest in northern Thailand.

In the temperate zone, most insects have discrete generations due to winter so that studies of population cycles and synchrony among populations have been mostly focused on changes in abundance among years. Insects in the tropics usually have continuous generations throughout the year, although some are known to show generation cycles with a period of approximately one generation (Godfray and Hassell 1989). However, the time-series data in Sanguansub et al. (2020) seemed to show a 1-year cycle in the trap captures. Therefore, in this paper, we hypothesized that a 1-yr cycle of climate had caused a 1-yr cycle in the trap captures. To test this hypothesis, cycles of total trap captures (TTC) and of each species, synchrony in time-series trap captures, and causality of temperature and rainfall to the TTC were determined.

Materials and methods

Data source

The dataset used in this study was obtained in northern Thailand (N 18° 50′ 23.11", E 98° 53′ 53.31") (Sanguansub et al. 2020). Three ethanol-baited traps were set at each of the four sites (total of 12 traps) for three years from 1 January 2014 to 21 December 2016, and the captured insects were collected every two weeks. Eighty-nine species of wood-boring insects belonging to the three taxonomic groups of the order Coleoptera (Bostrichidae and Curculionidae (Scolytinae and Platypodinae)) and 7,390 individuals were recorded and reanalyzed in this study.

Meteorological variables were observed at Kog-Ma Watershed (N 18° 48′ 45.52", E 98° 54′ 08.15") (Tanaka et al. 2008), approximately 3 km apart from the trapping sites. On a scaffolding forest tower of the watershed, air temperature was recorded with a 10-min interval at a height of 10 m above the forest canopy, using a temperature and humidity probe (HMP155, Vaisala, Helsinki, Finland). The 10-min air temperature data were stored in a data logger (CR1000, Campbell Scientific, Utah, USA) and was averaged over a day to obtain daily mean air temperature. Rainfall was measured by a tipping-bucket rain gauge with a resolution of 0.5 mm (No. 34 T, Ota Keiki Seisakusho, Tokyo, Japan) at an open area near the forest tower. The rainfall record was registered by a data logger (Hobo Event, Onset Computer Co., MA, USA). The mean temperature and total rainfall for the two weeks corresponding to each collection date were calculated from the daily data. Four years of climate data, from 2013 to 2016, were used because it is likely that the influence of climate on the trap captures has a time lag. The first date of collection was defined as the first time of collection.

Data analysis

All data analyses were performed using R software (ver. 3.6.1) (R Development Core Team 2019).

Cyclicity in TTC and climate data

To diagnose cyclicity in the trap captures of each species from spectral density, a multitaper method with conventional AR1 noise test (MTMAR) was employed. A package "astrochron (Version 0.9)" (Meyers 2014) was used in this analysis. A periodogram of each time series was computed to determine a peak maximum (=greatest spectral peak) (i.e. to determine if each species, each group, or TTC showed a 1-year cycle). The calculated periodogram was fitted with an Ornstein-Uhlenbeck state space (OUSS) null model using maximum-likelihood. The statistical significance of the periodogram peak maximum against the OUSS null hypothesis was evaluated. A package "peacots (ver 1.3)" (Louca and Doebeli 2015; Louca 2016) was used for this analysis. The cyclicities of temperature and rainfall were also diagnosed by the same two methodologies using biweekly data of the same period as trap captures from 2014 to 2016. Species with three individuals or more captured were used for these analyses. Cyclicity was determined for each species, each taxonomic and ecological group (Bostrichidae, Platypodinae, Scolytinae, bark beetles, and ambrosia beetles), and TTC.

Synchrony among species

To diagnose synchrony of the time-series among species, which is necessary to generate 1-year cycles in groups and TTC, Pearson's correlation function and Phillips-Ouliaris test of cointegration (Phillips and Ouliaris 1990) were employed between TTC and each species. For Pearson's correlation function, positive significant coefficients ($p < 0.05$) were diagnosed as synchronous. A package "tseries (ver. 0.10–47)" (Trapletti and Hornik 2019) was used for these analyses.

Causality test

To determine the influence of climate variables (temperature (TE) and rainfall (RA)) on TTC, causality detection was performed by convergent cross mapping (CCM) (Sugihara et al. 2012) followed by the Granger causality test (Granger 1980) using feed-forward neural networks for non-linear models. Packages "rEDM (ver. 1.3.0)" (Sugihara et al. 2019) and "NlinTS (ver. 1.3.8)" (Hmamouche 2020) were used for CCM and the Granger causality test, respectively.

Analysis of CCM was carried out according to Sugihara et al. (2019). Solar elevation angle obtained using the following equation (Cooper 1969) was included as an indicator of season (SE) as well as TE and RA.

$$\mathrm{SE} = 90 - \left| \mathrm{x} - 23.45 \times \cos\left(\frac{360}{365} \times (\mathrm{d} + 10)\right) \right|,$$

where x was the latitude of the research site (18.8397), was the day of the year with January 1 as $d = 1$, and 365 (the number of days in the year) was replaced with 366 for bissextile (2016). As a preliminary analysis, the most practical embedding dimension (E) was determined by examining simplex predictability, followed by a test for state dependency (nonlinearity) using the sequential locally weighted global linear map (S-map) analysis. Because simplex predictability improved when the embedding dimension (E) was 3–10 (Figure S1), a test for state dependency (nonlinearity) was employed for $E = 3$–10. As the result, prediction skill (ρ) versus S-map localization for the E values (3–10) proved that the best prediction was obtained at $E = 8$ (Figure S2) so that the most practical embedding dimension (E) was determined as $E = 8$ and used for the further analyses. For a rigorous test of causality, a two-part criterion for CCM was adopted:

(1) The cross-map prediction skill is statistically significant when using the full time series as the library.
(2) Cross map prediction demonstrates convergence, i.e. prediction skill increases as more of the time series is used.

For an initial summary, the cross-map skill (measured with Pearson's ρ) was computed for each variable pair. For comparison, lagged cross-correlation was also computed, allowing lags of up to ±13 times of collection (≈half a year, ≈1 year in total 26 times). For the second, namely convergence in cross-map predictability, Pearson's ρ was computed as a function of library size to determine if the ρ value at maximum library size significantly exceeding the magnitude of the cross-correlation between TTC and the cross-mapped variable (SE, TE, or RA). There still remains the possibility that the cross-map results are an artifact of shared seasonal forcing because all the three factors are related to the seasonal cycle. We need to reject the null hypothesis that the level of cross-mapping obtained for each factor can be solely explained by seasonality so that, at the last part of the CCM, randomization tests based on surrogate data were employed to test this hypothesis. Surrogate time series with the same level of shared seasonality were generated. A null distribution for the ρ value was generated by cross mapping between the real time series and these surrogates. The actual cross-map ρ value was compared against the null distribution.

For the Granger causality test, p values of Granger causality index (GCI) for TE and RA were computed, allowing lags of up to 26 times of collection (≈ 1 year). A generalized linear model (GLM) with a Poisson error structure and a log link function was also employed to determine the effects, where the response variable was TTC and either of TE or RA was the explanatory variable. Coefficients of each of the explanatory variables were computed for the same lags as Granger causality. The mechanism of how temperature and rainfall influenced TTC was discussed by the coefficients of TE and RA for the lags with significant p values for GCI.

Direct effect of climatic variables

The GLM with the same error structure as above was employed to determine direct effects (lag = 0) of TE and RA on TTC. Model selection was conducted for all models from a null to a full model using Akaike Information Criterion (AIC). Coefficients of TE and RA were determined.

Results

Figure 1 shows the time-series data used in this study. The first collection on January 15 is collection time 1. The TTC seemed to fluctuate annually as well as other elements

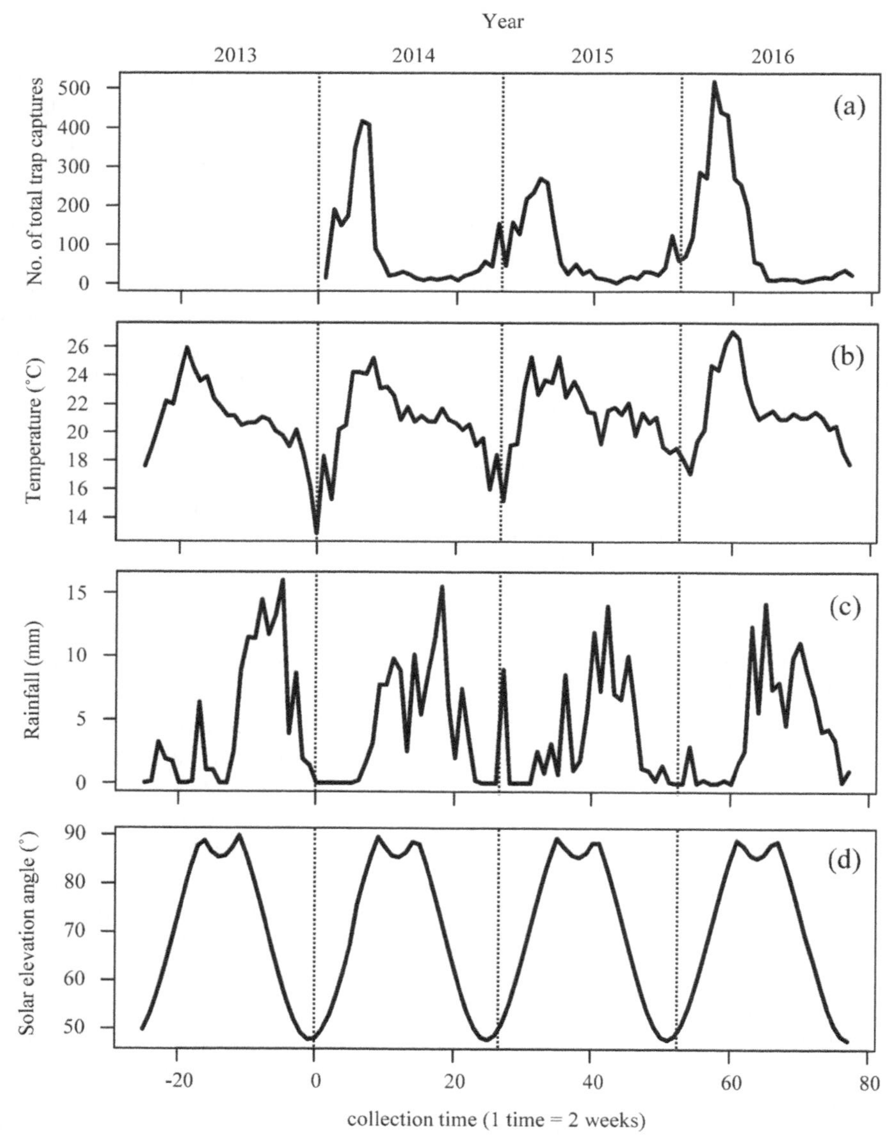

Figure 1. Four time series datasets analysed this study. Zero and one on x-axis indicate the dates of setting traps (1 January, 2014) and first collection (15 January, 2014), respectively. (a) Total trap captures of wood-boring insects at Doi-Pui National Park, Chiang Mai, Thailand in 2014–2016 (Original data from Sanguansub et al. (2020)). (b) Biweekly mean temperature corresponding to the timings of the trap captures, observed at Hui Kog Ma, approximately 10 km apart from the trapping sites in 2013–2016. (c) Biweekly total rainfall corresponding to the timings of the trap captures, observed at the same site as temperature (2013–2016). (d) Solar elevation angle for a day as an indicator of season.

(Figure 1(a)). An annual peak appeared on 5th or 6th collection times of each year in mid-March or early April. After the peak, TTC decreased rapidly by mid- to late May and was small by November. TTC increased rapidly from January. Temperature changed smoothly by repeating a similar pattern every year, i.e. cooled down gradually and warmed up rapidly between peaks from late March to early April and bottoms from late December to early January (Figure 1(b)). As a result, the time-series curve of temperature showed an asymmetric shape. The time-series curve of rainfall also repeated a similar pattern every year with more symmetric shape but less smooth with many more spikes than temperature (Figure 1(c)). Rainfall was slight between November and April but heavy between May and October. Solar elevation angle peaked in April and August and was at a minimum in December each year (Figure 1(d)).

Regarding cyclicity in the climate variables, both the temperature and rainfall had a significant peak at about one year (25.7 or 25.8 collection times), which was also the periodogram peak maximum (Table 1). Both had (a) shorter significant peak(s).

Regarding cyclicity in trap captures of each group including TTC (Table 2), the periodogram peak maximum was found at 25.7 collection times ($\approx$ 1 year) for all the groups but significant only for TTC, Scolytinae, and bark beetles, of which abundance was large. By MTMAR, a significant peak around one year was detected for four groups (these three and ambrosia beetles), whereas the period was 27.6 collection times with one exception of bark beetles. In TTC, significant shorter peaks were detected at 12.9 ($\approx$ half a year) and 2.38 collection times. The same peak at 2.38 collection times was found in the subfamily Scolytinae but different (5.01 collection times) in bark beetles.

Table 1. Periodogram peak maximum with its statistical significance against an Ornstein-Uhlenbeck state space null model (Periodogram OUSS) and cyclicities diagnosed by a multitaper method with conventional AR1 noise test (MTMAR) in temperature and rainfall (2014–2016, Doi-Pui National Park, Chiang Mai, Thailand).

	Periodgram Peak Maximum	MTMAR*2
	(*p*-value)*1	Significant peak
Temperature	25.7 (0.003)	25.8 12.9 2.08
Rainfall	25.7 (0.048)	25.7 2.23

*1: The statistical significance was tested against Ornstein-Uhlenbeck state space null hypothesis
*2: Significant cycles detected by a multitaper method with conventional AR1 noise test ($p < 0.05$)

Among the 89 species, three individuals or more were captured in 55 species (Table 3). Among the 55, 30 species showed the periodogram peak maximum at 25.7 collection times ($\approx$ 1 year), although only three were significant ($p < 0.05$, "PPM"). Two species, *Xylosandrus crassiusculus* and *Xylosandrus eupatorii*, had (a) significant peak(s) shorter than one year ($p < 0.05$, "MTMAR"). Regarding synchrony, 20 species with 5,149 individuals (69.7% of TTC) and 38 species with 6,729 (91.1%) were diagnosed to have significant synchrony with TTC by Phillips-Ouliaris cointegration test and Pearson's correlation function, respectively.

Regarding CCM, with one exception of a pair (SE and TTC as a source and a target), Pearson's ρ in all the pairs continued to increase with library size (Figure S3). The ρ at maximum library size exceeded the linear correlation most greatly in a case with SE as a target (Figure S3(a)) followed by a case with TE as a target (Figure S3(b)). Tables 4 and 5 show cross-map skill (Pearson's ρ) for each variable pair in both directions and the magnitude of cross-correlation with lags of up to $\pm$13 times of collections, respectively. Not only correlations of TTC with the three environmental variables but those of SE with TE and RA were also high. Furthermore, the cross-map results indicated that SE could almost perfectly recover TE ($\rho = 0.951$). These suggest a possibility that cross mapping using TE and RA might be an artifact of shared seasonal forcing without actual causal mechanism. However, randomization tests based on surrogate data rejected the null hypothesis that the level of cross mapping obtained for the two climate variables could be solely explained by SE, both for TE ($p < 0.001$) and RA ($p = 0.033$), which indicates that CCM influence of TE and RA (Table 4) was significantly higher than the linear correlation (Table 5) in relation to a surrogate null distribution. The CCM proved the significant causalities of SE, TE, and RA to TTC.

According to Granger causality test, GCI was significant at lags 1–2 and 26 for TE and at lags 13–16 for RA, where coefficients obtained by GLM showed relatively large positive values with one exception of lag = 3 in TE (Figure 2).

Table 2. Periodogram peak maximum with its statistical significance against an Ornstein-Uhlenbeck state space null model (Periodogram OUSS) and cyclicities diagnosed by a multitaper method with conventional AR1 noise test (MTMAR) in trap captures for all (TTC), each taxonomic group (Bostrichidae, Platypodinae, and Scolytinae), and each ecological group (bark beetles and ambrosia beetles) (Original data from Sanguansub et al. (2020)).

	Abundance	Periodgram Peak Maximum (*p*-value)*1	MTMAR*2 Significant peak
Total Trap Captures (TTC)	7,390	25.7 (0.019)	27.6 12.9 2.38
Taxonomic group			
Bostrichidae	1,103	25.7 (0.331)	ND
Curculionidae:			
Scolytinae	6,267	25.7 (0.017)	27.6 2.38
Platypodinae	20	25.7 (0.118)	ND
Ecological group			
Bark beetles	2,636	25.7 (0.011)	25.7 5.01
Ambrosia beetels	3,651	25.7 (0.053)	27.6

*1: The statistical significance was tested against Ornstein-Uhlenbeck state space null hypothesis
*2: Significant cycles detected by a multitaper method with conventional AR1 noise test ($p < 0.05$)
ND: Not detected

Table 3. The number of trap captures (ABD), cyclicity, and synchrony with the total trap captures for 89 species of wood-boring Coleoptera (Bostrichidae and Curculionidae (Scolytinae and Platypodinae)) using ethanol-baited traps in a seasonal tropical forest of northern Thailand from 2014 to 2016 (Original data from Sanguansub et al. 2020).

ID	Family or Subfamily	Species name	Group[*1]	ABD	Cyclicity PPM[*2]	(p)	MTMAR[*3]	Synchrony COR[*4]	PO[*5]
S01	Bostrichidae	*Parabostrychus acuticollis* Lesne	BOS	24	25.7	(0.11)			
S02	Bostrichidae	*Sinoxylon* sp. (broken)*	BOS	1					
S03	Bostrichidae	*Sinoxylon unidentatum* (F.)	BOS	3	9.63	(0.99)			
S04	Bostrichidae	*Octomeristes pusillus* Liu & Beaver	BOS	1					
S05	Bostrichidae	*Xylocis tortilicornis* Lesne	BOS	70	25.7	(0.04)	27.6	0.64	0.01
S06	Bostrichidae	*Xylodectes ornatus* (Lesne)	BOS	6	25.7	(0.97)		0.54	0.019
S07	Bostrichidae	*Xylodrypta* sp.	BOS	73	25.7	(0.13)	25.7		
S08	Bostrichidae	*Xylopsocus acutespinosus* Lesne	BOS	363	12.8	(0.34)	13.3, 5.21	0.54	0.021
S09	Bostrichidae	*Xylopsocus capucinus* (F.)	BOS	240	25.7	(0.87)		0.64	0.012
S10	Bostrichidae	*Xylothrips flavipes* (Illiger)	BOS	206	25.7	(0.49)	12.9, 8.58	0.51	
S11	Bostrichidae	*Dinoderus favosus* Lesne	BOS	33	25.7	(0.21)		0.54	0.01
S12	Bostrichidae	*Dinoderus* sp.	BOS	83	25.7	(0.93)		0.26	
S13	Platypodinae	*Baiocis pernanulus* (Schedl)	AMB	2					
S14	Platypodinae	*Crossotarsus externedentatus* (Fairmaire)	AMB	1				0.29	0.029
S15	Platypodinae	*Crossotarsus terminatus* Chapuis	AMB	10	25.7	(0.76)			
S16	Platypodinae	*Euplatypus parallelus* (F.)	AMB	2					
S17	Platypodinae	*Peroplatypus laosi* (Schedl)	AMB	2					
S18	Platypodinae	*Platypus vetulus* Schedl	AMB	1					
S19	Platypodinae	*Platypus* sp.	AMB	1					
S20	Scolytinae	*Gnatharus tibetensis* Wood & Yin	AMB	1					
S21	Scolytinae	*Cosmoderes* sp.	BAR	1				0.29	0.029
S22	Scolytinae	*Cryphalus scabricollis* Eichhoff	BAR	231	25.7	(0.80)	10.4	0.63	0.042
S23	Scolytinae	*Cryphalus* sp. 1	BAR	1					
S24	Scolytinae	*Cryphalus* sp. 2	BAR	511	77	(0.92)		0.31	
S25	Scolytinae	*Cryphalus* sp. 3	BAR	12	77	(0.99)			
S26	Scolytinae	*Cryphalus* sp. 4	BAR	97	77	(0.97)		0.23	
S27	Scolytinae	*Hypocryphalus mangiferae* (Stebbing)	BAR	1319	25.7	(0.38)		0.80	0.047
S28	Scolytinae	*Hypothenemus artocarpi* Browne	BAR	2					
S29	Scolytinae	*Hypothenemus birmanus* (Eichhoff)	BAR	9	2.08	(1.00)			
S30	Scolytinae	*Hypothenemus eruditus* Westwood	BAR	59	25.7	(0.92)		0.51	0.014
S31	Scolytinae	*Hypothenemus* sp.	BAR	6	2.14	(0.80)	10.4	0.36	0.021
S32	Scolytinae	*Scolytogenes* sp. 1	BAR	1					
S33	Scolytinae	*Scolytogenes* sp. 2	BAR	169	25.7	(0.69)			
S34	Scolytinae	*Scolytogenes* sp. 3	BAR	82	77	(0.71)			
S35	Scolytinae	*Coccotrypes advena* Blandford	BAR	4	38.5	(0.91)			
S36	Scolytinae	*Coccotrypes carpophagus* (Hornung)	BAR	1					
S37	Scolytinae	*Coccotrypes cyperi* (Beeson)	BAR	20	77	(0.76)			
S38	Scolytinae	*Coccotrypes graniceps* Eichoff	BAR	9	19.25	(0.98)			
S39	Scolytinae	*Coccotrypes longior* (Eggers)	BAR	28	38.5	(0.91)			
S40	Scolytinae	*Coccotrypes papuanus* (Eggers)	BAR	1					
S41	Scolytinae	*Coccotrypes rugicollis* (Eggers)	BAR	1					
S42	Scolytinae	*Coccotrypes* sp.	BAR	1					
S43	Scolytinae	*Coccotrypes vulgaris* (Eggers)	BAR	1					
S44	Scolytinae	*Dryocoetiops moestus* (Blandford)	BAR	58	25.7	(0.05)			0.038
S45	Scolytinae	*Pseudoxylechinus umbonatus* Beaver MS	BAR	12	77	(0.97)			
S46	Scolytinae	*Sueus niisimai* (Eggers)	AMB	5	25.7	(1.00)			
S47	Scolytinae	*Scolytoplatypus brahma* Blandford	AMB	3	7	(1.00)			
S48	Scolytinae	*Scolytoplatypus mikado* Blandford	AMB	6	77	(1.00)			
S49	Scolytinae	*Scolytoplatypus minimus* Hagedorn	AMB	2005	25.7	(0.03)	25.7	0.80	0.019
S50	Scolytinae	*Scolytoplatypus pubescens* Hagedorn	AMB	338	25.7	(0.02)	25.7, 2.90	0.73	0.01
S51	Scolytinae	*Scolytoplatypus raja* Blandford	AMB	14	25.7	(0.93)		0.51	0.045
S52	Scolytinae	*Ambrosiophilus* sp.	AMB	1					
S53	Scolytinae	*Anisandrus apicalis* (Blandford)	AMB	1					
S54	Scolytinae	*Anisandrus hirtus* (Hagedorn)	AMB	8	25.7	(0.64)			
S55	Scolytinae	*Arixyleborus lannaensis* Smith et al. MS	AMB	1				0.24	
S56	Scolytinae	*Beaverium dihingensis* (Eggers)	AMB	1					
S57	Scolytinae	*Cnestus bicornioides* (Schedl)	AMB	344	25.7	(0.22)		0.70	0.01
S58	Scolytinae	*Cnestus aterrimus* (Eggers)	AMB	313	25.7	(0.06)	25.7	0.51	
S59	Scolytinae	*Cnestus nitidipennis* (Schedl)	AMB	94	25.7	(0.93)		0.24	
S60	Scolytinae	*Cnestus testudo* (Eggers)	AMB	2				0.42	0.030
S61	Scolytinae	*Cyclorhipidion aff. punctatopilosum* (Schedl)	AMB	12	77	(0.99)			
S62	Scolytinae	*Cyclorhipidion bodoanum* (Reitter)	AMB	1					
S63	Scolytinae	*Cyclorhipidion fukiense* (Eggers)	AMB	17	25.7	(0.75)			
S64	Scolytinae	*Cyclorhipidion nr punctilicolle* (Schedl)	AMB	2					
S65	Scolytinae	*Cyclorhipidion pilipenne* (Eggers)	AMB	2					
S66	Scolytinae	*Cyclorhipidion* sp.	AMB	1					
S67	Scolytinae	*Diuncus corpulentus* (Eggers)	AMB	3	2.85	(0.94)			
S68	Scolytinae	*Diuncus haberkorni* (Eggers)	AMB	13	25.7	(0.98)		0.29	0.023
S69	Scolytinae	*Diuncus justus* (Schedl)	AMB	2				0.35	
S70	Scolytinae	*Eccoptopterus limbus* Sampson	AMB	22	25.7	(0.99)		0.35	0.046
S71	Scolytinae	*Euwallacea fornicatus* (Eichhoff)	AMB	7	3.35	(1.00)		0.22	
S72	Scolytinae	*Euwallacea velatus*(Sampson)	AMB	3	4.05	(1.00)		0.23	
S73	Scolytinae	*Hadrodemius comans* (Sampson)	AMB	3	25.7	(0.95)		0.34	
S74	Scolytinae	*Hadrodemius pseudocomans* (Eggers)	AMB	5	25.7	(0.96)		0.29	
S75	Scolytinae	*Hadrodemius* sp.	AMB	1				0.29	
S76	Scolytinae	*Microperus alpha* (Beeson)	AMB	4	2.08	(0.20)			

(Continued)

Table 3. (Continued).

ID	Family or Subfamily	Species name	Group*1	ABD	Cyclicity PPM*2 (p)	MTMAR*3	Synchrony COR*4	PO*5
S77	Scolytinae	*Microperus nudibrevis* (Schedl)	AMB	1				
S78	Scolytinae	*Microperus perparvus* (Sampson)	AMB	47	15.4 (1.00)			
S79	Scolytinae	*Planiculus bicolor* (Blandford)	AMB	1			0.29	
S80	Scolytinae	*Steptocranus fragilis* (Browne)	AMB	1			0.31	
S81	Scolytinae	*Truncaudum agnatum* (Eggers)	AMB	3	25.7 (0.99)		0.44	
S82	Scolytinae	*Xyleborinus andrewesi* (Blandford)	AMB	24	25.7 (0.85)		0.49	0.022
S83	Scolytinae	*Xyleborinus subgranulatus* (Eggers)	AMB	3	2.08 (0.83)			
S84	Scolytinae	*Xyleborus* sp. (damage)	AMB	1				
S85	Scolytinae	*Xylosandrus compactus* (Eichhoff)	AMB	1				
S86	Scolytinae	*Xylosandrus crassiusculus* (Motschulsky)	AMB	91	19.3 (0.90)	13.3, 2.04	0.27	
S87	Scolytinae	*Xylosandrus discolor* (Blandford)	AMB	213	25.7 (0.80)		0.37	
S88	Scolytinae	*Xylosandrus eupatorii* (Eggers)	AMB	8	3.50 (0.65)	3.57		
S89	Scolytinae	*Xylosandrus subsimilis* (Eggers)	AMB	3	3.85 (1.00)		0.35	

* 1: BOS, Bostrichidae; AMB, ambrosia beetle; BAR, bark beetle.
*2: Periodogram peak maximum for species with 3 individuals or more. The statistical significance was tested against Ornstein-Uhlenbeck state space null hypothesis.
*3: Significant cycles detected by a multitaper method with conventional AR1 noise test ($p < 0.05$).
*4: Positive significant coefficient of Pearson's correlation ($p < 0.05$).
*5: Significant p-value by Phillips–Ouliaris cointegration test ($p < 0.05$).

Table 4. Cross-map skill (measured with Pearson's ρ) for each variable pair in both directions. Note that "target" is influencing variable and "source" is influenced one.

	Source: Influenced variable			
	TTC	SE	TE	RA
Target: Influencing variable				
TTC	NA	0.719	0.805	0.742
SE	0.947	NA	0.933	0.697
TE	0.795	0.802	NA	0.397
RA	0.691	0.533	0.589	NA

TTC: Total trap captures
SE: Seasonality (solar elevation angle)
TE: Temperature
RA: Rainfall
NA: Not available

Table 5. Maximum of the lagged cross-correlation for each variable pair, allowing lags of up to ±13 times of collections.

	TTC	SE	TE	RA
TTC	NA	0.688	0.642	0.615
SE		NA	0.659	0.692
TE			NA	0.508
RA				NA

TTC: Total trap captures
SE: Seasonality (solar elevation angle)
TE: Temperature
RA: Rainfall
NA: Not available

Regarding the direct effect of TE and RA on TTC, AIC of a full model (TE + RA) was significantly smaller than those of the other models (Table 6). In the best model, coefficients of TE and RA are positive and negative, respectively. AIC of the model with RA was significantly smaller than that with TE.

Discussion

Population cycles are well-known phenomena in forest insects. However, most of the research on population cycles have been conducted for insects in temperate zone or cooler regions, in which insect generations are discrete due to the winter season (Liebhold and Kamata 2000). In these cases, population density of each generation was used as a time series to discuss population cycling. However, most insect populations in the tropics have continuous generations (Nair 2007) so that population cycles have been discussed by analyzing time-series datasets recorded at certain intervals. In the tropics, population cycles with a period of roughly one generation, so-called "generation cycles", have been reported (Godfray and Hassell 1989; Knell 1998; Nakamura et al. 2004). Cycles (= spectral peaks) shorter than one year were recognized in TTC (12.9 and 2.38 collection times, Table 2) and two species (Table 3). Therefore, a short spectral peak (2.08 collection times) in *X. crassiusculus* was likely a generation cycle because it was reported that its development time was 30–40 days (Mizell et al. 1998). Although the life cycles of wood-boring Bostrichid beetles are not well known (Lan-Yu Liu, personal communication), development times of bark beetles and ambrosia beetles are generally short and sensitive to the temperature (Bale et al. 2002): e.g. 15–18 days at 23–24°C for *Xylosandrus germanus* (Kaneko 1965; Kaneko et al. 1965). However, such short cycles were detected only in two species among the eighty-nine. Cycles with approximately one year were detected as the periodogram peak maximum in TTC, more abundant groups, and 30 species, although only three among the 30 species were significant. Twenty species with about 70% of individuals and 38 species with about 90% of individuals were identified to synchronize with TTC by strict (Phillips-Ouliaris test of cointegration) and moderate (Pearson's correlation function) diagnoses, respectively. This suggests that the time series of more abundant species tended to synchronize. Synchrony among more abundant species that had a periodogram peak maximum at one year, regardless of its statistical significance, likely generated 1-year cycle in abundant groups and TTC.

The next question is what mechanism causes 1-year cycles? The CCM proved that temperature and rainfall as well as the seasonal indicator (solar elevation angle) had a significant causal effect on TTC. The Granger causality test detected significant causality at lags of 1–2 collection times (= 2–4 weeks) in temperature and lags of 13–16 (= 26–32 weeks ≈ half a year or more) in rainfall, with both the environmental variables influenced positively (GLM, Figure 2). Regarding direct influence (lag = 0), both temperature (positively) and rainfall (negatively) influenced TTC (GLM, Table 6). Temperature in northern Thailand changes in a

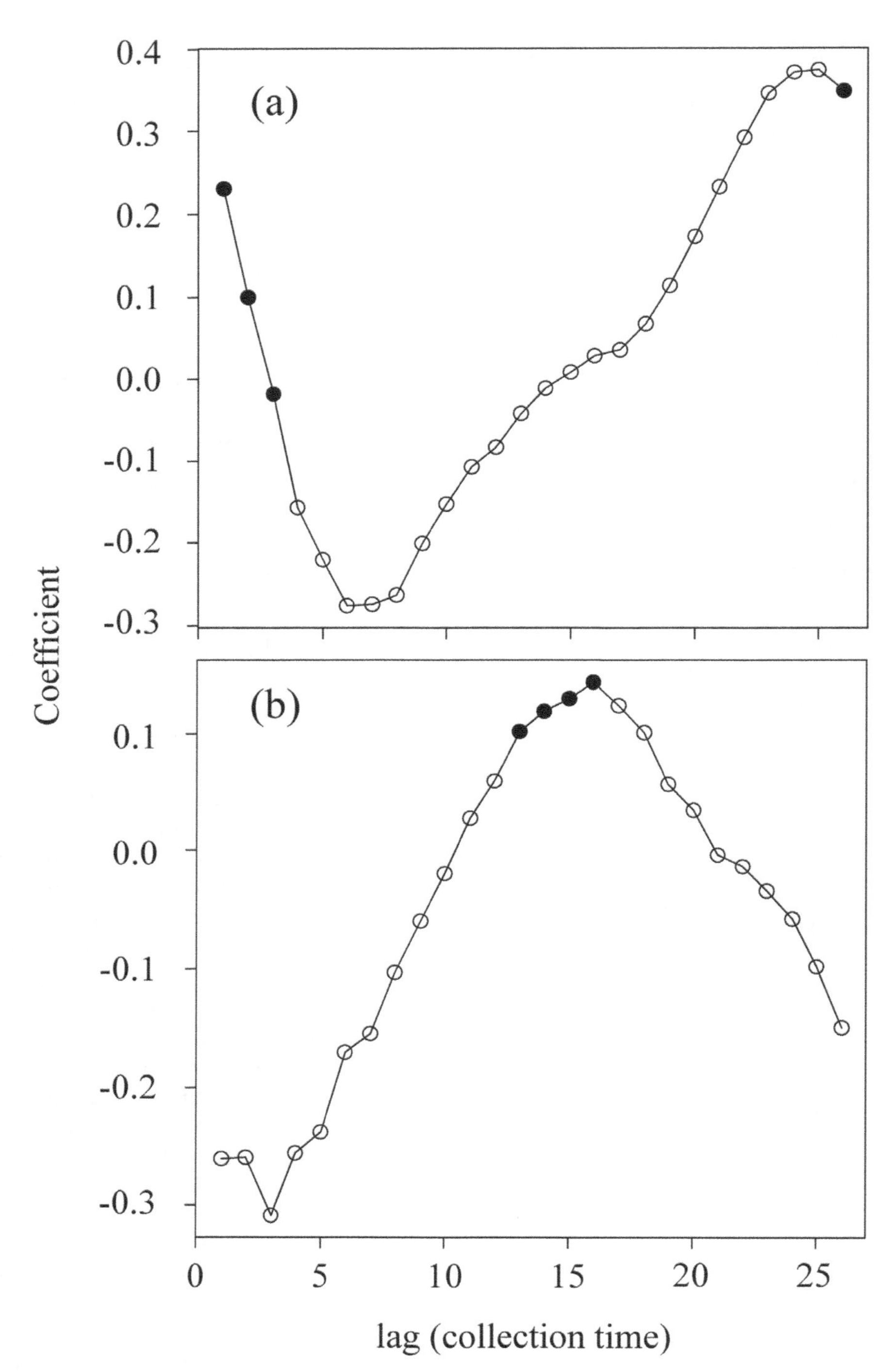

Figure 2. Coefficients of an explanatory variable obtained by a generalized linear model to explain influence on the total trap captures. The coefficients against a lag of up to 26 times of collections (= 52 weeks ≈ 1 year) are shown. Solid circles indicate that significant Granger Causality Indices (GCIs) at the lags. Open circles indicate the GCIs at the lags are not significant. (a) Temperature (TE) and (b) rainfall (RA).

Table 6. Model selection with a generalized linear model to explain total trap captures by temperature (TE) and rainfall (RA) using Akaike Information Criterion (AIC) and coefficients of the two explanatory variables in each model. A Poisson error structure with a log link function was used.

	Explanatory variable(s)			
	TE+RA	TE	RA	null
AIC	4071.5	7946.9	5801.7	10,291
Coefficient				
TE	0.166	0.232		
RA	−0.255		−0.261	

TE: Temperature
RA: Rainfall

different manner from the solar elevation angle (Figure 1(b)). In seasonal tropic zones, there is a long dry season, in which many woody plants lose their foliage. In northern Thailand, the dry season is composed of winter and summer, meaning that there are three seasons, i.e., rainy season, dry and cool season (winter), and dry and hot season (summer). During the dry season, the temperature decreases gradually and reaches its lowest in December–January due to the low sun elevation at winter solstice, then increases until April due to the high sun elevation and sunny climate. However, the temperature decreases during the rainy season due to lack of sunlight. Even during the second period of high sun elevation in August, temperature continues to decrease. After the second period of high sun elevation, the sun elevation drops until winter solstice, and thus the temperatures also continue to decrease until December–January. TTC was small in the rainy season, which was a cause of a negative coefficient of RA in the GLM without lag, and smaller AIC in the model with only RA than that with only TE (Table 6). The greater amount of rainfall first depressed TTC, probably due to a direct negative effect of rain on the flight behaviour of beetles. Second, during the dry season, TTC increased with temperature, as indicated by a positive coefficient in the GLM without lag (Table 6) probably because beetles flew more actively at high temperatures. It is known that the flight behaviour of beetles is influenced by temperature. For example, the ambrosia beetle, *Platypus quercivorus*, starts to fly when the air temperature reaches 19°C and actively flies at >20°C (Ueda and Kobayashi 2000).

In our study, the response of TTC to the two climatic factors was consistent for the three years. Similar results in relation to climatic factors have been reported in a seasonal tropical forest in Zambia (Beaver and Löyttyniemi 1991), in which two non-consecutive periods of 1-year monitoring were carried out. The number of trap captures increased rapidly during dry seasons in both years of monitoring, with the exception of Scolytinae ("Scolytidae" in the original article) in the second year. However, in both years, the trap captures peaked at the beginning of rainy season (October in the first year and December in the second). In Beaver and Löyttyniemi (1991), monthly data of trap captures and climate variables were analyzed so that coarse temporal resolution may have confused the relationship between the timing of the peak and the beginning of the rainy season, especially in the first year. The universality of the seasonal fluctuation pattern that was recognized in this study should be discussed in future when more similar datasets from seasonal tropical forests will be available.

The Granger causality test detected significant causality of temperature with lags 1–2 collection times (= 2–4 weeks). The development of the immature stages of insects is temperature-dependent (e.g. Stamp 1993). Females of ambrosia beetles are known to lay eggs for an extended period of time (Kirkendall et al. 1997) so extended progeny emergence as a result of continued maternal oviposition can occur (e.g. Oliver and Mannion 2001). Furthermore, teneral adults of many wood-boring insects are known to stay in their brood trees until the condition outside becomes preferable (Coulson and Witter 1984; Vega and Hofstetter 2015). These are likely factors causing the lag in positive effects of TE. On the other hand, positive effects of RA with longer lags (half a year or longer) are unexpected because there are few possibilities of direct positive effects of rain on the beetles. However, indirect effects of rain via host plants may have acted positively on the number of flying adults with relatively longer time lags as follows: Ambrosia beetles feed on fungi cultivated on the gallery surface so that wood moisture is important. Rain prevents desiccation of wood. Even for bark beetles which feed on phloem, deterioration of inner bark and cambium can be slowed down by rain. Therefore, rain keeps host plant condition suitable for the immature stages of both bark and ambrosia beetles for a longer time. In the seasonal tropics, heavy rainfall is sometimes accompanied by strong winds, which leaves many fallen trees and broken branches. These are preferred hosts for the reproduction of the beetles. Thus, there exist pathways by which rainfall may have caused positive effects on the wood-boring beetles with lags about half a year.

In the CCM, causalities of the two climate variables, especially RA, were weaker than SE. The seasonal indicator SE (solar elevation angle) is a product of the revolution and tilt of the earth. Seasonal changes in climate variables are also caused by these two. Therefore, even in a seasonal tropical forest, revolution and tilt of the earth act as driving forces of the 1-year cycle of flying wood-boring beetles via temperature and rainfall.

Acknowledgments

We express our sincere thanks to the two anonymous reviewers and four editors for their valuable comments to the earlier versions of this manuscript. Former students at Kasetsart University helped sorting insects. Biing-Tzuang Guan provided useful information on spectral density analysis. We also thank them.

Disclosure statement

No potential conflict of interest was reported by the authors.

Funding

This work was supported by the Japan Society for the Promotion of Science [16H02760]; Japan Society for the Promotion of Science [Core-to-core Project (FY2019—FY2021)]; Japan Society for the Promotion of Science [Core-to-core Project (FY2016—FY2018)]; Japan Society for the Promotion of Science [23255011].

References

Bale JS, Masters GJ, Hodkinson ID, Awmack C, Bezemer TM, Brown VK, Butterfield J, Buse a, Coulson JC, Farrar J, et al. 2002. Herbivory in global climate change research: direct effects of rising temperature on insect herbivores. Glob Chang Biol. 8:1–16.

Beaver RA. 1989. Insect-fungus relationships in the bark and ambrosia beetles. In: Wilding N, Collins NM, Hammond PM, Webber JF, editors. Insect-fungus interactions. London: Academic Press; p. 121–143.

Beaver RA, Löyttyniemi K. 1991. Annual flight patterns and diversity of bark and ambrosia beetles (Col., Scolytidae and Platypodidae) attracted to bait logs in Zambia. J Appl Entomol. 112:505–511. doi:10.1111/j.1439-0418.1991.tb01084.x.

Cooper PI. 1969. The absorption of radiation in solar stills. Sol Energy. 12:333–346. doi:10.1016/0038-092X(69)90047-4.

Coulson RN, Witter JA. 1984. Forest entomology: ecology and management. New York (NY): Wiley.

Crowson RA. 1981. The biology of Coleoptera. London: Academic Press.

Godfray HCJ, Hassell MP. 1989. Discrete and continuous insect populations in tropical environments. J Anim Ecol. 58:153–174. doi:10.2307/4992.

Granger CWJ. 1980. Testing for causality: a personal viewpoint. J Econ Dyn Control. 2:329–352. doi:10.1016/0165-1889(80)90069-X.

Hmamouche Y 2020. A package 'NlinTS': models for non linear causality detection in time series. R package version 1.3.8. accessed 2020 Mar 14:[12 p.]. https://cran.r-project.org/web/packages/NlinTS/NlinTS.pdf

Hulcr J, Beaver RA, Puranasakul W, Dole SA, Sonthichai S. 2008. A comparison of bark and ambrosia beetle communities in two forest types in northern Thailand (Coleoptera: Curculionidae: Scolytinae and Platypodinae). Environ Entomol. 37:1461–1470. doi:10.1603/0046-225X-37.6.1461.

Kaneko T. 1965. Biology of some scolytid ambrosia beetles attacking tea plants. I. Growth and development of two species of scolytid beetles reared on sterilized tea plants. Appl Entomol Zool. 9:211–216. doi:10.1303/jjaez.9.211.

Kaneko T, Tamaki Y, Takagi K. 1965. Preliminary report on the biology of some Scolytid beetles, the tea root borer, *Xyleborus germanus* Blandford, attacking tea roots, and the tea stem borer, *Xyleborus compactus* Eichhoff, attacking tea twigs. Appl Entomol Zool. 9:23–28. doi:10.1303/jjaez.9.23.

Kirkendall LR, Kent DS, Raffa KA. 1997. Interactions among males, females and offspring in bark and ambrosia beetles: the significance of living in tunnels for the evolution of social behaviour. In: Choe J, Crespi B, editors. The evolution of social behaviour in insects and arachnids. Cambridge (UK): Cambridge University Press; p. 181–215.

Knell RJ. 1998. Generation cycles. Trends Ecol Evol. 13:186–190. doi:10.1016/S0169-5347(97)01321-9.

Liebhold AM, Kamata N. 2000. Are population cycles and spatial synchrony a universal characteristic of forest insect populations? Population dynamics of forest-defoliating insects. Popul Ecol. 42:205–209. doi:10.1007/PL00011999.

Liu LY, Schönitzer K, Yang JT. 2008. A review of the literature on the life history of Bostrichidae (Coleoptera). Mitt Münch Ent Ges. 98:91–97.

Louca S 2016. A package 'peacots': periodogram peaks in correlated time series. accessed 2020 Mar 14:[19 p.]. https://cran.r-project.org/web/packages/peacots/peacots.pdf.

Louca S, Doebeli M. 2015. Detecting cyclicity in ecological time series. Ecology. 96:1724–1732. doi:10.1890/14-0126.1.

Macedo-Reis LE, Novais SM, Monteiro GF, Flechtmann CA, Faria ML, Neves Fde S. 2016. Spatio-temporal distribution of bark and ambrosia beetles in a Brazilian tropical dry forest. J Insect Sci. 16(1):48; 1–9. doi:10.1093/jisesa/iew027.

Meyers SR 2014. Astrochron: an R Package for astrochronology. accessed 2020 Mar 14:[132 p.]. https://cran.r-project.org/web/packages/astrochron/astrochron.pdf

Mizell RF III, Bolques a, Crampton P. 1998. Evaluation of insecticides to control the Asian ambrosia beetle, *Xylosandrus crassiusculus*. Proc Sou Nursery Assoc. 43:162–165.

Nair KSS. 2007. Tropical forest insect pests: ecology, impact, and management. Cambridge (UK): Cambridge University Press.

Nakamura K, Hasan N, Abbas I, Godfray HCJ, Bonsall MB. 2004. Generation cycles in Indonesian lady beetle populations may occur as a result of cannibalism. Proc Roy Soc Biol Sci. 271:S501–S504. doi:10.1098/rsbl.2004.0231.

Oliver JB, Mannion CM. 2001. Ambrosia beetle (Coleoptera: Scolytidae) species attacking chestnut and captured in ethanol-baited traps in middle Tennessee. Environ Entomol. 30:909–918. doi:10.1603/0046-225X-30.5.909.

Phillips PCB, Ouliaris S. 1990. Asymptotic properties of residual based tests for cointegration. Econometrica. 58:165–193. doi:10.2307/2938339.

R Development Core Team. 2019. R: a language and environment for statistical computing. Vienna (Austria): R Foundation for Statistical Computing. accessed 2019 Oct 31. https://www.R-project.org/.

Sandoval RC, Cognato AI, Righi CA. 2017. Bark and ambrosia beetle (Curculionidae: Scolytinae) diversity found in agricultural and fragmented forests in Piracicaba-SP, Brazil. Environ Entomol. 46:1254–1263. doi:10.1093/ee/nvx160.

Sanguansub S, Buranapanichpan S, Saowaphak T, Beaver RA, Kamata N. 2020. List of wood-boring beetles (Coleoptera: Bostrichidae, Curculionidae; Platypodinae, and Scolytinae) captured by ethanol-baited traps in a lower montane forest in northern Thailand. Misc Info Univ Tokyo For. 62:15–54.

Stamp NE. 1993. a temperate region view of the interaction of temperature, food quality, and predators on caterpillar foraging. In: Stamp NE, Casey TM, editors. Caterpillars: ecological and evolutionary constraints on foraging. New York (NY): Chapman & Hall; p. 478–508.

Sugihara G, May R, Ye H, Hsieh CH, Deyle E, Fogarty M, Munch S. 2012. Detecting causality in complex ecosystems. Science. 338:496–500. doi:10.1126/science.1227079.

Sugihara G, Park J, Deyle E, Saberski E, Smith C, Ye H 2019. rEDM: an R package for empirical dynamic modeling and convergent cross mapping. accessed 2020 Mar 14:[21 p.]. https://github.com/SugiharaLab/rEDM.

Tanaka N, Kume T, Yoshifuji N, Tanaka K, Takizawa H, Shiraki K, Tantasirin C, Tangtham N, Suzuki M. 2008. A review of evapotranspiration estimates from tropical monsoon forests in Thailand and adjacent regions. Agric For Meteorol. 148:807–819. doi:10.1016/j.agrformet.2008.01.011.

Trapletti a, Hornik K 2019. Package 'tseries': time series analysis and computational finance. R package version 0.10-47. accessed 2020 Mar 14:[54 p.]. https://cran.r-project.org/web/packages/tseries/tseries.pdf.

Ueda a, Kobayashi M. 2000. Relationship between flight of *Platypms quercivorus* (Coleoptera: Platypodidae), temperature and sunshine. Ap For Sci. 9:93–97. Japanese with English summary.

Vega FE, Hofstetter RW, editors. 2015. Bark beetles: biology and ecology of native and invasive species. London: Academic Press.

Wood SL. 1982. The bark and ambrosia beetles of North and Central America (Coleoptera: scolytidae), a taxonomic monograph. Great Basin Nat. 6:1–1359.

Spatio-temporal variation in egg-laying dates of nestbox-breeding varied tits (*Poecile varius*) in response to spring pre-breeding period temperatures at long-term study sites in South Korea and Japan

Min-Su Jeong, Hankyu Kim and Woo-Shin Lee

ABSTRACT

Climate change can alter and disrupt the phenology and phenological interaction between organisms from various trophic levels in forest ecosystems. In temperate forests, the breeding phenology of birds is correlated to local microclimate, especially spring temperature to match the timing of food availability. Recent studies revealed that the temperature warming is more pronounced in high-elevation areas (elevation-dependent warming), while the breeding phenology shift of birds in this condition needs further investigation. We studied the annual change in the egg-laying dates of varied tits (*Poecile varius*) and a pre-breeding temperature index in three plots located along with the elevational gradient in South Korea and a low-elevation plot in Japan. We found strong support for disproportionate rates of changes in higher elevation for warming trends in pre-breeding period and advances in egg-laying dates over the last decade. Next, we compared three segments of 36-year data from Akazu Research Forest. The evidence from pre-breeding temperature during 36 years indicates that we could detect the change in thermal environment and breeding phenology with longer years of data, especially in lower elevation regions. This result shows the need for long-term research to understand the change in local temperatures and the ecology of forest birds. Our study presents evidence of elevation-dependent phenological advance in avian breeding activities and discusses the need for systematic long-term research on multiple taxa and climatic drivers in Asia.

Introduction

Global climate change has accelerated over the last few decades, and the previous 4-year period (2015–2018) was the four warmest years on record globally (Siegmund et al. 2019). There is profound evidence showing that such change can cause phenological shifts and asynchrony among organisms, which can lead to the deterioration of ecosystem functions and population declines (Both et al. 2006; Thackeray et al. 2010; Donnelly et al. 2011; Saino et al. 2011; Renner and Zohner 2018). The asynchrony is due to the variation in phenological sensitivity to the warming among taxa, trophic levels, and ecosystems (Visser and Both 2005; Thackeray et al. 2016; Burgess et al. 2018). In temperate forest ecosystems, songbirds use the pre-breeding season temperature as one of the most important environmental cues to determine when to start to breed (Visser et al. 2009; Schaper et al. 2012; Verhagen et al. 2020). The phenological response of songbirds to the change in such cue is crucial for maintaining the synchrony between the timing of when songbirds rear their chicks and the peak availability of arthropod prey; hence, matching phenology to resources is essential for breeding success in many birds (van Noordwijk et al. 1995; Visser et al. 2006; Reed et al. 2013). As global temperature, especially spring temperature rose, the timing of breeding of songbirds advanced over the last few decades across the world (Crick and Sparks 1999; Both and Marvelde 2007; Bell et al. 2019). However, previous studies have shown that the degrees of phenological shifts of songbirds were different between populations, mainly due to the heterogeneity of the local climate, the variation of other environmental conditions, and breeding strategy between populations (Visser et al. 2003; Both et al. 2004; Torti and Dunn 2005; Porlier et al. 2012).

One of the major drivers of local temperature variability across the globe is altitude (Geiger et al. 2009). Air temperature near ground decreases as elevation increases in the troposphere, and thus phenological events such as budburst and the flowering of plants, and breeding of animals in the forest ecosystems progress along with elevational gradient in spring (Hwang et al. 2011; Jeong et al. 2019). However, recent studies also found that the rate of warming is greater in high-elevation regions around the globe (Rangwala and Miller 2012; Pepin et al. 2015). This elevation-dependent warming can cause stronger phenological advances in plants at higher elevations, leading to more uniform phenology of trees across elevations over a few decades (Chen et al. 2018; Vitasse et al. 2018). Yet there is very limited information on how animals respond to these increased rates of warming in higher elevation forest ecosystems, compared to the lower elevation forests.

Changes in phenology of forest ecosystems and its potential consequences from climate change are one of the many things that can be achieved only by continued efforts from long-term ecological studies. While warming spring and advancing phenology is a global phenomenon, these responses of ecosystems and organisms to climate change often only occur once a year, and a single site might only yield a single datapoint each year (Franklin 1989). Long-term studies across many years only can provide opportunities to collect data under annual variability in

Table 1. Summary of study plots and the number of breeding nests (*n*), overall mean and standard error (SE) of individual egg-laying dates over entire survey periods (mean egg-laying date; day of year) of varied tits, and pre-breeding period (the period from 44 to 14 days before mean egg-laying dates; day of year).

Plot	Location	Altitude (m)	Period	*n*	Mean egg-laying date (Mean ± SE)	Pre-breeding period
Mt. Sanage 300 m	35°12N, 137°30E	300–360	1983–2018	376	101.04 ± 0.43	57–87
Mt. Jiri 350 m	35°15N, 127°34E	340–400	2006–2018	69	108.33 ± 1.13	64–94
Mt. Jiri 900 m	35°18N, 127°39E	900–960	2006–2018	117	120.65 ± 0.84	77–107
Mt. Jiri 1300 m	35°17N, 127°31E	1270–1340	2009–2018	49	132.05 ± 1.42	88–118

climate, as well as statistical power to detect such responses (Lindenmayer et al. 2012).

We studied the breeding phenology of nestbox-breeding populations of varied tits (*Poecile varius*; Paridae) from long-term study sites in university forests in Japan and Korea, to understand the variability in early spring, pre-breeding period temperatures and egg-laying dates across multiple years. Varied tit is a common and abundant species in forested habitats of South Korea and Japan across a broad elevational gradient and consumes herbivorous insects during the breeding season (Gosler et al. 2019). Birds in the Paridae family are excellent model species for studying effects of climate change on breeding phenology – (a) since they breed in cavities and readily use nestboxes, (b) short-distance migrant or resident species thus influenced by local climatic patterns, (c) and heavily rely on seasonal herbivorous arthropod prey, especially lepidopteran larvae for breeding. Many species of birds in this taxa have been studied widely as a model species to understand the phenological response of animals to climate change and its consequences and their fitness (Reed et al. 2013; Shiao et al. 2015; Yanase et al. 2018; Jeong et al. 2019).

If the rates of warming are greater in higher-elevation forests, we can predict that the breeding timing of birds would be more advanced in higher elevation areas, while birds in low-elevation forests may retain their breeding schedule. In this paper, we test this hypothesis of elevation-dependent phenological shift in varied tits by comparing temperature and breeding phenology change across multiple long-term study plots at different elevations in montane forests of Korea and Japan. In addition, we also show the temporal pattern of trends of the pre-breeding period temperature and mean egg-laying dates using a long-term dataset from Akazu Research Forest in Japan, to demonstrate the importance of long-term studies.

Methods

Study sites

The breeding phenology data of varied tits were collected from three plots in the Nambu University Forest of Seoul National University (Mt. Jiri) in South Korea over 11 years from 2006 to 2018 (except 2007 and 2014). The size of each plot in South Korea is approximately 2 ha, and the elevations of each plot are 340 m–400 m (Mt. Jiri 350 m), 900 m–960 m (Mt. Jiri 900 m), and 1270 m–1340 m (Mt. Jiri 1300 m) above sea level (a.s.l.) (Table 1, Figure 1). For Mt. Jiri 1300 m, we excluded the egg-laying date data in 2006 and 2008 because the ambient temperature measurements started from 2009. A plot in Mt. Sanage in the Akazu Research Forest of the University of Tokyo in Japan (Mt. Sanage 300 m) is 8 ha in area, with elevation ranging 300–360 m a.s.l. Mt. Sanage 300 m plot has the longest record of breeding phenology data, covering 36 years from 1983 to 2018 (Table 1, Figure 1; Yanase et al. 2018; Yanase et al. 2019).

Three plots in Mt. Jiri were located in mixed deciduous forests (Lee et al. 2016), and Konara oak (*Quercus serrata*), Japanese loose-flowered hornbeam (*Carpinus laxiflora*), and Japanese snowbell (*Styrax japonicus*) were the dominant woody vegetation in Mt. Jiri 350 m, while the other two plots contained Mongolian oak (*Quercus mongolica*) and Korean maple (*Acer pseudosieboldianum*). Mt. Sanage 300 m was located in a natural secondary forest (Yanase et al. 2018, 2019), mainly composed of Konara oak (*Quercus serrata*), Japanese red pine (*Pinus densiflora*), and Hinoki cypress (*Chamaecyparis obtusa*).

Breeding data

At Mt. Jiri in South Korea, 48 nestboxes were placed 1.5 m above ground in each plot. Nestbox monitoring was conducted from mid-March to early July, and all nestboxes were visited at an interval of about 7 days from 2006 to 2015 and about every 14–21 days from 2016 to 2018. We used wooden nestboxes with equal dimension (height 25.0 cm × width 16.0 cm × depth 15.0 cm, wall thickness = 1.0 cm) and set the equal number of nestboxes for three entrance hole sizes (3.0 cm, 3.5 cm, 4.0 cm) of each plot. We also placed a miniaturized temperature data logger (TDL; iButton DS 1291G, Maxim Integrated, San Jose, USA) at the bottom of each nestbox from 2016 in three plots in Korea. All TDLs were set to record the temperature at intervals of 45 min to determine the egg-laying dates using the thermal signatures of the nestbox from breeding activities. In Mt. Sanage 300 m in Japan, nestbox monitoring was conducted from 42 (1983–1993), 70 (1994–2009), and 60 (2010–2018) nestboxes in the same study area, and all nestboxes were checked every 2–3 days from early March to early July each year. The dimensions of used nestboxes were height 20.0 cm, width 15.0 cm, and depth 15.0 cm (wall thickness 1.0–1.5 cm), and all of the entrances had 3 cm diameter (Yanase et al. 2018, 2019).

The first egg-laying dates of breeding pairs in three plots in Mt. Jiri from 2006 to 2015 and in Mt. Sanage 300 m (Yanase et al. 2018, 2019) were estimated by backdating the number of eggs assuming that one egg was laid per day during the egg-laying stage (van Balen 1973) when eggs were first detected. For the breeding pairs in Mt. Jiri from 2016 to 2018, we deployed TDLs in all nestboxes and used the temperature signatures to estimate the egg-laying dates while checking all nestboxes at least once every 14–21 days to confirm species and nest fate. The temperature in an active breeding nestbox is always higher than the ambient temperature of the plot or empty nestbox in the vicinity, and there are spikes in early morning (5–7 am) temperatures during the egg-laying period when the female lays egg. We used this difference to estimate the first egg-laying dates together with other thermal signatures using a random forest algorithm to

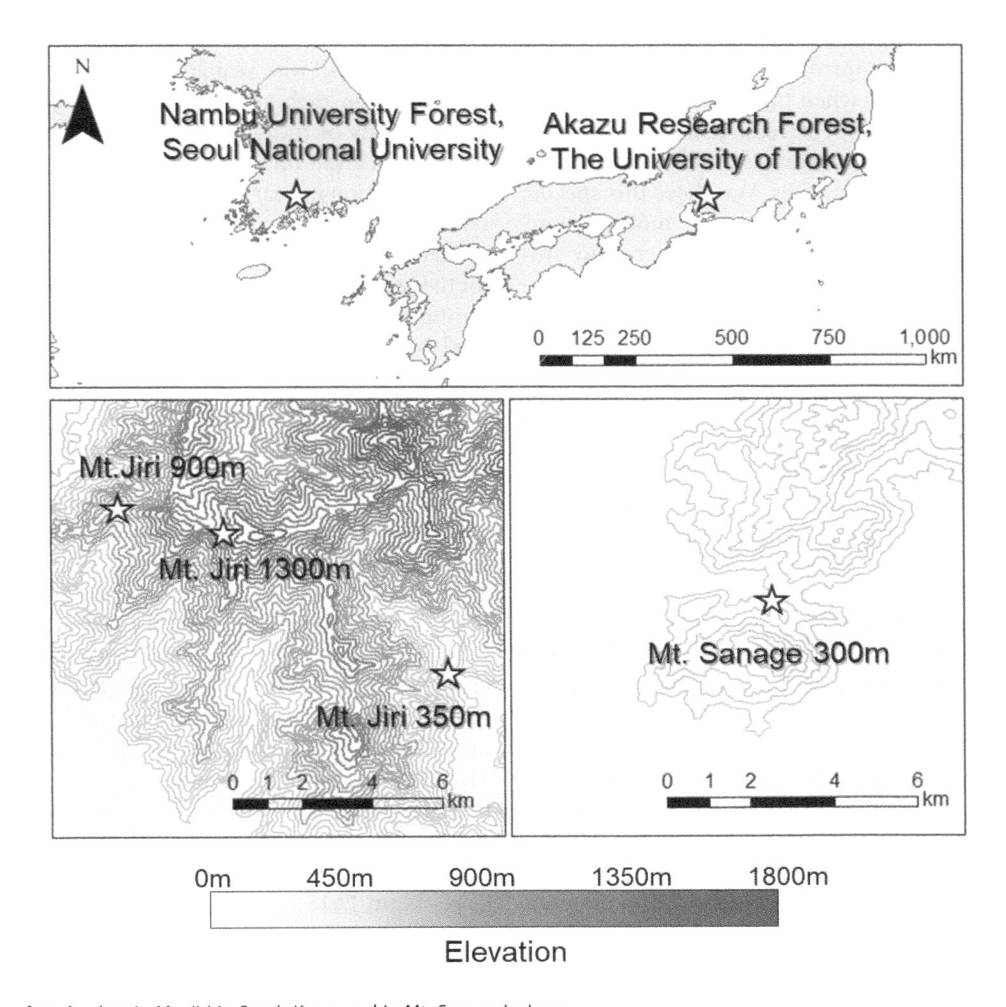

Figure 1. Locations of study plots in Mt. Jiri in South Korea and in Mt. Sanage in Japan.

classify the condition of the nest for each day, and extracted the first day of nesting activity (egg-laying) for egg-laying dates (see Jeong 2020 for more details in this method). We assessed the reliability of this method by comparing 19 nests from 2016 to 2018 in Mt. Jiri that we can estimate the egg-laying dates with a backdating method (nests visited before the clutch was finished). The clutch size of varied tits in the three plots in Mt. Jiri was 6.23 ± 0.08 (mean ± SE; $n = 237$). The mean difference of the egg-laying dates estimated with thermal signatures using random forest algorithm and the dates estimated with the backdating method from the field was 0.32 days ($n = 19$, SE = 0.18; Pearson's correlation coefficient = 0.998, $p < 0.001$). Thus, we considered the TDL method comparable to the field observation. We used a total of 611 nests initiated within 30 days from the first egg-laying dates in each year in each plot for the analysis to exclude the initiation dates of the second clutch (Table 1; Visser et al. 2003; Bourgault et al. 2010) from the analysis.

Climate data

We used the ambient air temperature of the 350 and 900 m plots in Mt. Jiri from an automatic weather station managed by the Korea Meteorological Administration approximately 300 m and 1 km away from each plot. Each weather station was located in the range of elevation of each plot, and measurements were taken every hour. For the 1300 m plot in Mt. Jiri, the ambient temperature was measured every hour with a data logger (HOBO U23 Pro v2, Onset Computer Corporation, Bourne, USA), which was placed 2 m above the ground at the center of the plot. In Mt. Sanage 300 m, the ambient temperature data from 1983 to 2018 were obtained from the Shirasaka Meteorological Observation Station in Mt. Sanage (35° 12′ N, 137°10′ E) at 300 m a.s.l. (Yanase et al. 2018, 2019).

The seasonal shift of phenology is delayed in higher elevation and latitude due to the lapse rate of temperature. Among our study plots, this difference is 3–5 weeks different between our lowest elevation study plot, Mt. Sanage 300 m and highest elevation study plot, Mt. Jiri 1300 m. Due to this difference, we cannot apply a single fixed-temporal window for pre-breeding period temperature indices across all plots.

Previous studies utilized a single temporal window that reflects pre-breeding season specific to each location and species (Visser and Both 2005; Husby et al. 2009). However, temperature indices right before the egg laying did not influence egg-laying dates of birds in many studies (Gienapp et al. 2005; Williams et al. 2015), indicating that longer term thermal conditions are more important predictors in bird breeding phenology (Williams 2012). This may be partly related to the time lag due to other breeding processes, such as the development of the eggs and nest building (up to 15 days). In addition to this lagged process and the need for reflecting a plot-specific temporal window for temperature indices, we chose a 31-day window period (pre-breeding period) from 44 days prior to the average egg-laying dates across all years for each plot. This window will reflect the temporal window when the most birds from each plot will be exposed to the pre-breeding thermal environment, given that the range of breeding initiation at each plot is 18–24 days of window, across sites. We chose this specific length of the window to be analogous to the monthly temperature indices that are commonly used in phenology studies (Sanz et al. 2003; Bourgault et al. 2010), while accounting for variation in nest initiation date among individuals and maximum time spent building nests. The time windows for temperature indices at each plot are February 26–March 27 (Mt. Sanage 300 m), March 4–April 3 (Mt. Jiri 350 m), March 17–April 16 (Mt. Jiri 900 m), March 28–April 27 (Mt. Jiri 1300 m), for all years (Table 1).

Data analysis

Various temperature parameters have been used in previous studies on breeding phenology (Visser et al. 2003; Wawrzyniak et al. 2015; Drake and Martin 2018), and one experimental study on the captive population of the *Parus* species showed the increasing pattern of temperature influence on the egg-laying initiation (Schaper et al. 2012). We calculated three temperature variables, including the average of the daily mean and daily maximum temperature, and the slope of the daily mean temperature. The slope of daily mean temperature was the coefficient of linear regressions between the date and daily mean temperature for each site during the pre-breeding period.

Some of these parameters were highly correlated; thus, for simplicity, we used a variable selection procedure employing an information criteria approach to choose a single most representative pre-breeding temperature variable to describe the thermal environment of breeding varied tits in our study sites. We used linear mixed-effect models with each of three temperature variables as predictor variables and individual egg-laying dates (n = 597) as a response variable to compare and choose a temperature covariate that best explains the phenology of birds. To account for repeated measurement of bird populations in multiple years at the same plot and individual nesting pairs measured within each year, we included plot and year as two random variables to allow the intercepts to vary for these variables in the models. All data across years and plots were used in these models. We ranked model fit using Akaike Information Criteria adjusted for a small sample size (AICc; Burnham and Anderson 2002) and selected the variable with the lowest AICc value. Akaike weights, proportion of the likelihood of the model compared with all others, were calculated to measure the probability that the best model is a better fit to the data than alternative models (Burnham and Anderson 2002).

We investigated how yearly trends for pre-breeding temperature and mean egg-laying timing of birds at each plot changes by elevation using a linear model and a linear mixed-effect model with year and elevation interaction term, using the data from all four plots from 2006 to 2018. For these analyses, we limited the study period to the most recent decade to compare trends among plots because the data from Korean plots were limited to the 2006–2018 period. To test the variation in temporal trends of spring pre-breeding period temperature in different elevations, we used the selected temperature variable from the above model selection process on a linear regression model with year and elevation as an interaction term in addition to each variable (Tables 2 and 3). To show how yearly trends of mean egg-laying date vary by elevation, we employed a linear mixed-effect model with year, elevation, two-way interaction of year and elevation, and plot and year as two random variables that allow intercept to vary among plots. We estimated the slopes and 95% confidence intervals of fitted lines for the temperature variable and the egg-laying date of each plot during the study period. For a linear mixed-effect model, we used bootstrapping simulations (n = 1000) to estimate 95% confidence intervals for estimates.

We also compared the trend of 36-year data and three 12-year period subset segments of the pre-breeding temperature and annual mean egg-laying dates from Mt. Sanage 300 m plot. We created a categorical dummy variable (period) to divide 36-year data into three 12-year segment periods (categories: period 1: 1983–1994, period 2: 1995–2006, period 3: 2007–2018). We fitted two linear regression models: one with the whole 36-year data (36-year model) and the other with three-segmented categories (12-year model). The 36-year model was built simply with the year as an independent variable. For the 12-year model, period, year and two-way interaction term were provided to estimate trends for each 12-year segment. We compared the slopes and 95% confidence interval of each trend from two models.

All analysis was done on a program R, version 3.5.1 (R Core Team 2018). The linear mixed-effect model analysis was conducted using "lme4" package (Bates et al. 2018) and compared with "MuMin" package (Barton 2019). Bootstrapped confidence intervals were estimated using "ciTools" package (Haman and Avery 2019). Linear models were fitted using base R function "lm" and the linear combinations of estimates of linear mixed-effect models and linear regression models were calculated with "emmeans" package (Lenth 2018).

Table 2. Model selection results based on AICc for linear mixed-effect model for the individual egg-laying dates of varied tits with the effect size of the fixed effect of each model covariates and 95% confidence intervals (CI).

Model	AICc	ΔAICc	Weight	Effect size	95% CI
Average daily mean temperature	4187.8	0.00	0.995	−2.27	−2.93 to −1.59
Average daily maximum temperature	4198.4	10.61	0.005	−1.79	−2.49 to −1.13
Temperature slope	4218.0	30.26	0.000	9.59	1.24–17.92
Null (random effect only)	4221.1	33.29	0.000	-	-

Table 3. Effect size and 95% confidence interval (CI) for yearly trends for average daily mean temperature during pre-breeding period (temperature) and mean egg-laying dates of four study plots from 2006 to 2018.

Response variable	Source of variance	Effect size	95% CI	t-value	p-value
Temperature (°C)	Intercept	6.86	4.96–8.75	7.31	<0.001
	Year	−0.03	−0.25–0.20	−0.22	0.826
	Elevation	−3.16	−5.82 to −0.50	−2.40	0.021
	Year × Elevation	0.36	0.05–0.67	2.37	0.022
Egg-laying dates	Intercept	91.42	82.93–97.45	19.33	<0.001
	Year	0.46	0.01–1.11	1.23	0.238
	Elevation	37.84	28.86–47.63	6.93	0.002
	Year × Elevation	−1.23	−1.98 to −0.40	−3.15	0.002

Results

In Mt. Jiri, the timing of egg-laying of varied tits delayed with elevational gradient (Table 1), and annual mean egg-laying dates of each plot varied among years; ranging from April 9 to April 28 (19 days) at Mt. Jiri 350 m, from Apr 24 to May 10 (18 days) at Mt. Jiri 900 m, from Apr 30 to May 24 (24 days) at Mt. Jiri 1300 m from 2006 to 2018. In Mt. Sanage 300 m, annual mean egg-laying dates ranged April 3 and April 21 (19 days) for all survey years (all 36 years), and Apr 3 and April 19 (17 days) from 2006 to 2018.

The linear mixed-effect models showed that the egg-laying dates advanced along the increase in daily mean temperatures and daily maximum temperatures during the pre-breeding period, but not for the temperature slope (Table 2). The egg-laying dates delayed as temperature slope increased, but the 95% confidence interval and low AIC value indicated that the effect of temperature slope was subtle rather than other variables. The model comparison based on Akaike's Information Criteria indicated that the model including average daily mean temperature was the best model with the lowest AICc value, and the probability that the model is the best one of candidate models was 99.5% (Table 2). Such strong evidence suggests choosing the mean daily temperature of the pre-breeding period rather than other indices. The average daily mean temperature model suggested that the average egg-laying date of varied tits advanced 2.27 days (95% CI = −2.93 to −1.59 days) as the average daily mean temperature during the pre-breeding period increased by 1° C, across all plots in our study.

The linear model for average daily mean temperatures during the pre-breeding period from 2006 to 2018 showed a strong evidence of elevation-dependent warming that the annual change of average daily mean temperature increased 0.36°C/year (95% CI = 0.05–0.67°C/year) for every 1 km increase in elevation (Table 3). While the temperature was 3.16°C (95% CI = 0.50–5.81°C) cooler for a kilometer increase in elevation across all plots and years (Table 3). However, on average across all plots, the temperature in the pre-breeding period did not show strong evidence of change (mean = −0.03°C/year, 95% CI = −0.25 to 0.20°C/year; Table 3). From our model, there was almost no change (Figure 2) in average daily mean temperatures in Mt. Sanage 300 m (mean = 0.08°C/year, 95% CI = −0.07 to 0.24°C/year) and Mt. Jiri 350 m (mean = 0.10°C/year, 95% CI = −0.04 to 0.25°C/year). On the other hand, there was substantial evidence of increases of the average breeding period daily mean temperatures in the other two higher elevation plots. The pre-breeding period average daily mean temperatures increased 0.30°C annually (95% CI = 0.16–0.44°C/year) in Mt. Jiri 900 m and 0.45°C/year (95% CI = 0.21–0.68°C/year) in Mt. Jiri 1300 m (Figure 2).

Trends of annual mean egg-laying dates in the linear-mixed effect model supported elevation-dependent shift in annual egg-laying dates, per 1 km increase in elevation (mean = −1.23 days/year, 95% CI = −1.98 to −0.40 days/year), while the average egg-laying dates were 37.85 days later (95% CI = 28.86–47.63 days) as a kilometer increase in elevation in our study plots during the study period (Table 3). Our model results did not show evidence of advanced egg-laying dates during this recent period in both Mt. Sanage 300 m (mean = 0.09 days/year, 95% CI = −0.60 to 0.79 days/year) and Mt. Jiri 350 m (mean = 0.03 days/year, 95% CI = −0.66 to 0.72 days/year; Figure 3). However, the mean estimates of annual change in egg-laying dates were 0.65 days earlier in Mt. 900 m (95% CI = −1.35 to 0.06 days/year) and 1.14 days earlier in Mt. 1300 m (95% CI = −1.98 to −0.29 days/year) each year, though the support for Mt. Jiri 900 m plot is weaker than Mt. Jiri 1300 m plot (Figure 3).

From 1983 to 2018, in Mt. Sanage 300 m plot, there was some evidence of slight increase in the average daily mean temperature (mean = 0.04°C/year, 95% CI = 0.00–0.08°C/year), while there was no strong trend of the mean egg-laying

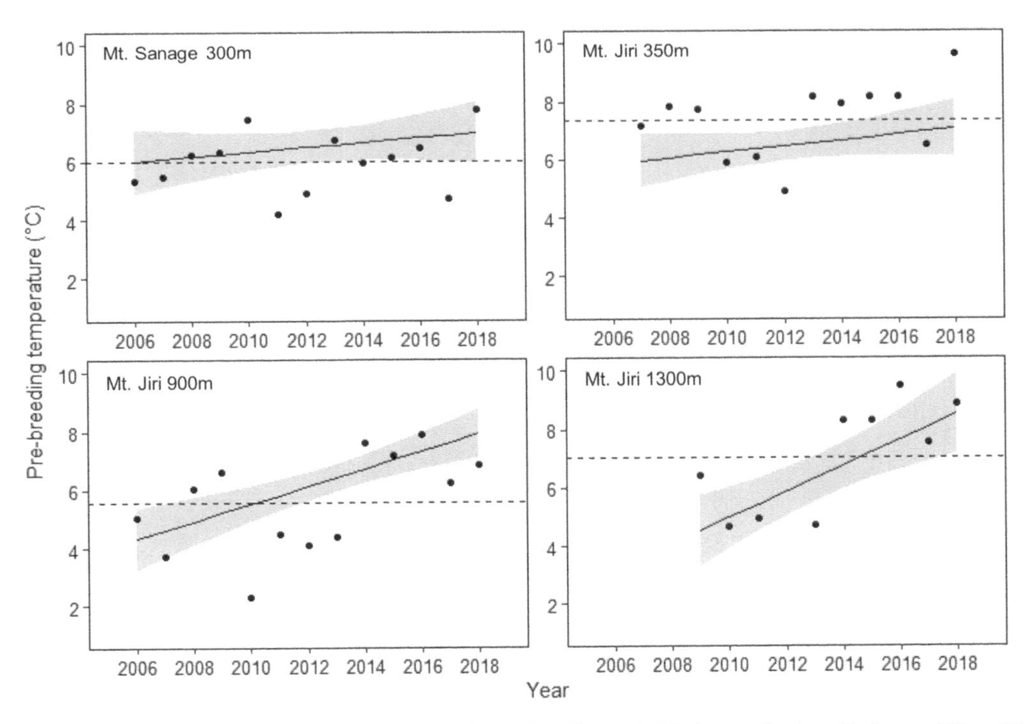

Figure 2. Yearly trends for the average daily mean temperatures during the pre-breeding period in four study plots: Mt. Sanage 300 m, Mt. Jiri 350 m, Mt. Jiri 900 m, Mt. Jiri 1300 m. The black solid line and grey shading represent the regression line and 95% confidence interval, respectively. The dashed line represents the average of pre-breeding temperatures of each plot from 2006 to 2018.

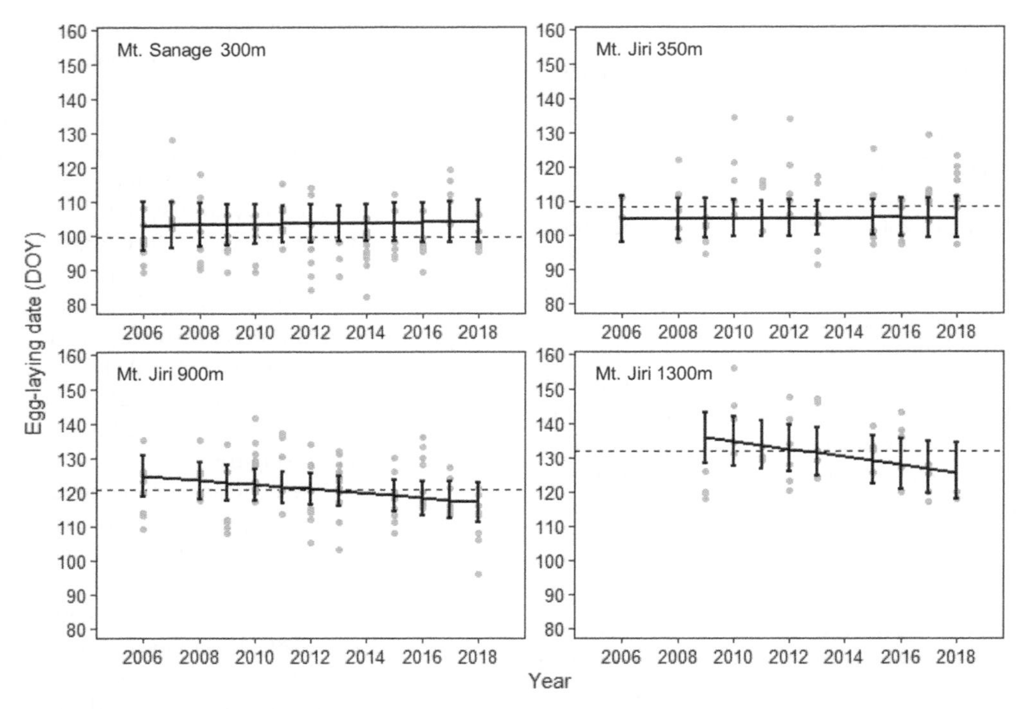

Figure 3. Yearly trends for egg-laying dates (day of year; DOY) in four study plots: Mt. Sanage 300 m, Mt. Jiri 350 m, Mt. Jiri 900 m, Mt. Jiri 1300 m. The black solid line and error bars represent the regression lines and 95% confidence intervals for each year estimates, respectively. The dashed line represents the overall mean of egg-laying dates of each plot from 2006 to 2018.

dates (mean = −0.09 days/year, 95% CI = −0.26 to 0.09 days/year; Figure 4). For 12-year segment periods, we failed to find supportive evidence in the change in yearly trends for both pre-breeding temperature and mean egg-laying dates in all three shorter periods (Figure 4). For each shorter period, annual changes of mean daily temperature of pre-breeding period were 0.18°C/year (95% CI = −0.04 to 0.41°C/year), −0.05 (95% CI = −0.27 to 0.18°C/year) and 0.05 (95% CI = −0.18 to 0.27°C/year) for period 1, period 2 and period 3, respectively, and the mean egg-laying dates changed −0.32 days/year (95% CI = −1.29 to 0.65 days/year), −0.21 days/year (95% CI = −1.18 to 0.76 days/year) and −0.02 days/year (95% CI = −0.99 to 0.95 days/year) for each period (Figure 4).

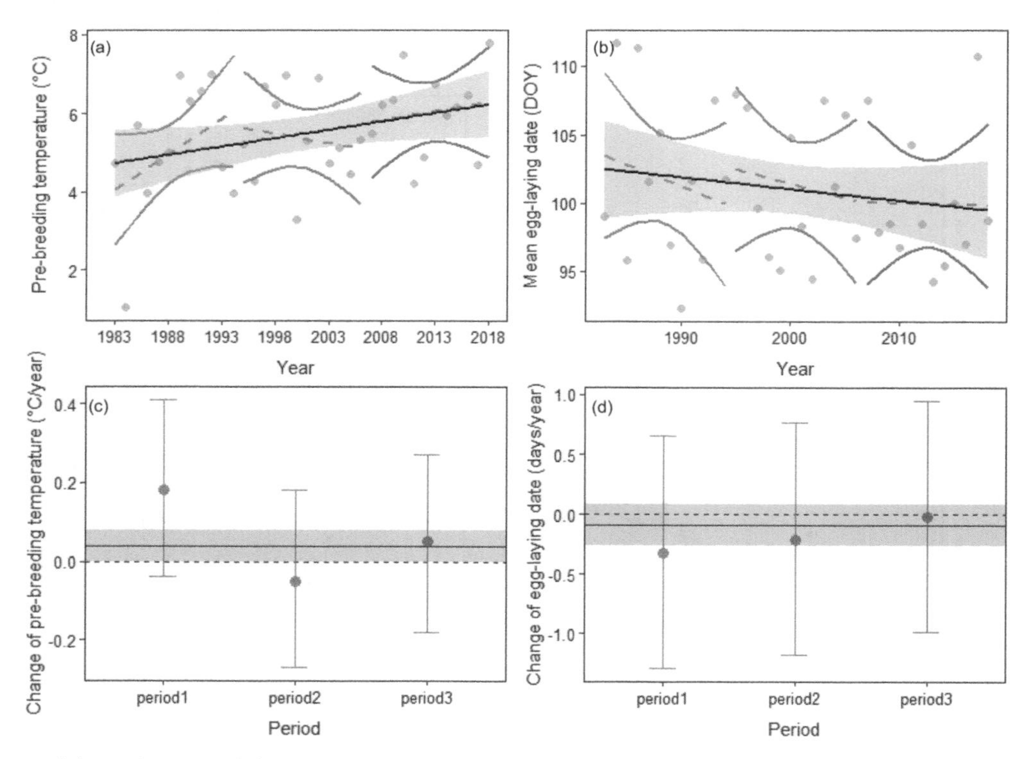

Figure 4. (a, c) Pattern of change in average daily mean temperatures during the pre-breeding period and (b, d) mean egg-laying dates in Mt. Sanage 300 m between full 36-year period (grey shading and black lines) and three 12-year periods: period 1: 1983–1994, period 2: 1995–2006, period 3: 2007–2018 (dotted lines and point estimate with error bars). Error bars, grey shading and error lines represent 95% confidence intervals.

Discussion

Our results showed the spatial and temporal variability in egg-laying dates of varied tits across our study plots in Japan and Korea, between 2006 and 2018. The warming of pre-breeding period temperature and egg-laying dates were greater in higher elevations, while lower elevation plots in research forests did not show strong changes in temperature nor egg-laying dates in our 13 years period. The patterns of trend in egg-laying dates in study plots correspond well with the patterns of annual trends in pre-breeding period temperatures. This relationship matches well with the known relationship between early spring pre-breeding period temperatures and onset of breeding in many species of forest birds (Visser et al. 2009; Schaper et al. 2012; Verhagen et al. 2020), which was also shown from our study. Local temperature indices during the pre-breeding period that reflect microclimatic conditions in montane forests are an important measure for understanding bird phenology. This is especially important in our warming world since the differential rate of warming across landscapes can drive species distributions, population and individual fitness of animals and plants, and consequently alter ecosystem functions and structures that provide ecosystem services (Harrington et al. 1999; Gilman et al. 2010; Creed et al. 2014; Ma et al. 2017; Tougeron et al. 2018).

The annual increase in the pre-breeding temperature and earlier egg-laying dates along elevation gradient takes effect around 1000 m elevation above sea level from our models (Figure 5), which resulted in strong annual advances in breeding phenology of varied tits and thermal environment that cues breeding at two high-elevation plots (Mt. Jiri 900 m and Mt. Jiri 1300 m) in our study, but relatively weak in two low-elevation plots (Mt. Jiri 350 m and Mt. Sanage 300 m). This difference of annual trends for the pre-breeding temperature between high- and low-elevation areas was similar to that of previous studies, demonstrating that the warming rate enhanced with elevation globally (Wang et al. 2014; Pepin et al. 2015, 2019). One of the suggested mechanisms for elevation-dependent warming is feedback of decrease in snow-cover in high elevations and followed by albedo loss causing warmer near-ground temperature in winter (Im and Ahn 2011). This potential mechanism can be applied in early spring temperatures when resident birds take cues for breeding, as higher elevation sites (i.e. over 1,000 m a.s.l) often maintain snow cover in this period. One of our study sites, for example, Mt. Jiri 1300 m usually has some snow cover in early March from our observations in the field (Personal observations of authors across the study period). This pattern of elevation-dependent warming was also observed from December to February across Korea (Im and Ahn 2011), which can influence early spring temperatures those birds and other forest organisms may cue on for their phenology.

While other environmental cues such as photoperiod and social information (i.e. ambient conspecific or heterospecific songs) also alter onset of breeding in birds (Dawson 2008; Chmura et al. 2017), these cues are shared between individuals in a plot and regional spatial scale, and hence may not vary across years. Similar phenomena were observed in plants in different ecosystems across the world (Way and Montgomery 2015). Even though the photoperiod is a major driver of phenology of birds in a broad scale, the annual shift in phenology was more often driven by changes in thermal environment, that are now warming rapidly each year, due to anthropogenic climate change (Pearce-Higgins et al. 2005; Goodenough et al. 2010; Fletcher et al. 2013). We are not clear yet how much either thermal environment or many other cues contribute to the onset of breeding for varied tits, and how those relationships are different among organisms in the forest food web that songbirds like varied tits rely on. However, if there is a different rate of change to warming in those organisms, either from using different cue or differential rates of change, consumers in food webs that require synchrony of phenology in ecosystems may lose their fitness in the current speed of warming of spring, especially in forests in higher elevations where growing season is shorter (Thackeray et al. 2016).

Buse et al. (1999) showed that the arthropods were able to shift their phenology with the advance of leaf phenology by hatching earlier and developing faster at warmer conditions. Such mismatch might cause worse effects on long-distance migratory birds as they have strict limitations on annual time budget for migration and breeding in temperate regions where resources are seasonal (Both et al. 2010). Studies from oak forests in Europe with long-distance migratory songbird, the pied flycatcher (*Ficedula hypoleuca*), showed that their egg-laying timing did not match up with the advance of the leaf phenology along with the rising temperature and consequently the reproductive success decreased (Sanz et al. 2003), or even population size decreased (Both et al. 2006). An ecological counterpart of the pied flycatchers, the narcissus flycatchers (*Ficedula narcissus*) in Japan also have declined severely in parts of their breeding range (Higuchi and Morishita 1999), but we do not have systematic long-term data to understand the drivers of the cause of decline in breeding habitat. From this deep need of understanding potential loss of ecosystem functions and interactions due to climate change in Asia, we strongly suggest that future research in university research forests in Asia needs to focus on the food-web level response to climate change, by studying multi-taxa concurrently with abiotic factors such as microclimate and hydrology for multi-decadal period.

Understanding these long-term ecological patterns requires persistent effort to detect changes, especially when the changes are subtle due to complex ecological interactions with multiple drivers. Thirty-six-year long data from The University of Tokyo's Akazu Research Forest showed no strong evidence from all of the 12-year segmented periods for the change in pre-breeding temperatures and the advance of egg-laying dates. However, for a long-term period (36 years), pre-breeding temperatures showed some level of evidence of warming (0.04°C/year) though the magnitude was very low, and 95% confidence interval was barely over zero. Meanwhile, the mean egg-laying dates were stable across 36 years in Mt. Sanage 300 m and for each 12-year segment as well, which is consistent with Mt. Jiri 350 m. The detection of the subtle change in temperatures across 36 years, but not in a shorter period, is most likely due to the increased number of sample years for the whole period, though segment periods had not enough statistical power to detect subtle changes. This supports our observations from three plots in Korea. The advancing trend of egg-laying dates was relatively weak and had almost no statistical support, while the pre-breeding temperature in the lower elevation plot did not show any substantial evidence of trends. If we

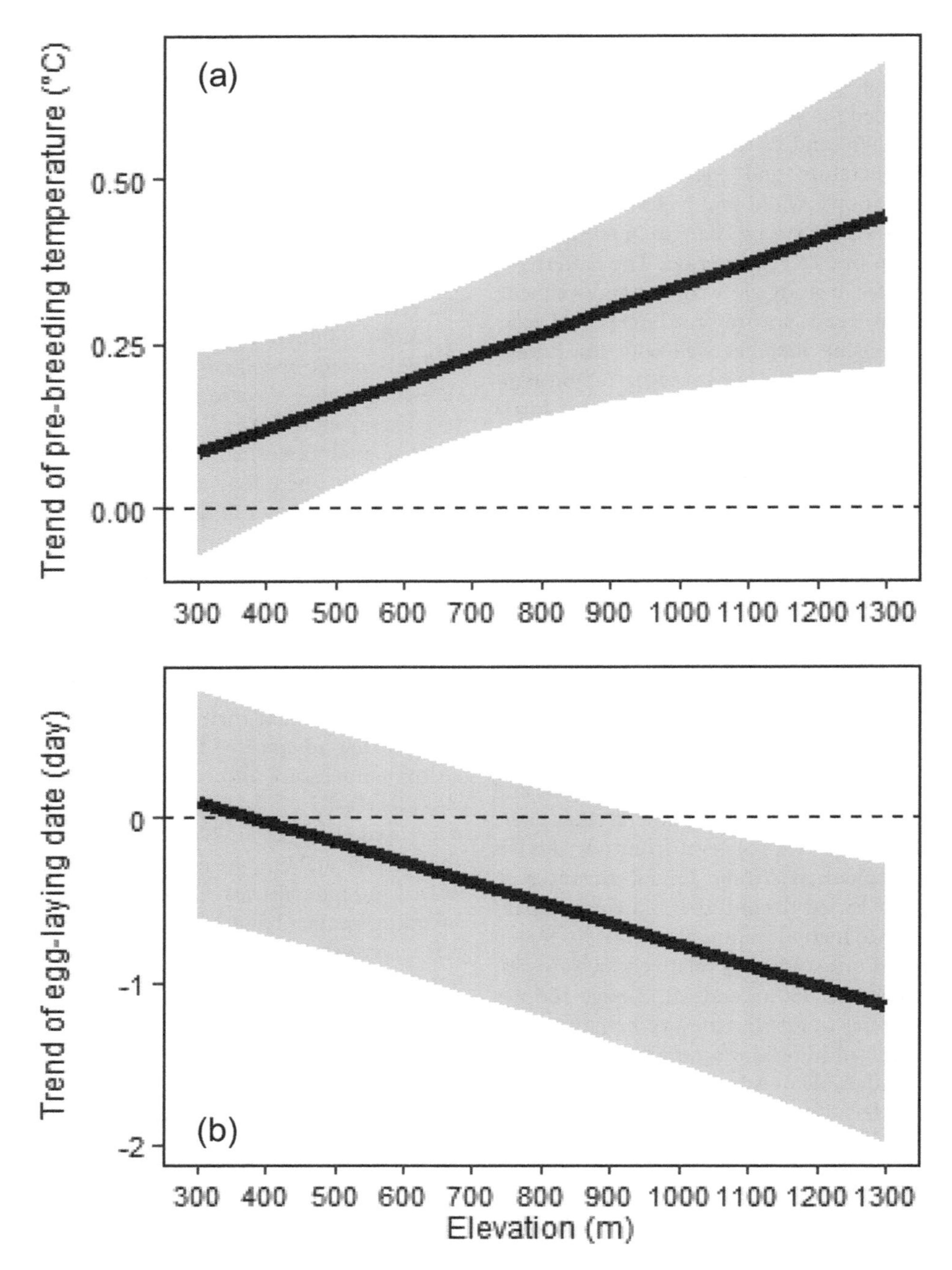

Figure 5. Effect of elevation on annual trend of: (a) average daily mean temperature during the pre-breeding period and (b) egg-laying dates of varied tits. Note the elevations when the 95% confidence intervals (grey shading) start to stop overlapping with zero, and the slope of the lines.

observed from Mt. Sanage with more years of data, the statistical evidence for trends of temperature and egg-laying dates could have changed. This would be especially important in the lower elevation plots where the effect size is small and hence difficult to detect the evidence of change with a smaller number of years.

In summary, our results suggest that there is strong evidence of elevation-dependent warming in early spring temperatures that drives elevation-dependent shift in breeding phenology of varied tits in our study sites in Korea and Japan over the last decade. This implies that varied tit populations at high-elevation forest habitats are expected to experience greater change in their breeding phenology, in the current climate warming conditions. This will lead to narrower differences in phenology of birds along the elevational gradient, as it is observed in our study and from other studies on plants (Chen et al. 2018; Vitasse et al. 2018). On the other hand, we did not detect significant changes in temperatures nor the breeding phenology of varied tits in lower elevation in our study sites. The data from Akazu Research Forest suggest that this might be due to the lack of power to detect a subtle trend with a smaller set of years. When such changes are subtle due to the complex nature of ecological interactions, long-term studies on organisms and communities across multi-trophic levels become essential to fully understand such spatiotemporal variation in ecological interactions with desired confidence levels. As the climate change warms spring temperatures across the montane forests around the world, understanding the consequences of disproportionate warming along the elevational gradients would be important for managing and conserving forest ecosystems.

Acknowledgments

We are grateful to Prof. Kamata Naoto in the University of Tokyo for providing help in developing this study in the initial stage, and suggesting the data source in Japan, collected by his colleagues; Yanase Kiriko, Mizutani Mizuki, Sato Takanori, Arakida Yoshitaka, Matsui Masaki, Takatoku Kae and Saiki Michio in Ecohydrology Research Institute, the University of Tokyo. We also acknowledge the members of the Laboratory of Wildlife Management and Ecology, Department of Forest Sciences in Seoul National University for assisting nestbox monitoring. The staff of Seoul National University Research Forest supported this study to great extent, especially Jongyeong Park and Giho Ha for their many years of efforts on nestbox survey in Mt. Jiri, that made this study possible, we are very thankful for their contribution for the data collection and support in the field logistics. Hankyu Kim was supported by Oregon State University while preparing this manuscript. We are very grateful to the editors Dr. Masahiro Takagi and Dr. Satoshi Ito and anonymous reviewers who reviewed and commented on our submitted manuscripts. Thanks to their keen review, we were able to improve this manuscript to a great extent.

Disclosure statement

No potential conflict of interest was reported by the authors.

Funding

This study was supported by 'R&D Program for Forest Science Technology (Project No. 2014109C10-2020-AA01)' by Korea Forest Service (Korea Forestry Promotion Institute), LG Evergreen Foundation, and College of Agriculture and Life Sciences of Seoul National University.

References

Barton K. 2019. MuMIn: multi-model inference. [accessed 2020 May 01]. https://cran.r-project.org/web/packages/MuMIn/index.html.

Bates D, Maechler M, Bolker B, Walker S, Christensen RHB, Singmann H, Dai B, Scheipl F, Grothendieck G, Green P, et al. 2018. lme4: linear mixed-effects models using "Eigen" and S4. [accessed 2020 May 01]. https://CRAN.R-project.org/package=lme4.

Bell JR, Botham MS, Henrys PA, Leech DI, Pearce-Higgins JW, Shortall CR, Brereton TM, Pickup J, Thackeray SJ. 2019. Spatial and habitat variation in aphid, butterfly, moth and bird phenologies over the last half century. Global Change Biol. 25(6):1982–1994. doi:10.1111/gcb.14592.

Both C, Artemyev AV, Blaauw B, Cowie RJ, Dekhuijzen AJ, Eeva T, Enemar A, Gustafsson L, Ivankina EV, Jarvinen A, et al. 2004. Large-scale geographical variation confirms that climate change causes birds to lay earlier. Proc R Soc B Biol Sci. 271(1549):1657–1662. doi:10.1098/rspb.2004.2770.

Both C, Bouwhuis S, Lessells CM, Visser ME. 2006. Climate change and population declines in a long-distance migratory bird. Nature. 441 (7089):81. doi:10.1038/nature04539.

Both C, Marvelde L. 2007. Climate change and timing of avian breeding and migration throughout Europe. Clim Res. 35(1–2):93–105. doi:10.3354/cr00716.

Both C, van Turnhout CAM, Bijlsma RG, Siepel H, van Strien AJ, Foppen RPB. 2010. Avian population consequences of climate change are most severe for long-distance migrants in seasonal habitats. Proc R Soc B Biol Sci. 277(1685):1259–1266. doi:10.1098/rspb.2009.1525.

Bourgault P, Thomas D, Perret P, Blondel J. 2010. Spring vegetation phenology is a robust predictor of breeding date across broad landscapes: a multi-site approach using the Corsican Blue Tit (*Cyanistes caeruleus*). Oecologia. 162(4):885–892. doi:10.1007/s00442-009-1545-0.

Burgess MD, Smith KW, Evans KL, Leech D, Pearce-Higgins JW, Branston CJ, Briggs K, Clark JR, Du Feu CR, Lewthwaite K, et al. 2018. Tritrophic phenological match–mismatch in space and time. Nat Ecol Evol. 2(6):970. doi:10.1038/s41559-018-0543-1.

Burnham KP, Anderson DR. 2002. Model selection and multimodel inference: a practical information-theoretic approach. 2nd ed. New York (NY): Springer.

Buse A, Dury SJ, Woodburn RJW, Perrins CM, Good JEG. 1999. Effects of elevated temperature on multi-species interactions: the case of Pedunculate Oak, Winter Moth and Tits. Funct Ecol. 13 (Suppl.1):74–82. doi:10.1046/j.1365-2435.1999.00010.x.

Chen L, Huang JG, Ma Q, Hänninen H, Rossi S, Piao S, Bergeron Y. 2018. Spring phenology at different altitudes is becoming more uniform under global warming in Europe. Global Change Biol. 24 (9):3969–3975. doi:10.1111/gcb.14288.

Chmura HE, Meddle SL, Wingfield JC, Hahn TP. 2017. Effects of a social cue on reproductive development and pre-alternate molt in seasonally breeding migrant and resident female songbirds (*Zonotrichia leucophrys*). J Exp Biol. 220(16):2947–2956. doi:10.1242/jeb.160994.

Creed IF, Spargo AT, Jones JA, Buttle JM, Adams MB, Beall FD, Booth EG, Campbell JL, Clow D, Elder K, et al. 2014. Changing forest water yields in response to climate warming: results from long-term experimental watershed sites across North America. Global Change Biol. 20(10):3191–3208. doi:10.1111/gcb.12615.

Crick HQP, Sparks TH. 1999. Climate change related to egg-laying trends. Nature. 399(6735):423. doi:10.1038/20839.

Dawson A. 2008. Control of the annual cycle in birds: endocrine constraints and plasticity in response to ecological variability. Philos Trans R Soc B Biol Sci. 363(1497):1621–1633. doi:10.1098/rstb.2007.0004.

Donnelly A, Caffarra A, O'Neill BF. 2011. A review of climate-driven mismatches between interdependent phenophases in terrestrial and aquatic ecosystems. Int J Biometeorol. 55(6):805–817. doi:10.1007/s00484-011-0426-5.

Drake A, Martin K. 2018. Local temperatures predict breeding phenology but do not result in breeding synchrony among a community of resident cavity-nesting birds. Sci Rep. 8(1):2756. doi:10.1038/s41598-018-20977-y.

Fletcher K, Howarth D, Kirby A, Dunn R, Smith A. 2013. Effect of climate change on breeding phenology, clutch size and chick survival of an upland bird. Ibis. 155(3):456–463.

Franklin JF. 1989. Importance and justification of long-term studies in ecology. In: Likens GE, editor. Long-term studies in ecology. New York (NY): Springer; p. 3–19.

Geiger R, Aron RH, Todhunter P. 2009. The climate near the ground. 7th ed. Lanham (MD): Rowman & Littlefield Publisher.

Gienapp P, Hemerik L, Visser ME. 2005. A new statistical tool to predict phenology under climate change scenarios. Global Change Biol. 11 (4):600–606. doi:10.1111/j.1365-2486.2005.00925.x.

Gilman SE, Urban MC, Tewksbury J, Gilchrist GW, Holt RD. 2010. A framework for community interactions under climate change. Trends Ecol Evol. 25(6):325–331. doi:10.1016/j.tree.2010.03.002.

Goodenough AE, Hart AG, Stafford R. 2010. Is adjustment of breeding phenology keeping pace with the need for change? Linking observed response in woodland birds to changes in temperature and selection pressure. Clim Change. 102:687–697.

Gosler A, Clement P, Kirwan GM. 2019. Varied Tit (*Sittiparus varius*). In: Del Hoyo J, Elliott A, Sargatal J, Christie DA, de Juana E, editors. Handbook of the birds of the world alive. Barcelona: Lynx Edicions; [accessed 2019 Apr 19]. http://www.hbw.com/species/varied-tit-sittiparus-varius.

Haman J, Avery M. 2019. ciTools: confidence or prediction intervals, quantiles, and probabilities for statistical models. R package version 0.5.1. https://CRAN.R-project.org/package=ciTools

Harrington R, Woiwod I, Sparks T. 1999. Climate change and trophic interactions. Trends Ecol Evol. 14(4):146–150. doi:10.1016/S0169-5347(99)01604-3.

Higuchi H, Morishita E. 1999. Population declines of tropical migratory birds in Japan. Actinia. 12:51–59.

Husby A, Kruuk LEB, Visser ME. 2009. Decline in the frequency and benefits of multiple brooding in Great Tits as a consequence of a changing environment. Proc R Soc B Biol Sci. 276 (1663):1845–1854. doi:10.1098/rspb.2008.1937.

Hwang T, Song C, Vose JM, Band LE. 2011. Topography-mediated controls on local vegetation phenology estimated from MODIS vegetation index. Landscape Ecol. 26(4):541–556. doi:10.1007/s10980-011-9580-8.

Im ES, Ahn JB. 2011. On the elevation dependency of present-day climate and future change over Korea from a high resolution regional climate simulation. J Meterol Soc Jpn. 89(1):89–100. doi:10.2151/jmsj.2011-106.

Jeong MS. 2020. The effects of climate change on the breeding ecology and phenological asynchrony of the Varied Tit (*Sittiparus varius*) in Korea [dissertation]. Seoul: Seoul National University.

Jeong MS, Choi CY, Kim HK, Lee WS. 2019. Predicting climate-driven shifts in the breeding phenology of Varied Tits (*Sittiparus various*) in South Korean forests. Anim Cells Syst. 23(6):422–432. doi:10.1080/19768354.2019.1675759.

Lee JK, Jang WS, Chung OS, Lee WS. 2016. The relationships between prey size, nestling age, provisioning rate, and elevation in the Varied Tit *Parus Varius*. Ornithol Sci. 15(1):29–36. doi:10.2326/osj.15.29.

Lenth R. 2018. emmeans: estimated marginal means, aka least-squares means. R package version 1.3.1. https://CRAN.R-project.org/package=emmeans

Lindenmayer D, Cunningham S, Young A, editors. 2012. Land use intensification: effects on agriculture, biodiversity and ecological processes. Collingwood: CSIRO publishing.

Ma Z, Liu H, Mi Z, Zhang Z, Wang Y, Xu W, Jiang L, He JS. 2017. Climate warming reduces the temporal stability of plant community biomass production. Nat Commun. 8(1):1–7. doi:10.1038/ncomms15378.

Pearce-Higgins JW, Yalden DW, Whittingham MJ. 2005. Warmer springs advance the breeding phenology of golden plovers Pluvialis apricaria and their prey (Tipulidae). Oecologia. 143(3):470–476.

Pepin N, Bradley RS, Diaz HF, Baraer M, Caceres EB, Forsythe N, Fowler H, Greenwood G, Hashmi MZ, Liu XD, et al. 2015. Elevation-dependent warming in mountain regions of the world. Nat Clim Change. 5(5):424–430.

Pepin N, Deng H, Zhang H, Zhang F, Kang S, Yao T. 2019. An examination of temperature trends at high elevations across the Tibetan Plateau: the use of MODIS LST to understand patterns of elevation-dependent warming. J Geophys Res Atmos. 124 (11):5738–5756.

Porlier M, Charmantier A, Bourgault P, Perret P, Blondel J, Garant D. 2012. Variation in phenotypic plasticity and selection patterns in Blue Tit breeding time: between- and within-population comparisons: variation in plasticity among populations. J Anim Ecol. 81 (5):1041–1051. doi:10.1111/j.1365-2656.2012.01996.x.

R Core Team. 2018. R: a language and environment for statistical computing. Version 3.5.1. Vienna: R Core Team. https://www.R-project.org/

Rangwala I, Miller JR. 2012. Climate change in mountains: a review of elevation-dependent warming and its possible causes. Clim Change. 114(3):527–547. doi:10.1007/s10584-012-0419-3.

Reed TE, Jenouvrier S, Visser ME. 2013. Phenological mismatch strongly affects individual fitness but not population demography in a woodland passerine. J Anim Ecol. 82(1):131–144. doi:10.1111/j.1365-2656.2012.02020.x.

Renner SS, Zohner CM. 2018. Climate change and phenological mismatch in trophic interactions among plants, insects, and vertebrates. Annu Rev Ecol Evol Syst. 49(1):165–182. doi:10.1146/annurev-ecolsys-110617-062535.

Saino N, Ambrosini R, Rubolini D, von Hardenberg J, Provenzale A, Hüppop K, Hüppop O, Lehikoinen A, Lehikoinen E, Rainio K, et al. 2011. Climate warming, ecological mismatch at arrival and population decline in migratory birds. Proc R Soc B Biol Sci. 278 (1707):835–842. doi:10.1098/rspb.2010.1778.

Sanz JJ, Potti J, Potti J, Moreno J, Merino S, Frias O. 2003. Climate change and fitness components of a migratory bird breeding in the Mediterranean region. Global Change Biol. 9(3):461–472. doi:10.1046/j.1365-2486.2003.00575.x.

Schaper SV, Dawson A, Sharp PJ, Gienapp P, Caro SP, Visser ME. 2012. Increasing temperature, not mean temperature, is a cue for avian timing of reproduction. Am Nat. 179(2):E55–E69. doi:10.1086/663675.

Shiao MT, Chuang MC, Yuan HW, Wang Y. 2015. Effects of weather variation on the timing and success of breeding in two cavity-nesting species in a subtropical montane forest in Taiwan. Auk. 132 (3):671–684. doi:10.1642/AUK-15-10.1.

Siegmund P, Abermann J, Baddour O, Canadell P, Anny C, Derksen C, Garreau A, Stephen H, Huss M, Isensee K, et al. 2019. The global climate in 2015–2019. Geneva: World Meteorological Organization.

Thackeray SJ, Henrys PA, Hemming D, Bell JR, Botham MS, Burthe S, Helaouet P, Johns DG, Jones ID, Leech DI, et al. 2016. Phenological sensitivity to climate across taxa and trophic levels. Nature. 535(7611):241–245. doi:10.1038/nature18608.

Thackeray SJ, Sparks TH, Frederiksen M, Burthe S, Bacon PJ, Bell JR, Botham MS, Brereton TM, Bright PW, Carvalho L, et al. 2010. Trophic level asynchrony in rates of phenological change for marine, freshwater and terrestrial environments. Global Change Biol. 16(12):3304–3313. doi:10.1111/j.1365-2486.2010.02165.x.

Torti VM, Dunn PO. 2005. Variable effects of climate change on six species of North American birds. Oecologia. 145(3):486–495. doi:10.1007/s00442-005-0175-4.

Tougeron K, Damien M, Le Lann C, Brodeur J, van Baaren J. 2018. Rapid responses of winter aphid-parasitoid communities to climate warming. Front Ecol Evol. 6:173. doi:10.3389/fevo.2018.00173.

van Balen JH. 1973. A comparative study of the breeding ecology of the Great Tit *Parus major* in different habitats. Ardea. 55 (1–2):1–93.

van Noordwijk AJ, McCleery RH, Perrins CM. 1995. Selection for the timing of Great Tit breeding in relation to caterpillar growth and temperature. J Anim Ecol. 64(4):451. doi:10.2307/5648.

Verhagen I, Tomotani BM, Gienapp P, Visser ME. 2020. Temperature has a causal and plastic effect on timing of breeding in a small songbird. J Exp Biol. 223(8):1–7. doi:10.1242/jeb.218784.

Visser ME, Adriaensen F, van Balen JH, Blondel J, Dhondt AA, van Dongen S, Du Feu C, Ivankina EV, Kerimov AB, de Laet J, et al. 2003. Variable responses to large-scale climate change in European *Parus* populations. Proc R Soc Lond B Biol Sci. 270(1513):367–372. doi:10.1098/rspb.2002.2244.

Visser ME, Both C. 2005. Shifts in phenology due to global climate change: the need for a yardstick. Proc R Soc B Biol Sci. 272 (1581):2561–2569. doi:10.1098/rspb.2005.3356.

Visser ME, Holleman LJM, Caro SP. 2009. Temperature has a causal effect on avian timing of reproduction. Proc R Soc B Biol Sci. 276 (1665):2323–2331. doi:10.1098/rspb.2009.0213.

Visser ME, Holleman LJM, Gienapp P. 2006. Shifts in caterpillar biomass phenology due to climate change and its impact on the breeding biology of an insectivorous bird. Oecologia. 147(1):164–172. doi:10.1007/s00442-005-0299-6.

Vitasse Y, Signarbieux C, Fu YH. 2018. Global warming leads to more uniform spring phenology across elevations. Proc Natl Acad Sci. 115 (5):1004–1008. doi:10.1073/pnas.1717342115.

Wang Q, Fan X, Wang M. 2014. Recent warming amplification over high elevation regions across the globe. Clim Dyn. 43(1):87–101. doi:10.1007/s00382-013-1889-3.

Wawrzyniak J, Kaliński A, Glądalski M, Bańbura M, Markowski M, Skwarska J, ZielińSki P, Cyżewska I, Bańbura J. 2015. Long-term variation in laying date and clutch size of the Great Tit *Parus major* in Central Poland: a comparison between urban parkland and deciduous forest. Ardeola. 62(2):311–322. doi:10.13157/arla.62.2.2015.311.

Way DA, Montgomery RA. 2015. Photoperiod constraints on tree phenology, performance and migration in a warming world. Plant Cell Environ. 38(9):1725–1736. doi:10.1111/pce.12431.

Williams TD. 2012. Physiological adaptations for breeding in birds. Princeton (NJ): Princeton University Press. Chapter 3, Timing of breeding; p. 52–99.

Williams TD, Bourgeon S, Cornell A, Ferguson L, Fowler M, Fronstin RB, Love OP. 2015. Mid-winter temperatures, not spring temperatures, predict breeding phenology in the European Starling *Sturnus vulgaris*. R Soc Open Sci. 2(1):140301. doi:10.1098/rsos.140301.

Yanase K, Mizutani M, Sato T, Arakida Y, Matsui M, Takatoku K, Saiki M. 2018. Elucidation of long-term trends in reproductive characteristics of *Poecile varius* and *Parus minor* using nest-box surveys. Chubu For Res. 66:45–48. (in Japanese)

Yanase K, Mizutani M, Sato T, Arakida Y, Matsui M, Takatoku K, Saiki M. 2019. Investigation of reproductive traits of *Poecile varius* and *Parus minor*. Chubu For Res. 67:43–46. (in Japanese)

Modeling stand basal area growth of *Cryptomeria japonica* D. Don under different planting densities in Taiwan

Tzeng Yih Lam and Biing T. Guan

ABSTRACT

Stand basal area (BA) is an important parameter, yet significantly influenced by initial planting density, in describing the developments of plantation forests. The effects of initial density on the growth of sugi (*Cryptomeria japonica* D. Don), an important plantation tree species in Taiwan, have seldom been studied. The goals of this study are to (1) model sugi stand BA growth under different initial densities, and (2) quantify model forecast accuracy. The data were from a spacing trial established in 1950 at the National Taiwan University Experimental Forest. The initial densities were 2500, 1111, 625, and 400 trees ha^{-1}. Ten measurements were carried out up to stand age 65. Using a mixed-effects modeling approach, we fitted a Gompertz model with the initial density as the covariate to describe stand BA growth trends. Results showed that stand BA was the largest for stands with the highest initial density. The maximum current annual increment of the highest initial density was also the largest and reached earlier in stand development than that of the other spacings. Data up to stand age 60 were needed to yield a forecast accuracy within 6% for BA at stand age 65. This study showed that the fitted Gompertz model could adequately capture the general growth trends in stand BA despite unequal measurement intervals. The results agreed with other spacing trials in other regions and tree species, and the model accuracy was acceptable given the availability of data. The prediction accuracy results underlined the importance of long-term growth monitoring.

Introduction

Stand basal area (BA), the total BA of all trees per unit area, is one of the most frequently reported parameters to describe conditions of a forest stand (Kershaw et al. 2016). It can reflect the successional stage, competition response, and productive capacity of a plant community. Stand BA is also a surrogate for stand characteristics such as biomass and density (Kershaw et al. 2016). As such, the measure is commonly used in forest management and planning, such as density management with Reineke's Stand Density Index (Reineke 1933) and BA stocking diagrams (Gingrich 1967). Furthermore, stand BA is an essential component in modeling stand growth (Gadow and Hui 1999). The dynamics of stand BA throughout stand development are greatly influenced by the initial number of planted trees (i.e. density) together with survival rates and site quality (Antón-Fernández et al. 2012). Thus, understanding the close relationship between stand BA and initial density is crucial for plantation forest management.

Forest managers know that initial density will influence the type and timing of intermediate silvicultural treatments and affect the quantity and quality of wood harvested at the end of a rotation (Amateis and Burkhart 2012). Trees planted at a higher density compete for resources more intensively, leading to smaller average tree size (Forrester et al. 2013). However, a higher initial planting density accelerates crown recession and reduces the crown length, which in turn could improve wood quality through effects on ring width, length of branch-free bole, and stem taper (Garber et al. 2008). Therefore, spacing trials have been established across regions and tree species for decades to understand the underlying ecological processes and to quantify the effects on stand BA development, among other parameters of primary interest. Early spacing trials from Oliver (1979) and Reukema (1979) found that mean tree diameter at breast height (dbh) was larger for trees planted at a lower initial density, and *vice versa*, for *Pinus ponderosa* and *Pseudotsuga menziesii*. The results were also echoed by Jiang et al. (2007) for *Populus xiaohei* in China. On the other hand, stand BA was lower for plantations planted at a lower initial density (Curtis et al. 2016). Forrester et al. (2013) observed this relationship for stand BA in *Eucalyptus globulus* plantations in southwestern Australia regardless of site quality. In addition to this general relationship, Antón-Fernández et al. (2012) found that stand BA of *Pinus taeda* plantations with a high initial density reached its maximum stand BA at an earlier stand age and decreased afterward, whereas stand BA of plantations with a low initial density tended to increase more gradually and reach its maximum at a later age.

Sugi (or Japanese cedar, *Cryptomeria japonica* D. Don), a species native to Japan, was first introduced to Taiwan in the late 1890s (Guan et al. 2008a). It became one of the most important plantation species in Taiwan due to its quick and robust growth performances. According to the latest national forest resource inventory, the species still covers about 18% of the total forest plantation area in Taiwan and has the highest stand volume per unit area (389 m^3 ha^{-1}) among all the coniferous plantations (Taiwan Forestry Bureau 2017). Thus, although no longer planted, sugi plantations will still be intensively managed for timber production in the near foreseeable future. Despite being an important plantation species, studies on the effects of initial density on sugi growth in Taiwan have been limited. Guan et al. (2008a, 2008b) examined the relationship between growth efficiency and survivorship and initial size advantage of sugi growing under four different initial densities in Taiwan. At the same study site, Wang and Chen (1992) and Chuang and Wang (2001) studied the effects of initial density on the wood properties and standing tree quality. In Japan, Ishiguri et al. (2005) studied wood and lumber quality of 35 year-old sugi planted at a range of initial densities from 1500 to 10,000 trees ha^{-1}. Lastly, Fujisawa et al. (1995) and Tsushima et al. (2006) studied the interactions of the genetic variation and initial density on mean dbh and height, wood properties, and ring features of sugi. Both studies found that the genetic factor has a stronger influence than initial density.

Therefore, there is a need to understand how current sugi plantations have developed under different initial densities for timber production, and how far into the future a developed growth model could accurately forecast. While the accuracy of forecasting generally decreases with projections outside the range of data used (Weiskittel et al. 2011), long-term projection of stand development is often desired. To our knowledge, forecast error has not been quantified explicitly for sugi plantations. Quantifying forecast accuracy allows one to be cautious when designing future management schemes for current sugi plantations and developing strategies to plan and maintain current sugi permanent studies. The goals of this study are to (1) model stand BA growth of sugi stands planted under different initial densities to understand whether spacing effects diminished through time, and (2) quantify forecast accuracy of the model after accounted for the effects of unequal measurement intervals and serial correlation structures in longitudinal data.

Materials and methods

Data

Data were from a sugi spacing trial of the National Taiwan University Experimental Forest, located in central Taiwan (120°47′E, 23°40′N, elevation 1250 m). The trial was established in 1950 using 1-year cuttings of sugi to minimize potential effects from genetic variations. The trial was set up as a completely randomized design with the initial density as the treatment factor. Five square planting spacings were applied: 1 × 1 m, 2 × 2 m, 3 × 3 m, 4 × 4 m, and 5 × 5 m, which corresponded to initial densities of 10,000, 2500, 1111, 625, and 400 trees ha^{-1}, respectively. Fifteen 40 m × 25 m (0.1 ha) plots were established with a 5-m buffer between plots; the actual total area of the spacing trial was about 2 ha. Within this localized area, abiotic factors such as topography and climate were homogeneous. Thus, site quality was assumed to be identical among the 15 plots. Each initial density had three replicates (plots). The first inventory was conducted in 1955, five years after establishment. Subsequent measurements were taken in 1960, 1965, 1980, 1985, 1995, 2000, 2005, 2010, and 2015 for a total of 10 repeated measurements. At each measurement, all surviving trees within each of the plots were measured for dbh. Height was not measured for all measurement periods. The three 1 × 1 m plots were thinned in 1965. They were excluded from this study because other plots were not thinned. Thus, only 12 plots were analyzed in this study. The location of the sugi spacing trial, the experimental design, and some examples of the plots were presented in Figure S1 (Supplementary Materials). Further information on the spacing trial could be found in Guan et al. (2008a, 2008b).

Statistical analysis

The Gompertz equation (Gompertz 1825; Zeide 1993) was chosen for this study to model the stand BA growth of sugi planted under different initial densities. Gompertz models are considered to be able to capture biological growth adequately, both theoretically and empirically (ref. Zeide 1993), and many variants of the model have been extensively developed (Tjørve and Tjørve 2017). The basic form of a Gompertz model is,

$$BA_{ij} = \beta_0 \exp\left(-\beta_1 \exp\left(-\beta_2 A_{ij}\right)\right) + \varepsilon_{ij} \quad (1)$$

where BA_{ij} in the model was stand BA (m^2 0.1 ha^{-1}) for the ith plot at the jth measurement, and A_{ij} was the number of years since planting (year) for the ith plot at the jth measurement for $i = 1, \ldots, 12$ and $j = 1, \ldots, 10$. The parameters have biological interpretations (Zeide 1993): β_0 is an asymptote parameter representing the theoretical maximum stand BA, and it controls the position of the inflection point; β_1 is a displacement (i.e. location) parameter that shifts the growth curve along stand age describing the stand age at which the inflection point occurs; and β_2 describes growth rate.

Let $U_{3ij} = 1$ if the ith plot and the jth measurement had initial planting spacing of 3 × 3 m, else $U_{3ij} = 0$; $U_{4ij} = 1$ if the ith plot and the jth measurement had initial planting spacing of 4 × 4 m, else $U_{4ij} = 0$; and $U_{5ij} = 1$ if the ith plot and the jth measurement had initial planting spacing of 5 × 5 m, else $U_{5ij} = 0$. Then, the β_k parameter for $k = 0, 1, 2$ in Equation (1) could be expanded as,

$$\mathbf{X}\boldsymbol{\beta}_k = \begin{bmatrix} \mathbf{1} & \mathbf{U}_3 & \mathbf{U}_4 & \mathbf{U}_5 \end{bmatrix} \begin{bmatrix} \beta_{k0} \\ \beta_{k1} \\ \beta_{k2} \\ \beta_{k3} \end{bmatrix}$$

where, $\mathbf{1} = [1 \ldots 1\ 1 \ldots 1\ 1 \ldots 1\ 1 \ldots 1]'$, $\mathbf{U}_3 = [0 \ldots 0\ 1 \ldots 1\ 0 \ldots 0\ 0 \ldots 0]'$, $\mathbf{U}_4 = [0 \ldots 0\ 0 \ldots 0\ 1 \ldots 1\ 0 \ldots 0]'$, and $\mathbf{U}_5 = [0 \ldots 0\ 0 \ldots 0\ 0 \ldots 0\ 1 \ldots 1]'$. Thus, the basic Gompertz model (Equation 1) was expanded to include initial density as follows,

$$BA_{ij} = \mathbf{X}\boldsymbol{\beta}_0 \exp\left(-\mathbf{X}\boldsymbol{\beta}_1 \exp\left(-\mathbf{X}\boldsymbol{\beta}_2 A_{ij}\right)\right) + \varepsilon_{ij} \quad (2)$$

A non-linear mixed-effects (NLME) modeling approach (Pinheiro and Bates 2000) was applied to account for random effects among plots. To avoid overparameterizing the model in Equation (2), only random effects were added to the intercept term (β_{k0}) of each of the kth parameter, while other parameters associated with the dummy variables (β_{k1}, β_{k2}, β_{k3}) were held as fixed effects. Let e_{k0i} be the random effects for the intercept term of the kth parameter for the ith plot, thus, $\mathbf{e}_{0i} = [e_{00i}\ e_{10i}\ e_{20i}]'$ was assumed to follow a multivariate normal distribution (MVN) with mean $\mathbf{0}$ and a variance-covariance matrix $\boldsymbol{\Psi}$, i.e. $\mathbf{e}_{0i} \sim \text{MVN}(\mathbf{0}, \boldsymbol{\Psi})$. The model was fitted using the nlme package (Pinheiro and Bates 2000) of R statistical software (R Development Core Team 2019).

Preliminary analyses were carried out with sequential likelihood tests to check for the inclusion of initial density as a predictor and the elimination of random effects. Results suggested that the β_2 parameter was not significantly depended on the initial densities, and the random effects e_{20i} could be dropped without affecting the overall model goodness of fit. Thus, the revised model was,

$$BA_{ij} = \mathbf{X}\boldsymbol{\beta}_0 \exp(-\mathbf{X}\boldsymbol{\beta}_1 \exp(-\beta_2 A_{ij})) + \varepsilon_{ij} \quad (3)$$

The revised model (Equation 3) assumed that the within-group errors ε_{ij} was independent for different the ith plot and the jth measurement and also was independent of random effects (Pinheiro and Bates 2000). Standardized residual plots of the revised model suggested that variances were different among the initial densities. Therefore, the varIdent function in the nlme package was used to account for this within-group heteroscedasticity (Pinheiro and Bates 2000). Furthermore, assuming within-group errors to be independent of the jth measurement might not be appropriate because the data were longitudinal. To properly account for the autocorrelation structure, the empirical autocorrelation function (ACF) of residuals was used to investigate the correlations at different lags. Results suggested that lag-1 to lag-3 autocorrelations were significant at α = 5% level. Four autocorrelation models based on the first- and second-order autoregressive correlation (AR) and moving average (MA) models were tested: AR(1), AR(2), MA(1), and MA(2). Fitted models were compared using the Akaike Information Criterion and Bayesian Information Criterion. Results of the Akaike Information Criterion and Bayesian Information Criterion suggested that MA(2) provided the best fit, and with it, the empirical ACF showed lag-1 to lag-3 autocorrelations were not significant at α = 5% level. Lastly, Pinheiro and Bates (2000) suggested that incorporating a within-group autocorrelation structure into an NLME model might reduce the need to specify some random effects in the model. Thus, sequential log-likelihood tests suggested that e_{10i} could be dropped without affecting the overall model goodness of fit. In summary, the final model for modeling stand BA growth of sugi under different initial densities was specified as Equation (3) with random effects on β_{00}, a **varIdent** variance function to account for within-group heteroscedasticity, and an MA(2) autocorrelation structure for modeling within-group errors.

Two analysis steps were taken to meet the second objective of quantifying forecast accuracy. In the first step, data up to stand age 55 years (DATA55) were fitted through the model building process described above, and the resulted Gompertz model was used to forecast stand BA at stand age 60 and 65 years. In the second step, data up to stand age 60 years (DATA60) were again fitted through the above model building process, and forecasts were made for stand BA at stand age 65 years. In both steps, bias (B_{ij}) at the jth measurement was calculated as the difference between the forecasted and observed stand basal area, $B_{ij}=\widehat{BA}_{ij}-BA_{ij}$, where $\widehat{BA}_{ij}$ and BA_{ij} was the forecasted and observed stand basal area for the ith plot and the jth measurement, respectively, and j was at either stand age 60 or 65. Percent bias (PB_{ij}) for the jth measurement was calculated as $PB_{ij}={}^{B_{ij}}/_{BA_{ij}}\times 100\%$. Accuracy was assessed by mean bias (MB), mean percent bias (MPB), root-mean-square bias (RMSB), and root-mean-square percent bias (RMSPB) for the jth measurement as $MB_j = \sum_{i=1}^{12} B_{ij}/12$, $MPB_j = \sum_{i=1}^{12} PB_{ij}/12$, $RMSB_j = \sqrt{\sum_{i=1}^{12} (B_{ij} - MB_j)^2/12}$, and $RMSPB_j = \sqrt{\sum_{i=1}^{12} (PB_{ij} - MPB_j)^2/12}$, respectively.

Results

Stand basal area growth

Residual of the final fitted Gompertz model was 0.311 m^2 0.1 ha^{-1} suggesting relatively precise model fit. Residual plot of standardized residuals against fitted values indicated homogeneity of variance in each initial density as well as a similar range in the residuals across initial densities except for two large negative residuals for 2 × 2 spacing (Figure S2; Supplementary Materials). On the other hand, the standard deviation for the random effect e_{00} was 0.386 m^2 0.1 ha^{-1}, suggesting that there was still a considerable variation in maximum stand basal area among plots. The parameter estimates of the fitted Gompertz model were provided in Table 1. There was suggestive, but inconclusive, evidence that β_0 parameters of 3 × 3 m and 4 × 4 m spacing were significantly lower than that of 2 × 2 m spacing (p = 0.063 and 0.043, respectively). In contrast, there was strong evidence that β_0 parameter of 5 × 5 m spacing was significantly lower than that of 2 × 2 m spacing (p < 0.0001). The β_1 parameter of 3 × 3 m spacing was not significantly different from that of 2 × 2 m spacing (p = 0.25), whereas others were significantly larger than that of 2 × 2 m spacing (p = 0.02 and 0.004). Furthermore, the initial density did not affect the growth rate parameter β_2. Lastly, estimates of the fitted MA (2) model parameters were $\widehat{\theta}_1$ = 0.69 and $\widehat{\theta}_2$ = 0.41, suggesting strong underlying serial correlation structures at the first two lags.

The fitted Gompertz model adequately captured the general trends of the data for each initial density (Figure 1). More specifically, the observed data of 2 × 2 m spacing for one plot exhibited significantly smaller stand BA for stand age 45 and 50, but its fitted Gompertz model could accommodate such deviations from the general trend and produced a relatively well-fitted curve (Figure 1(a)). As expected, the fitted curve of 5 × 5 m spacing was significantly lower than that of 2 × 2 m spacing, with its inflection point being prominently located toward a larger stand age than that of

Table 1. Parameter estimates of the fitted Gompertz model for sugi stand basal area growth under different initial densities. Parameter estimates of 3 × 3 m (β_{k1}), 4 × 4 m (β_{k2}), 5 × 5 m (β_{k3}) spacings are contrasts, which are relative to the parameter estimates of 2 × 2 m spacing (β_{k0}).

	Estimate	Standard Error	p-value
Fixed Effects			
β_{00}	8.249	0.430	< 0.0001
β_{01}	−0.943	0.502	0.063
β_{02}	−1.060	0.518	0.043
β_{03}	−3.076	0.495	< 0.0001
β_{10}	2.476	0.361	< 0.0001
β_{11}	0.497	0.432	0.252
β_{12}	1.285	0.548	0.021
β_{13}	1.835	0.617	0.004
β_2	0.066	0.005	< 0.0001
Random Effects			
sd(e_{00})[a]	0.386		
Minimum e_{00}	−0.546		
Maximum e_{00}	0.585		

[a]Standard deviation for the random effect e_{00}.

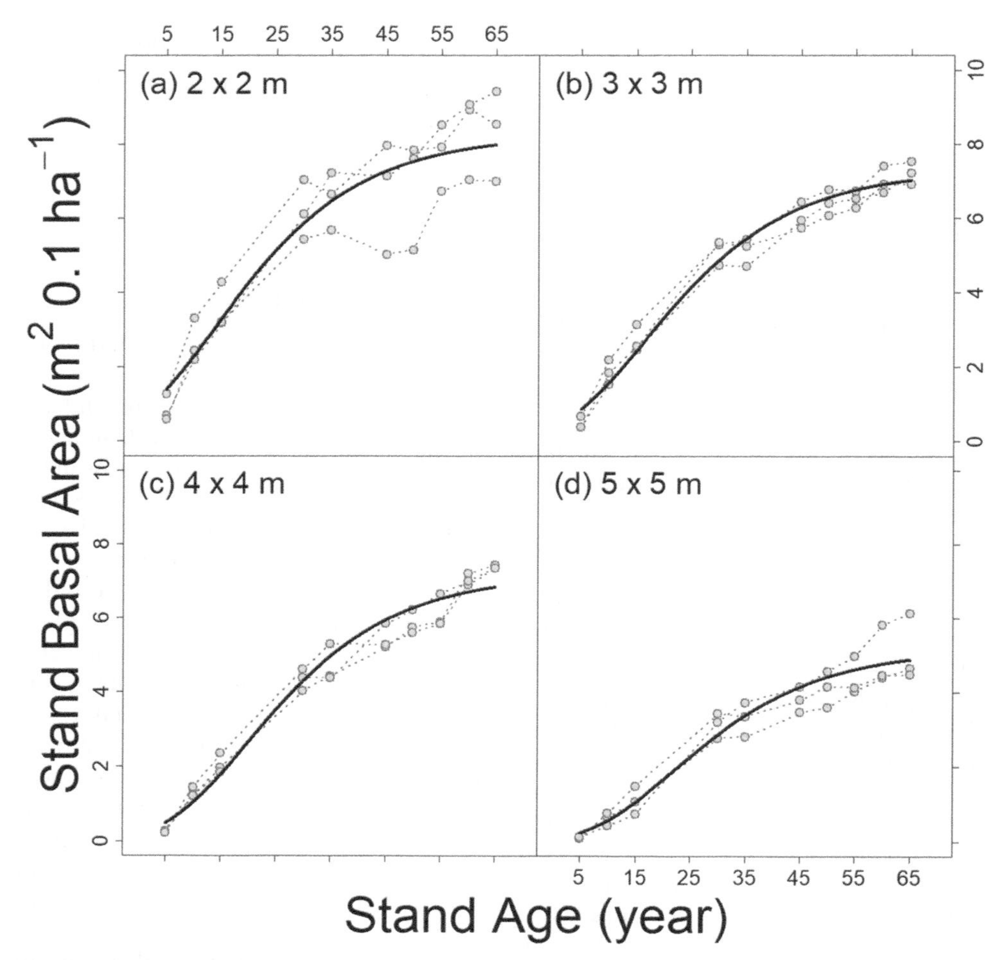

Figure 1. Stand basal area growth of sugi over 65 years for four initial densities: (a) 2 × 2 m (2500 trees ha^{-1}), (b) 3 × 3 m (1111 trees ha^{-1}), (c) 4 × 4 m (625 trees ha^{-1}), and (d) 5 × 5 m (400 trees ha^{-1}). The grey circles and dotted lines depict observed stand basal area at each stand age. The solid black lines depict the fitted Gompertz model.

2 × 2 m spacing (Figure 1(a,d)). All four fitted curves showed signs of reaching an asymptote, yet a clear asymptotic trend was still elusive.

From the fitted Gompertz model, we predicted the current annual increment (CAI) of stand BA (m^2 0.1 ha^{-1} year^{-1}) for each initial density (Figure 2). The maximum CAI for the four spacing of 2 × 2 m, 3 × 3 m, 4 × 4 m, and 5 × 5 m were 0.201, 0.178, 0.175, and 0.126 m^2 0.1 ha^{-1} year^{-1}, respectively. The stand age at which the four spacing reached their maximum CAI was 14, 17, 21, and 23 years, respectively. Thus, as expected, CAI for 2 × 2 m spacing reached the maximum earlier than other spacings. Lastly, while the CAI trends were decreasing at earlier stand ages, they have not approached zero increment at stand age 65 years.

Forecast accuracy

Using the first 55 years of stand BA growth data (DATA55), the fitted Gompertz model forecasted stand BA of the 12 plots at stand age 60 to have MB ± RMSB (MPB ± RMSPB) of – 0.748 ± 0.663 m^2 0.1 ha^{-1} (–10.259 ± 8.947%). The forecasts made by the same model for stand BA of the 12 plots at stand age 65 had MB ± RMSB (MPB ± RMSPB) of – 0.879 ± 0.724 m^2 0.1 ha^{-1} (–11.886 ± 9.665%). The residual plots agreed with the results that the forecasts at stand age 65 were greater, with most of the observations having larger negative biases (Figure S3(a); Supplementary Materials). Furthermore, mean bias increased negatively with increasing observed stand BA (Figure S3(a)). For β_0, 95% confidence intervals (CIs) of estimated β_{01} (3 × 3 m), β_{02} (4 × 4 m), and β_{03} (5 × 5 m) from DATA55 did not contain the respective estimated parameters of the Gompertz model fitted with the full dataset (FULL) suggesting significant differences in the estimated parameters between the two datasets (Figure 3(b–d); Table S1, Supplementary Materials). For example, the 95% CI of $\beta_{01}$from DATA55 was (6.130, 7.101), and the interval did not contain $\widehat{\beta}_{01}$ from FULL, which was 7.305 (Table S1). For β_1, however, its 95% CIs from DATA55 contained the estimated parameters from FULL, which suggested insignificant differences in the parameter estimates between the two datasets (Figure 4, Table S1). Lastly, the $\widehat{\beta}_2$ (the growth rate) from DATA55 was significantly larger than that from FULL because the 95% CI of β_2 from DATA55 (0.073, 0.093) did not contain the $\widehat{\beta}_2$ from FULL (0.066) (Figure 5, Table S1).

Using the first 60 years of stand BA growth data (DATA60), the fitted Gompertz model forecasted stand BA of the 12 plots at stand age 65 to have MB ± RMSB (MPB ± RMSPB) of – 0.453 ± 0.694 m^2 0.1 ha^{-1} (–5.638 ± 9.852%). Similar to the above, the residual plot depicted that mean bias increased negatively with increasing observed stand BA (Figure S3(b)). In all cases, parameter estimates (β_k, for k = 0, 1, 2) from the Gompertz model fitted with DATA60 were not

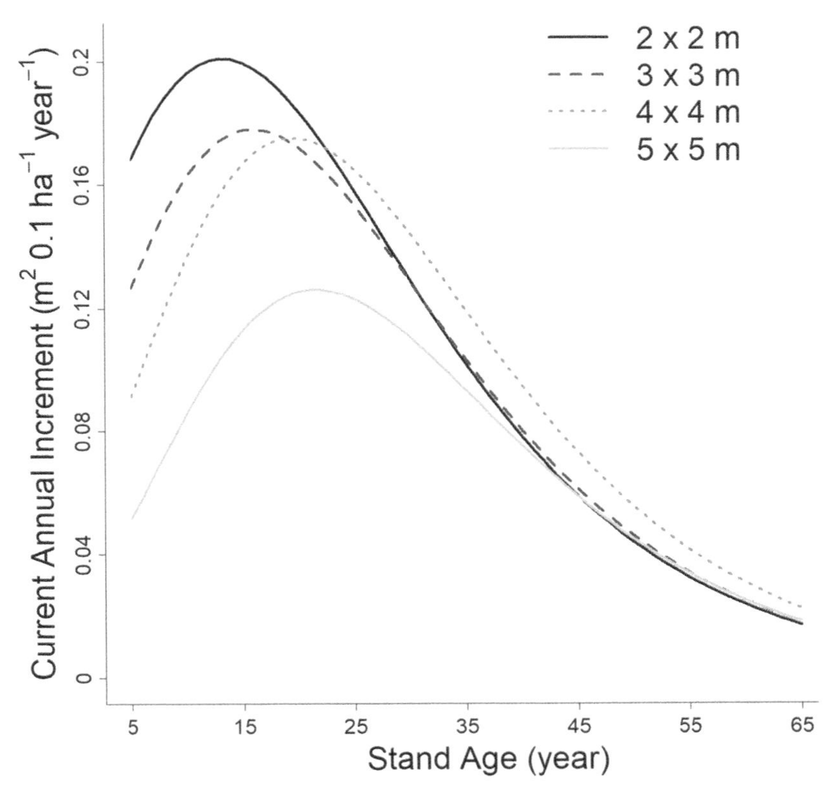

Figure 2. Current annual increment of stand basal area of sugi over stand age predicted by the fitted Gompertz model for four initial densities: (a) 2 × 2 m (2500 trees ha^{-1}), (b) 3 × 3 m (1111 trees ha^{-1}), (c) 4 × 4 m (625 trees ha^{-1}), and (d) 5 × 5 m (400 trees ha^{-1}).

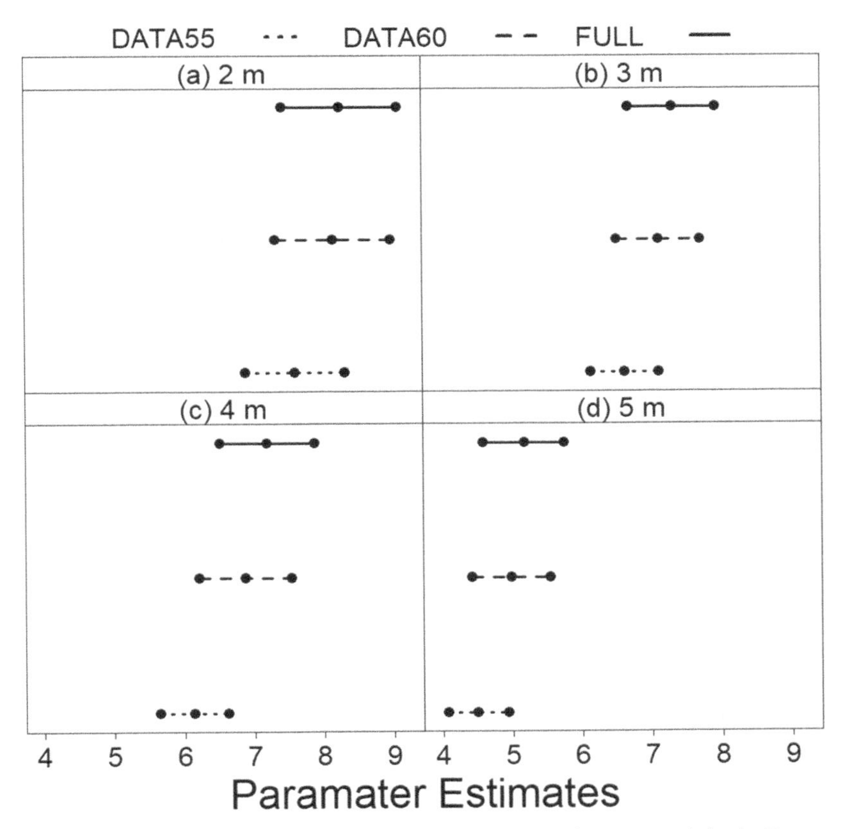

Figure 3. Parameter estimates of β_0 and their corresponding lower and upper bounds of the 95% confidence intervals for the Gompertz models fitted based on the full dataset (FULL), data up to 55 years (DATA55), and data up to 60 years (DATA60) for four initial densities: (a) 2 × 2 m (2500 trees ha^{-1}), (b) 3 × 3 m (1111 trees ha^{-1}), (c) 4 × 4 m (625 trees ha^{-1}), and (d) 5 × 5 m (400 trees ha^{-1}). The parameter estimates are not contrasts.

significantly different to those from the model fitted with FULL as the 95% CIs of β_k from DATA60 contained the $\widehat{\beta_k}$ from FULL (Figures 3–5; Table S1). Lastly, longer observation periods increased values in the estimated β_0 (Figure 3), but decreased values in the estimated β_1 and β_2 (Figures 4, 5; Table S1).

Discussion

Similar to other studies, such as Curtis et al. (2016) and Forrester et al. (2013), stand BA of sugi plantations is the largest when planted at the highest initial density and is the smallest at the lowest initial density. At a lower initial density, larger growing spacing is available per tree, which favors capturing sunlight, moisture, and nutrients for tree growth and therefore accelerates growth rate (Macdonald and Hubert 2002). While this leads to a larger average tree diameter, results show that it is not enough to compensate for the lower stand density to achieve a comparable stand BA of stands planted at a higher initial density, which is clearly depicted in the trends of stand density and quadratic mean diameter changing over stand development stages for different initial densities (Figures S4, S5; Supplementary Materials). For example, at stand age 65, the predicted stand basal area of 5 × 5 m spacing is about 40% less than that of 2 × 2 m spacing. Despite that the fitted models predicted significantly different asymptotes between initial densities, the data have not revealed clear and discernible asymptotes of stand BA development for all the initial densities. For example, stands with 4 × 4 m spacing still show evidence of a continuous increase in stand BA. Antón-Fernández et al. (2012) suggested that stand BA of stands with a high initial density would decrease at an earlier stand development stage, possibly due to mortality and slower growth. Cameron et al. (1989) and Chen et al. (2011) found that differences in stand BA between initial densities diminished in the longer term. Thus, the stand BA of all initial densities of the sugi spacing trial could perhaps intersect at some points in time. However, this will require longer observations to be made.

In Japan, growth studies about sugi mainly focus on the effects of thinning and other silvicultural treatments (e.g. Nagumo et al. 1981; Nishizono et al. 2008); studies on the effects of initial density are limited in comparison. Fukuchi et al. (2011) studied the density effects with a series of Nelder plots established in 1974 in the Miyazaki Prefecture. At stand age 32 years, the stand BA for the initial density of 2326, 1122, 779, and 376 trees ha^{-1} was 7.17, 5.88, 5.15, and 3.34 m^2 0.1 ha^{-1}, respectively. In this study, with comparable initial densities, the estimated stand BA at 32 years was 6.13, 5.11, 4.58, and 3.08 m^2 0.1 ha^{-1}, respectively. Besides environmental factors, the discrepancy could also possibly be due to the differences in the experimental designs, i.e. Nelder plot vs. completely randomized design. Osumi et al. (2000) and Masaki et al. (2015) analyzed the growth data of a sugi plantation, with an initial density of 3000 trees ha^{-1}, from the Soehatazawa Experimental Forest in the Akita Prefecture. They found that stand BA at stand age 45, 48, 54, and 61 years was 7.84, 8.35, 9.19, and 9.99 m^2 0.1 ha^{-1}, respectively, with an average CAI of 0.71 m^2 0.1 ha^{-1} year^{-1}. For the 2 × 2 m spacing (i.e. initial density 2500 trees ha^{-1}) in this study, the stand BA for those stand ages was estimated to be 7.27, 7.44, 7.70, and 7.90 m^2 0.1 ha^{-1}, respectively, with an average CAI of 0.21 m^2 0.1 ha^{-1} year^{-1}. The differences imply that the stand BA of the Soehatazawa Experimental Forest was still growing at a faster rate than that in our study site despite that the former plantation was planted at a higher initial density. Caution should be exercised when interpreting the comparisons between Taiwan and Japan because abiotic and biotic factors such as climate conditions could also contribute to the observed differences.

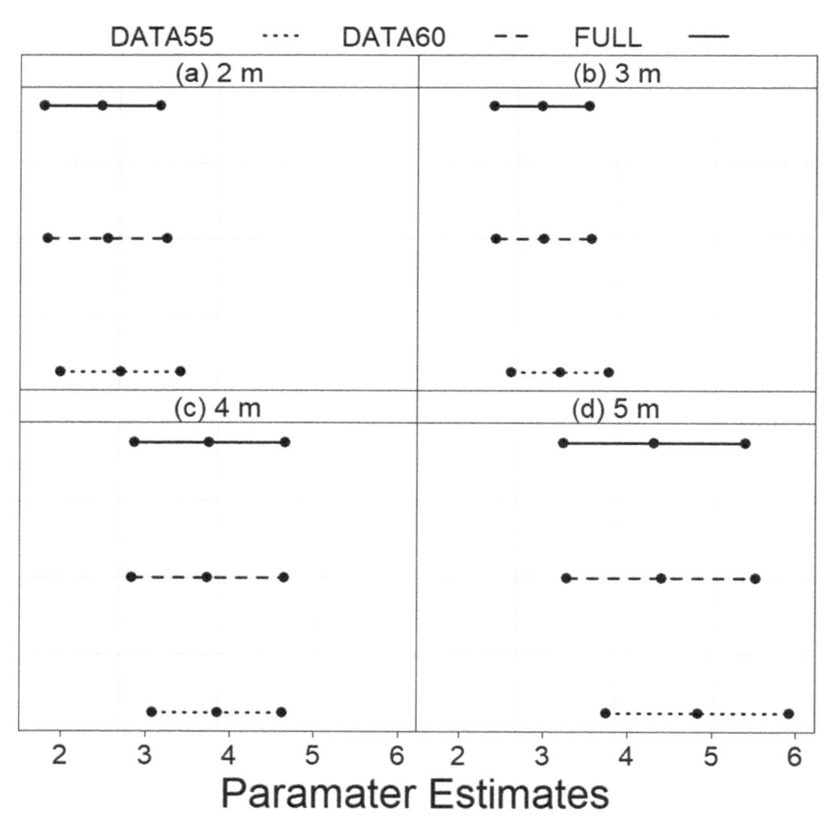

Figure 4. Parameter estimates of β_1 and their corresponding lower and upper bounds of the 95% confidence intervals for the Gompertz models fitted based on the full dataset (FULL), data up to 55 years (DATA55), and data up to 60 years (DATA60) for four initial densities: (a) 2 × 2 m (2500 trees ha^{-1}), (b) 3 × 3 m (1111 trees ha^{-1}), (c) 4 × 4 m (625 trees ha^{-1}), and (d) 5 × 5 m (400 trees ha^{-1}). The parameter estimates are not contrasts.

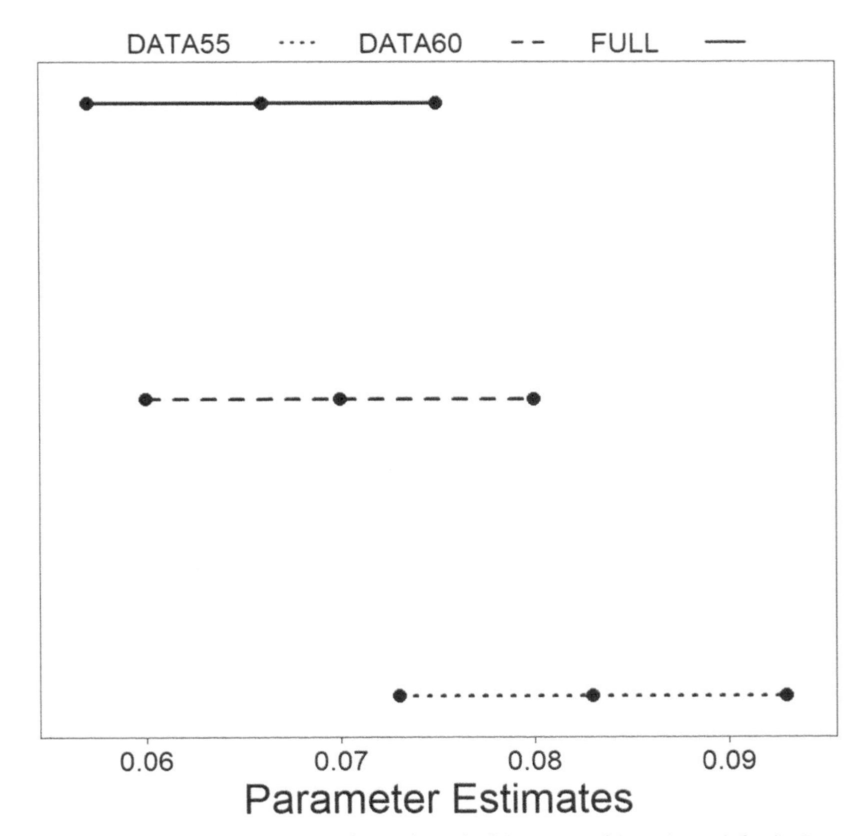

Figure 5. Parameter estimates of β_2 and their corresponding lower and upper bounds of the 95% confidence intervals for the Gompertz models fitted based on the full dataset (FULL), data up to 55 years (DATA55), and data up to 60 years (DATA60). The parameter estimates are not contrasts.

Similar to Antón-Fernández et al. (2012), decreasing initial density brings about a lower maximum increment that occurs at a later stand age. Ishiguri et al. (2005) noted that the period required for crown closure occurred earlier for stands planted at a higher initial density, and once crown closure was reached, individual tree growth decreased. This phenomenon may have contributed to the fact that the increment of stand BA of sugi spacing trial stands planted at the highest initial density reached its maximum at the earliest stand age and was the largest among the initial densities. Despite these, CAI of 2 × 2 m, 3 × 3 m, and 5 × 5 m converged around stand age 45 and began to taper off, which implies that differential gain in CAI due to spacing effects diminished around this age. From a silviculture perspective, this is the period when thinning or stand replacement treatments could take place, especially for the stands with 2 × 2 m spacing, which incidentally corresponds to the prescribed rotation age of 40 to 45 years of sugi planted in the study region suggested by Wang (1977) and Cheng et al. (2013). In Japan, the rotation age of sugi plantations is conventionally set between 40 and 60 years (Masaki et al. 2006). In Saitama Prefecture, Japan, its stand rotation age is set at 65 years for a clear-cutting system, 80 to 100 years for multi-storied silvicultural systems, and 100 to 150 years for long rotation systems (Tatsuhara and Doi 2006). Those rotation ages in Japan coincide with this study at the time when stand BA growth is gradually tapering off, and spacing effects are no longer prominent. For the stands with 4 × 4 m spacing, this study suggests the rotation age could perhaps be longer, but caution should be practiced as the results were from a single spacing trial specific to the study region. The fitted models suggested that the growth rate parameter β_2 did not significantly vary between initial densities, which implied that growth rates were similar among the four initial densities. The parameter β_2 describes the "intrinsic" growth rate in biological growth, which is the potential growth rate of a tree or a species. As mentioned previously, the planting materials in our spacing trial were 1-year cuttings of sugi that minimized genetic variations, which may have explained why the estimated β_2 was insignificantly different among initial densities. Despite this, the trends in CAI have captured the finer details in sugi growth under them, which points out that it is difficult to isolate the effects of initial density on β_2 from the fitted models as all parameters were simultaneously estimated.

Producing wood with desirable properties and product sizes from stands planted at a lower initial density could perhaps make up for the lower stand BA of those stands. Studies have shown that harvested wood sizes are affected by initial densities. Amateis and Burkhart (2012) showed that 25 year-old loblolly pine planted at 740 trees ha^{-1} could produce sawlog grade wood, which is due to a lower initial density produces on average larger diameter trees that are valuable as sawtimber (Forrester et al. 2013). On the other hand, an initial density of 1680 trees ha^{-1} of loblolly pine is best for pulpwood production on similar site quality as sawtimber production (Amateis and Burkhart 2012). In terms of sugi wood properties, past studies have found that increasing initial density reduces the number and average size of knots (Wang and Lin 1996; Ishiguri et al. 2005), reduces crook in timber (Takino and Sasaki 1979), and increases modulus of rupture and modulus of elasticity (Takino and Sasaki 1979; Wang and Ko 1998). These are the desired properties for producing lumber grade wood products. However, Jiang et al. (2007) found that increasing initial density decreased tree stem taper and increased slenderness (ratio of tree height to dbh), which would affect volume production per tree and its vulnerability to wind damage (Kershaw et al. 2016). Lastly, studies have found little effect of initial density on wood density (Zobel and Buijtenen 1989; Jiang et al. 2007), but the effects on fiber length are inconsistent (e.g. Yang and Hazenberg 1994). In short, management objectives on the quality of the final wood products should be carefully laid out prior to deciding on a preferable planting density.

Decreasing accuracy of estimates with increasing projection length occurs in long-term forecasting with growth and yield models (Kangas 1997). While this is common, the magnitude of accuracy in the successive forecast is often of great interest. This study showed that the accuracy of forecasting future stand BA was poorer for the Gompertz model fitted with data up to 55 years (about −10%) than for the model fitted with data up to 60 years (about −6%). One possible explanation is that data up to 55 years have yet to exhibit a distinct asymptote. As a result, the fitted model based on the data up to 55 years may not have adequately captured the asymptote where stand BA is no longer increasing. Such a situation would in turn affect prediction of the inflection point as the inflection point of the Gompertz model is at about one-third of the asymptote (Zeide 1993), which could further produce misleading maximum CAI. The 60-year dataset is better at indicating the asymptotic trend, which could have led to improved forecasts of future stand BA and present CAI. Such results highlight the necessity and importance of having long term observations. When evaluating the performance of growth models in the Swedish Forest Planning System, Fahlvik et al. (2014) found that BA growth was overestimated at about 2 to 3%, which were better than this study probably because they have accessed to a large long-term dataset unlike this study (Elfving 2010). We believe that a mean forecast error rate less than 6% is acceptable for management purposes. Furthermore, there are inherent plot-to-plot variations in stand BA growth trend within an initial density, but the use of random effects under a mixed-effects modeling framework could account for such variations (Pinheiro and Bates 2000; Lam et al. 2017). Lastly, the performances of our fitted models do not seem to be affected by the unequal measurement intervals, perhaps also due to the flexibility of the modeling framework.

This study has successfully modeled the development of stand BA under different initial densities with several important highlights. For one, the planted sugi trees were from 1-year cuttings and were planted in a small area with relatively homogeneous environment conditions, especially topography and climate (Guan et al. 2008a, 2008b). As a result, genetic and environmental variations were minimized, and their growth performances in this study entirely reflected the effects of initial density, such as inter-tree competition. Secondly, as the result of missing measurements between 1965 and 1980, the longitudinal stand BA data were unevenly spaced and would affect the assumptions underlying the four autocorrelation models. Despite this, results showed that the stand BA growth trends were adequately captured with a mixed-effects modeling framework, and the forecast accuracy was acceptable when the data itself started to depict asymptotic trends.

Findings from this study are relevant to many interested groups and the government agencies such as the Taiwan Forestry Bureau or silvicultural researchers. For one, the study shows evidence that stand basal area has not entirely reached an asymptote for all initial planting densities after 65 years, which suggests that the final cut should be planned at a later stand age to maximize timber volume production. To determine when would be best for a final cut, research organizations should continue to invest in monitoring this study area and others to fully understand stand development stages under different spacings and to increase forecast accuracy. Nonetheless, there are still some limitations and challenges. For one, the scope of inference is limited as the study is confined to a single location, which could constrain the generalization of the results. Secondly, one should note that the spacing trial is a squared one. Other spatial arrangements with the same initial density could induce different tree-to-tree competition effects and could lead to different stand BA growth trends.

Measurements between 1965 to 1980 were unfortunately missing, which was when the stands were between 15 and 30 years old. That was the crucial period in stand development stages where stands should be experiencing the highest growth rate and self-thinning. Thus, the predicted stand age at which the maximum CAI occurred in this study could be less accurate. Lastly, there are trees with partial measurements in the measurement series, which may have caused a decrease in stand basal area in some stands, e.g. most notably in years 45 and 50 for a stand in 2 × 2 m spacing (Figure 1(a)). Partial measurement series is sometimes unavoidable due to field practicality in long term observations in permanent plots. However, analysis on the stand-level and the use of a mixed-effects model approach could potentially minimize the effects of partial measurement series of some trees.

Acknowledgments

We express sincere appreciation to National Taiwan University Experimental Forest for permission to use the data and for providing field supports. We also thank many students and research assistants that have contributed to the collection of the long-term data.

Disclosure Statement

No conflict of interest declared.

Funding

This work was supported by the Ministry of Science and Technology of Taiwan under Grant [MOST 105-2628-B-002-010-MY3 for TYL and MOST 106-2313-B-002-007-MY3 for BTG] and by the National Taiwan University.

ORCID

Tzeng Yih Lam http://orcid.org/0000-0001-6865-5626
Biing T. Guan http://orcid.org/0000-0001-9860-0861

References

Amateis RL, Burkhart HE. 2012. Rotation-age results from a Loblolly pine spacing trial. South J Appl For. 36:11–18.

Antón-Fernández C, Burkhart HE, Amateis RL. 2012. Modeling the effects of initial spacing on stand basal area development of Loblolly pine. For Sci. 58:95–105.

Cameron DM, Rance SJ, Jones RM, Charles-Edwards DA, Barnes A. 1989. Project STAG: an experimental study in agroforestry. Aust J Agric Res. 40:699–714.

Chen S, Arnold R, Li Z, Li T, Zhou G, Wu Z, Zhou Q. 2011. Tree and stand growth for clonal *E. urophylla* × *grandis* across a range of initial stockings in southern China. New For. 41:95–112.

Cheng CH, Hung CY, Chen CP, Pei CW. 2013. Biomass carbon accumulation in aging Japanese cedar plantations in Xitou, central Taiwan. Bot Stud. 54:1–9.

Chuang ST, Wang SY. 2001. Evaluation of standing tree quality of Japanese cedar grown with different spacing using stress-wave and ultrasonic-wave methods. J Wood Sci. 47:245–253.

Curtis RO, Bansal S, Harrington CA. 2016. Relation of initial spacing and relative stand density indices to stand characteristics in a Douglas-fir plantation spacing trial [Internet]. Portland (OR, USA): U.S. Department of Agriculture, Forest Service, Pacific Northwest Research Station.

Elfving B. 2010. Growth modelling in the Heureka system [Internet]. Umeå (Sweden): Swedish University of Agricultural Sciences, Faculty of Forestry.

Fahlvik N, Elfving B, Wikström P. 2014. Evaluation of growth functions used in the Swedish Forest Planning System Heureka. Silva Fenn. 48:1013.

Forrester DI, Wiedemann JC, Forrester RI, Baker TG. 2013. Effects of planting density and site quality on mean tree size and total stand growth of *Eucalyptus globulus* plantations. Can J For Res. 43:846–851.

Fujisawa Y, Ohta S, Akashi T. 1995. Wood characteristics and genetic variation in sugi (*Cryptomeria japonica*) IV. Variation in growth ring features of plus tree clones in relation to the initial planting space. Mokuzai Gakkaishi. 41:631–639.

Fukuchi S, Yoshida S, Mizoue N, Murakami T, Kajisa T, Ota T, Nagashima K. 2011. Analysis of the planting density toward low-cost forestry: a result from the experimental plots of Obi-sugi planting density. J Jpn For Soc. 93:303–308.

Gadow K, Hui G. 1999. Modelling forest development [Internet]. 1st ed. Dordrecht (Netherlands): Springer Netherlands.

Garber SM, Monserud RA, Maguire DA. 2008. Crown recession patterns in three conifer species of the Northern Rocky Mountains. For Sci. 54:633–646.

Gingrich SF. 1967. Measuring and evaluating stocking and stand density in upland hardwood forests in the Central States. For Sci. 13:38–53.

Gompertz B. 1825. On the nature of the function expressive of the law of human mortality, and on a new mode of determining the value of life contingencies. Philos Trans R Soc Lond. 115:513–583.

Guan BT, Lin ST, Lin YH, Wu YS. 2008a. No initial size advantage for Japanese cedars in crowded stands. For Ecol Manag. 255:1078–1084.

Guan BT, Lin ST, Lin YH, Wu YS. 2008b. Growth efficiency-survivorship relationship and effects of spacing on relative diameter growth rate of Japanese cedars. For Ecol Manag. 255:1713–1723.

Ishiguri F, Kasai S, Yokota S, Iizuka K, Yoshizawa N. 2005. Wood quality of sugi (*Cryptomeria Japonica*) grown at four initial spacings. IAWA J. 26:375–386.

Jiang ZH, Wang XQ, Fei BH, Ren HQ, Liu XE. 2007. Effect of stand and tree attributes on growth and wood quality characteristics from a spacing trial with *Populus xiaohei*. Ann For Sci. 64:807–814.

Kangas AS. 1997. On the prediction bias and variance in long-term growth projections. For Ecol Manag. 96:207–216.

Kershaw JA Jr., Ducey MJ, Beers TW, Husch B. 2016. Forest mensuration. 5th ed. West Sussex (UK): John Wiley & Sons Ltd.

Lam TY, Kershaw JA Jr., Nur Hajar ZS, Abd Rahman K, Weiskittel AR, Potts MD. 2017. Evaluating and modelling genus and species variation in height-to-diameter relationships for Tropical Hill Forests in Peninsular Malaysia. Forestry. 90:268–278.

Macdonald E, Hubert J. 2002. A review of the effects of silviculture on timber quality of Sitka spruce. Forestry. 75:107–138.

Masaki T, Mori S, Kajimoto T, Hitsuma G, Sawata S, Mori M, Osumi K, Sakurai S, Seki T. 2006. Long-term growth analyses of Japanese cedar trees in a plantation: neighborhood competition and persistence of initial growth deviations. J For Res. 11:217–225.

Masaki T, Osumi K, Seki T, Mori S, Kajimoto T, Hitsuma G, Yagihashi T, Shibata M, Noguchi M. 2015. Long-term growth of a planted forest of Japanese cedar at Soehatazawa experimental forest under various thinning intensities of trees 45–104 years old. Bull For For Prod Res Inst. 14:65–72.

Nagumo H, Shiraishi N, Tanaka M. 1981. Systematic method constructing an yield table for sugi even-aged stand: a case study in experimental plots of the Tokyo University Forest in Chiba. Bull Univ Tokyo For. 71:269–330.

Nishizono T, Tanaka K, Awaya Y, Oishi Y, Hayashi M, Yokota Y, Amano M, Kuboyama H, Yamaki K, Furuido H. 2008. Age-related changes in stand volume growth of *Cryptomeria japonica* plantations in Akita District, Northeastern Japan. J Jpn For Soc. 90:232–240.

Oliver WW. 1979. Early response of ponderosa pine to spacing and brush: observations on a 12-year-old plantation [Internet]. Berkeley (CA, USA): U.S. Department of Agriculture, Forest Service, Pacific Northwest Research Station.

Osumi K, Mori M, Sakurai S, Saitou K, Satou S, Seki T. 2000. Long term growth records of old-aged sugi (*Cryptomeria japonica*) plantations in Akita Prefecture, North-eastern Japan. J Jpn For Soc. 82:179–187.

Pinheiro JC, Bates DM. 2000. Mixed-effects models in S and S-PLUS. 1st ed. New York (NY, USA): Springer-Verlag New York.

R Core Team. 2019. R: a language and environment for statistical computing. Vienna (Austria): R Foundation for Statistical Computing. https://www.R-project.org/.

Reineke LH. 1933. Perfecting a stand-density index for even-aged forests. J Agric Res. 46:627–638.

Reukema DL. 1979. Fifty-year development of Douglas-fir stands planted at various spacings [Internet]. Portland (OR, USA): U.S. Department of Agriculture, Forest Service, Pacific Northwest Research Station.

Taiwan Forestry Bureau. 2017. The fourth national forest resource inventory. Taipei (Taiwan): Taiwan Forestry Bureau, Council of Agriculture. https://www.forest.gov.tw/0002393.

Takino S, Sasaki H. 1979. Properties of sugi from thinning operation for structural use. Wood Res Note. 14:99–104. [in Japanese].

Tatsuhara S, Doi T. 2006. Comparing long-rotation silvicultural systems of a sugi (*Cryptomeria japonica*) plantation in regard to yield and labour requirements. Jpn J For Plan. 40:257–265.

Tjørve KMC, Tjørve E. 2017. The use of Gompertz models in growth analyses, and new Gompertz-model approach: an addition to the Unified-Richards family. PLoS One. 12:e0178691.

Tsushima S, Koga S, Oda K, Shiraishi S. 2006. Effects of initial spacing on growth and wood properties of sugi (*Cryptomeria japonica*) cutting cultivars. Mokuzai Gakkaishi. 52:196–205.

Wang SY, Chen KN. 1992. Effects of plantation spacings on tracheid lengths, annual-ring widths, and percentages of latewood and heartwood of Taiwan-grown Japanese cedar. Mokuzai Gakkaishi. 38:645–656.

Wang SY, Ko CY. 1998. Dynamic modulus of elasticity and bending properties of large beams of Taiwan-grown Japanese cedar from different plantation spacing sites. J Wood Sci. 44:62–68.

Wang SY, Lin SH. 1996. Effects of plantation spacings on the quality of visually graded lumber and mechanical properties of Taiwan-grown Japanese cedar. Mokuzai Gakkaishi. 42:435–444.

Wang TT. 1977. Tree biomass production in *Cryptomeria* stands of different age classes. J Agri Assoc China. 102:59–76.

Weiskittel AR, Hann DW, Kershaw JA Jr., Vanclay JK. 2011. Forest growth and yield modeling. 1st ed. Chichester (UK): John Wiley & Sons Ltd.

Yang KC, Hazenberg G. 1994. Impact of spacing on tracheid length, relative density, and growth rate of juvenile wood and mature wood in *Picea mariana*. Can J For Res. 24:996–1007.

Zeide B. 1993. Analysis of growth equations. For Sci. 39:594–616.

Zobel BJ, Buijtenen JP. 1989. Wood variation-its cause and control. Berlin (Germany): Springer-verlag.

Long observation period improves growth prediction in old Sugi (*Cryptomeria japonica*) forest plantations

Takuya Hiroshima, Keisuke Toyama, Satoshi N. Suzuki, Toshiaki Owari, Tohru Nakajima and Seiji Ishibashi

ABSTRACT

It is important to predict the growth of Sugi forest plantations in old age. When predictions about the growth of Sugi forest plantations are made and there is a lack of growth data from older trees, it is possible that the accuracy of these predictions becomes worse. For example, it is known that the growth of Sugi does not get slower at older ages as expected from past growth predictions based on growth data from young to middle-aged trees. This study investigated the changes in extrapolated values of diameter at breast height (DBH) in old Sugi forest plantations with changes in the observation period of training data for model calibration. The study sites were long-term growth observation sites of Sugi forest plantations in the University of Tokyo Chiba Forest and Chichibu Forest. In this study, both DBH of individual trees and mean DBH of stands were analyzed by fitting Richards growth functions. The results showed that the accuracy of growth predictions in old ages was improved by including growth data from a sufficient number of older trees. From another point of view, growth prediction in old ages tended to underestimate actual growth if growth data did not include enough older trees.

Introduction

Sugi (*Cryptomeria japonica*) forest plantations have recently been reaching maturity in Japan and currently, more than half of forest plantations are over 50 years old (Forestry Agency 2018). As a result, the trees are now taller and provide large diameter logs when felled. In such circumstances, it is important to predict the growth of Sugi forest plantations, particularly in old age.

For the purpose of predicting the growth of Sugi forest plantations, several yield tables were developed using stand variables such as age and mean height obtained from experimental plots. For instance, empirical yield tables for Sugi were developed by the University of Tokyo Chiba Forest, where the Mitscherlich equation was used for site classification and for development of a height growth curve (Nagumo et al. 1981; Shiraishi 1985a, 1985b, 1986). These yield tables were improved and remodeled into a computerized local yield prediction system and have been widely applied for practical growth predictions of Sugi forest plantations in Japan (Matsumoto et al. 2011; Nakajima et al. 2011). In other previous studies, stochastic models for diameter and height growth predictions were developed using Sugi stand variables in the University of Tokyo Chiba Forest, assuming several hypotheses such as a relationship between periodic annual increments and growth at given ages, independent of random effects and so on (Tanaka 1986, 1988, 1991) as an extension of Sloboda's model (Sloboda 1984). Nonlinear mixed-effects models were developed considering the effects of thinning and site productivity on stand volume growth using data from long-term experimental plots of Sugi by fitting the Richards growth function (Nishizono 2010). Process-based growth models were developed for Sugi forest plantations using long-term data, which incorporated a balance of matter among processes such as photosynthesis and respiration using a Bayesian calibration technique (Mitsuda et al. 2013, 2017). Individual tree growth prediction models for Sugi were also developed including neighborhood competition (Masaki et al. 2006; Matsushita et al. 2015) and excluding it as well (Takao and Minowa 1993).

When the growth of Sugi forest plantations is predicted using any kind of model, it is possible that the accuracy of growth prediction in old ages, i.e., the accuracy of extrapolation, gets worse as there is a paucity of growth data for trees of older ages. Several studies pointed out that the growth of Sugi did not get slower in old age as was expected based on past growth predictions based on growth data from young to middle-aged stands (Osumi et al. 2000; Takeuchi and Ito 2003; Takeuchi 2005; Masaki et al. 2015). For instance, Osumi et al. (2000) and Masaki et al. (2015) pointed out that growing stock maintained high growth rates even in the Sugi forest plantations over 100 years old.

In Japan, however, there are only a limited number of research plots that store enough growth data up to old ages; hence, empirical studies about growth have been limited particularly in old Sugi forest plantations. For instance, national forests in Japan hold a total of 60 yield experimental sites of Sugi as of March 1996, though only the part of the sites store enough data from plants over 90 years old (FFPRI 1996; Hosoda et al. 2009, 2014; Nishizono et al. 2019). University forests or experimental forests managed by universities also hold experimental sites of Sugi such as the Kagoshima university forests at Takakuma (Yoshida et al. 1992), Hirakura experimental forest of Mie university (Shiono et al. 2013), Utsunomiya university forests at Funyu (Matsue 2019), 11 sites in Xitou, Qingshuiguo and Duigaoyue districts in National Taiwan University Experimental Forest (Cheng et al. 2019), etc.

Among them, the University of Tokyo Forests hold a limited number of long-term experimental plots of old Sugi forest plantations in Japan (Owari et al. 2019). Particularly the University of Tokyo Chiba Forest and Chichibu Forest hold several long-term and very old plots and the ones in Chiba Forest must be the oldest long-term observational plot in Asia.

Under these circumstances, it is meaningful to verify the variability and accuracy of growth predictions of old Sugi forest plantations according to the availability of long-term growth data.

Thus, the purpose of this study was to investigate the changes in extrapolation values of DBH in old Sugi forest plantations by fitting a growth function according to changes in the observation period of training data for model calibration. Study sites included long-term growth observation sites of Sugi forest plantations in The University of Tokyo Chiba Forest and Chichibu Forest. In this study, we analyzed both DBH of individual trees and mean DBH of stands.

Materials and methods

Study sites

Table 1 shows the study sites of old Sugi forest plantations, which consisted of six sites in Chiba Forest: Anno1, Anno2, Gobozawa, Godai1, Metaki3 and Ninodai and five sites in Chichibu Forest of 005B, 032D, 036B, 048A and 503A (Takeuchi and Hasegawa 1975; Yamamoto et al. 1988; Suzuki et al. 1999; Oomura et al. 2004, 2005, 2012; Niwa et al. 2014; Takatoku et al. 2019). Chiba Forest belonged to the warm temperate zone with a mean annual precipitation of 2,242 mm and mean annual temperature of 13.2°C and Chichibu Forest belonged to the cool temperate zone with a mean annual precipitation of 1,498 mm and mean annual temperature of 11.2°C, according to the observations by local weather stations. In each site, every Sugi tree was tagged and their DBH was measured approximately every five years. Hence, time-series data of DBH were available at an individual tree level. In addition, these sites were artificially thinned several times based on standard thinning regimes: Chiba and Chichibu Forest management teams conduct low thinning one – three times before 40 years of age with the intensity of around 20–40% and sometimes give additional crown thinning one–two times after 40 years with relatively high intensity.

Individual tree-level analysis

First, we set reference ages for statistical tests, which were around 110 (108–111) years old in the case of Chiba Forest sites and around 90 (85–90) years old in the case of Chichibu Forest sites. In this analysis, targets were living trees at the reference ages. For instance at Anno1 site (Table 1), a total of 105 trees were living at the reference age of 108 years old in 2010, so we used time-series DBH data of only these 105 trees with a total measurement frequency of 20 times from 14 to 108 years old (from 1916 to 2010).

For a growth model, we used the Richards growth function:

$$DBH = a\left(1 - e^{-bt}\right)^{c}, \quad (1)$$

where t was age in years, and a, b and c are parameters to be estimated. In this research, we only applied the Richards function for growth curve fitting because the Richards function is the general function that contains the conventional growth curves of Mitcherlich, Logistic and Gompertz, and has high flexibility in model fitting (Osumi and Ishikawa 1983).

Because we focused on exploring how the parameters of the individual tree growth curve respond to the changes in the observation period, we fitted the Richards function to time-series DBH data for each target tree, following the previous studies (for example, Osumi and Ishikawa 1983; Taniguchi and Kayatani 1994). Fittings were conducted to time-series DBH data from first measurement age point to until several fitting age points: three points at around 60 (58–61), 80 (78–81) and 100 (97–102) years were set for the Chiba Forest sites and two points at around 60 (60–63) and 80 (80–83) years of age were set for Chichibu Forest sites (Table 1). Then, we extrapolated DBH at the reference ages using the Richards growth function. Finally, we conducted statistical analyses for extrapolated DBH and observed DBH by error evaluation and multiple comparison tests. For the purpose of error evaluation, we calculated percent prediction biases (= 100 * [mean extrapolated DBH – mean observed DBH]/mean observed DBH) and root mean squared errors (RMSE) to examine the prediction accuracies.

For the purpose of multiple comparison tests, we employed a non-parametric Friedman test because the assumption of normality was violated in the extrapolated and observed DBH in some sites and Scheffé paired comparison were also conducted for the case of paired and more than three group data sets. In common, the Friedman test is used to detect significant differences in treatments (extrapolation and observation values) across multiple test attempts (individual target trees in each site), and the Scheffé paired comparison test is used to identify which subgroup (extrapolation or observation values) was significantly different from other subgroups.

For instance at the Anno1 site (Table 1), we fitted Richards growth functions to each target tree at three age points: 58 years old (9 time-series DBH data from 14 to 58 years old), 78 years old (13 time-series DBH data from 14 to 78 years old) and 98 years old (18 time-series DBH data from 14 to 98 years old) and extrapolated DBH at the reference age of 108 years old using these three Richards functions. Fitting and extrapolating were conducted for all 105 target trees. Then, we statistically compared the three sets of extrapolated DBH and observed DBH at 108 years old for 105 target trees.

Stand level analysis

Reference ages and fitting ages in the case of stand-level analysis were the same in the case of individual tree level analysis for each site. In this analysis, we calculated the mean

Table 1. Summary of study sites.

Chiba Forest	Stand age	Frequency	Mean DBH(cm)	Number of tree	Chichibu Forest	Stand age	Frequency	Mean DBH(cm)	Number of tree
Anno1, 0.111 ha, 210 m, 10-15°, S,planted in 1903, survey 1916-2015	58 (in 1960)	9	18.9	165 (1486/ha)	005B, 0.050 ha, 1080 m, 38°, S,planted in 1930, survey 1956-2017	61 (in 1990)	6	25.8	75 (1500/ha)
	78 (in 1980)	13	23.4	145 (1306/ha)		83 (in 2012)	10	32.6	53 (1060/ha)
	98 (in 2000)	18	30.5	114 (1027/ha)		**88** (in 2017)	11	34.0	52 (1040/ha)
	108 (in 2010)	20	32.8	105 (945/ha)	032D, 0.071 ha, 950 m, 44°, SE,planted in 1930, survey 1956-2014	60 (in 1989)	8	30.5	94 (1323/ha)
Anno2, 0.076, 200 m, Flat, -,planted in 1902, survey 1916-2015	59 (in 1960)	9	22.4	103 (1355/ha)		81 (in 2010)	12	39.2	43 (605/ha)
	79 (in 1980)	13	27.0	85 (1118/ha)		**85** (in 2014)	13	40.9	43 (605/ha)
	99 (in 2000)	18	32.6	67 (881/ha)	036B, 0.128 ha, 800 m, 43°, S,planted in 1926, survey 1963-2015	60 (in 1985)	5	29.5	144 (1125/ha)
	109 (in 2010)	20	34.9	63 (828/ha)		80 (in 2005)	9	36.0	111 (867/ha)
Gobozawa, 0.539 ha, 200 m, 20-25°, N&S, planted in 1905, survey 1940-2015	61 (in 1965)	7	38.2	319 (591/ha)		**90** (in 2015)	11	38.9	104 (812/ha)
	81 (in 1985)	12	43.8	287 (532/ha)	048A, 0.123 ha, 940 m, 29°, N,planted in 1929, survey 1960-2016	63 (in 1991)	5	29.3	166 (1349/ha)
	102 (in 2006)	16	55.0	187 (346/ha)		83 (in 2011)	9	35.5	130 (1056/ha)
	111 (in 2015)	18	57.7	182 (337/ha)		**88** (in 2016)	10	37.2	121 (983/ha)
Godai1, 0.142 ha, 210 m, 30°, W,planted in 1905, survey 1916-2015	61 (in 1965)	11	33.4	129 (908/ha)	503A, 0.239 ha, 950 m, 16°, SE,planted in 1930, survey 1959-2014	60 (in 1989)	7	31.1	316 (1322/ha)
	81 (in 1985)	16	39.7	105 (739/ha)		81 (in 2010)	11	39.1	190 (794/ha)
	102 (in 2006)	20	49.8	66 (464/ha)		**85** (in 2014)	12	40.7	188 (786/ha)
	111 (in 2015)	22	52.7	65 (457/ha)					
Metaki3, 0.036 ha, 290 m, 22°, SE,planted in 1903, survey 1915-2015	58 (in 1960)	9	31.0	30 (833/ha)					
	78 (in 1980)	13	35.7	30 (833/ha)					
	98 (in 2000)	18	42.5	26 (722/ha)					
	108 (in 2010)	20	46.0	24 (666/ha)					
Ninodai, 0.057 ha, 280 m, 15°, S,planted in 1900, survey 1915-2015	61 (in 1960)	10	25.4	76 (1333/ha)					
	81 (in 1980)	14	30.8	60 (1052/ha)					
	97 (in 1996)	19	37.1	43 (754/ha)					
	111 (in 2010)	21	40.4	32 (561/ha)					

Information for each site in the left end column consists of site name, size of plot, elevation above sea level, mean slope angle, mean slope direction, planted year and survey period. Stand age with bold character shows the reference age in each site.

DBH of living trees at each measurement age points. For instance, at the Anno1 site, mean DBH of 388 living trees was 7.0 cm at 14 years old, mean DBH of 386 living trees was 8.3 cm at 19 years old, . . ., and mean DBH of 114 living trees was 30.5 cm at 98 years old. Table 1 shows the example of mean DBH and number of living trees at each fitting and reference age point.

A mean DBH growth function was estimated by fitting a Richards growth function to time-series mean DBH data from the first measurement age point to until several fitting age points. Then, we extrapolated mean DBH at the reference ages using the Richards growth function. Finally, we compared extrapolated mean DBH and observed mean DBH at the reference ages.

In both individual and stand-level analyses, fitting was conducted using the "optim" function in the R programming platform.

Results

Individual tree-level analysis

Chiba Forest sites

Figure 1 shows examples of fitting results, including time-series DBH data up to the reference age of 108 (Ref) and fitted growth curves at three fitting age points of 58 (T1), 78 (T2) and 98 (T3) for three sample trees of No. 265, 337, and 367 in the Anno1 site. Figure 2(a–c) shows the fitted growth curves for a total of 63 target trees at three fitting age points of 59 (T1), 78 (T2), and 99 (T3) in the Anno2 site. In general, fitting was good for all target trees at the three fitting age points in all six sites. For example, RMSE of fitted growth curve at T1, T2 and T3 for No. 265 were 0.36 (n = 9), 0.34 (n = 13) and 0.34 (n = 18); those for No.337 were 0.32, 0.54 and 0.57; and those for No. 367 were 0.64, 0.81 and 1.00. RMSEs for other trees were similarly enough small.

Table 2 shows the results of the error evaluation at six sites. The table includes prediction biases (%) and RMSEs between extrapolated and observed DBH at the reference age of around 110 years old on three growth curves at the fitting ages of around 60 (T1), 80 (T2) and 100 (T3) years old. Except for 60 (T1) of Ninodai, all other prediction biases were negative. Changes in prediction biases among the three fitting age points were as follows: In Gobozawa and Godai1 sites, the prediction biases got bigger from 60 to 80 years old and got smaller from 80 to 100 years old and were smallest at 100 years old. At Anno1, Anno2 and Metaki3 sites, the prediction biases got smaller from 60 to 80 and from 80 to 100 years old and were smallest at 100 years old. In Ninodai site, the prediction biases got bigger from 60 to 80 years old changed from positive to negative, and got smaller from 80 to 100 years old and were smallest at 60 years old. RMSEs got smaller from 60 to 80 and from 80 to 100 years old and were smallest at 100 years old in all six sites.

Table 3(a,b) shows the results of Friedman tests and Scheffé paired comparisons in the six sites. Table 3(a)

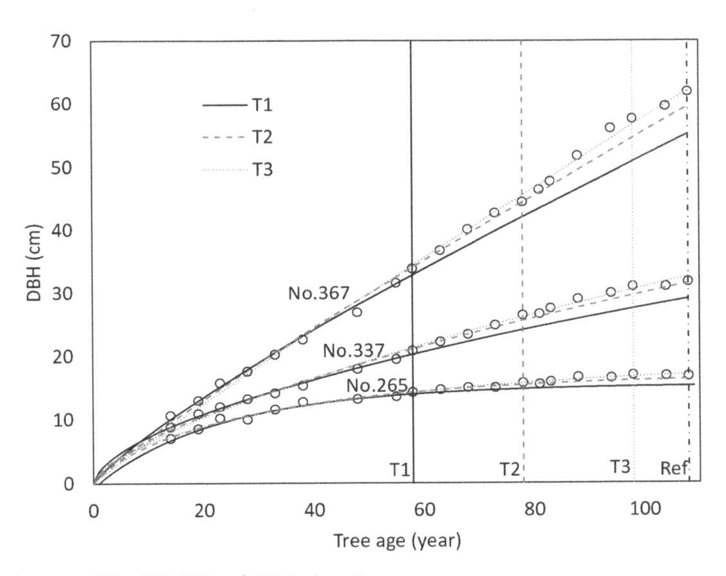

Figure 1. Fitting result for three sample trees of No. 265, 337 and 367 in Anno1.

DBH data are stored up to the reference age of 108 (Ref) and growth curves are fitted at three fitting age points of 58 (T1), 78 (T2) and 98 (T3).

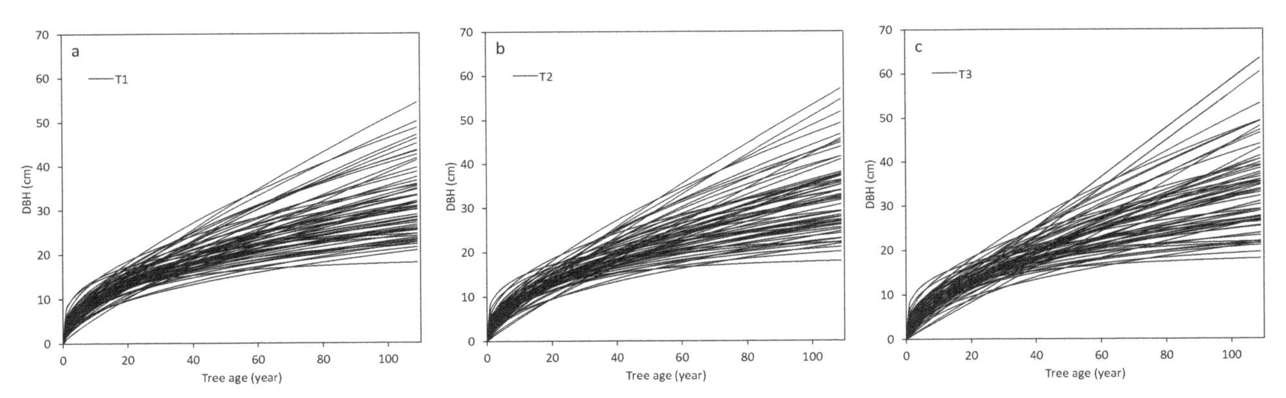

Figure 2. All fitted growth curves for a total of 63 target trees at three fitting age points of 59 (T1), 78 (T2) and 99 (T3) in Anno2.

Table 2. Prediction bias and root mean squared error (RMSE) between extrapolated and observed DBH at the reference age of around 110 years old in six sites of Chiba Forest.

	Prediction bias (%)		
	(RMSE)		
Site	60(T1)	80(T2)	100(T3)
Anno1 (n = 105)	−7.18↘	−3.32↘	−0.21
	(6.30)	(3.38)	(1.36)
Anno2 (n = 63)	−8.79↘	−5.93↘	−2.83
	(6.11)	(4.29)	(2.17)
Gobozawa (n = 182)	−4.76↗	−5.83↘	−0.75
	(8.43)	(5.12)	(3.04)
Godai1 (n = 65)	−3.60↗	−7.35↘	−3.23
	(5.88)	(4.94)	(2.53)
Metaki3 (n = 24)	−8.52↘	−6.51↘	−1.34
	(7.42)	(4.43)	(1.63)
Ninodai (n = 32)	0.98↗	−4.86↘	−2.23
	(3.61)	(2.92)	(1.41)

Arrows represent increase (□) or decrease (□) of prediction biases (%) between age points.

Table 3. Result of Friedman test (a) and Scheffé paired comparison (b) in six sites of Chiba Forest.

a.

	Mean rank of DBH					
Site	60(T1)	80(T2)	100(T3)	Obs	Chi-squared value	*P* value
Anno1	2.18	2.41	2.95	2.46	19.94	0.00**
Anno2	1.92	2.51	2.76	2.81	18.90	0.00**
Gobozawa	2.31	1.68	2.81	3.20	141.11	0.00**
Godai1	2.52	1.48	2.62	3.38	71.88	0.00**
Metaki3	1.96	2.00	2.88	3.17	16.25	0.00**
Ninodai	3.03	1.56	2.31	3.09	29.74	0.00**

b.

	Chi-squared value					
	(P value)					
Site	60(T1)-80(T2)	80(T2)-100(T3)	60(T1)-100(T3)	60(T1)-Obs	80(T2)-Obs	100(T3)-Obs
Anno1	1.65	9.28	18.75	2.40	0.07	7.73
	(0.65)	(0.03)*	(0.00)**	(0.49)	(1.00)	(0.05)
Anno2	6.52	1.22	13.38	14.93	1.72	0.04
	(0.09)	(0.75)	(0.00)**	(0.00)**	(0.63)	(0.99)
Gobozawa	21.42	69.95	13.95	43.26	125.56	8.08
	(0.00)**	(0.00)**	(0.00)**	(0.00)**	(0.00)**	(0.04)*
Godai1	21.34	25.27	0.17	14.47	70.97	11.54
	(0.00)**	(0.00)**	(0.98)	(0.00)**	(0.00)**	(0.00)**
Metaki3	0.01	5.51	6.05	10.51	9.80	0.61
	(1.00)	(0.14)	(0.11)	(0.01)*	(0.02)*	(0.89)
Ninodai	20.71	5.40	4.96	0.04	22.51	5.86
	(0.00)**	(0.14)	(0.17)	(1.00)	(0.00)**	(0.12)

Observation is abbreviated as Obs.
$^*P < 0.05$, $^{**}P < 0.01$.

shows the mean ranks of observation values (Obs) and extrapolation values at the reference age of around 110 years old on three growth curves at the fitting ages of around 60 (T1), 80 (T2) and 100 (T3) years old. To calculate the mean rank in each site, extrapolated and observed DBHs were ranked within each target tree in ascending order, and then the ranks were added and averaged for each treatment (i.e. T1, T2, T3 and Obs). *P* values showed that significant differences were found across extrapolation and observation values in all six sites. Table 3(b) shows the results of Scheffé paired comparisons. Significant differences were found among several extrapolation and observation values in the six sites. If we focus on the significant differences among extrapolation values (first three columns), in Gobozawa, significant differences were found in all three combinations of extrapolation values. In Anno1, Anno2, Godai1 and Ninodai, significant differences were found in one or two combinations. In metaki3, no significant difference was found in all three combinations. If we focus on the significant differences among extrapolation and observation values (last three columns), in Gobozawa and Godai1 sites, significant differences were found in all three combinations of extrapolation and observation values. In Anno2, Metaki3 and Ninodai sites, significant differences were found in one or two combinations. In Anno1, no significant difference was found in all three combinations.

Chichibu Forest sites

In the same way as Chiba Forest sites, Figure 3 shows examples of fitting results including time-series DBH data up to the reference age of 88 (Ref) and fitted growth curves at two fitting age points of 61 (T1) and 83 (T2) for three sample trees, specifically, Nos. 36, 13, and 67 in the 005B site. Figure 4(a,b) shows the fitted growth curves for a total of 43 target trees at two fitting age points of 60 (T1) and 81 (T2) in the 032D site.

Table 4 shows prediction biases (%) and RMSEs between extrapolated and observed DBH at the reference age of around 90 years old by two growth curves at the fitting ages of around 60 (T1) and 80 (T2) years old. All prediction biases were negative. The prediction biases got smaller from 60 to 80 years old and were smallest at 80 years old in all five sites. RMSEs got smaller from 60 to 80 years old and were smallest at 80 years old in all five sites.

Table 5(a,b) shows the results of Friedman tests and Scheffé paired comparisons in the five sites. Table 5(a) shows the mean ranks of observation values and extrapolation values at the reference age of around 90 years old on two growth curves at the fitting ages of around 60 (T1) and 80 (T2) years old. Significant differences were found across extrapolation and observation values in all five sites. In Table 5(b), if we focus on the first column, significant differences were found in extrapolation values between 60 and 80 years old in the four sites of 005B, 036B, 048A, and 503A, leaving only 032D, as the exception. If we focus on the last two columns, significant differences were found in all two combinations of extrapolation and observation values in all five sites.

Stand level analysis

Figures 5 and 6 show fitting results of mean DBH growth curves at each fitting age in the six sites of Chiba Forest and five sites of Chichibu Forest. Except for Metaki3 site of Chiba Forest, as fitting age increased, the growth curves shifted upwards in all other sites of Chiba and Chichibu Forests. In general, fitting was good in most sites. Among Chiba Forest sites, only Gobozawa at T1 had a different shape of a growth curve (Figure 5) because observation frequency of Gobozawa at T1 was lower, i.e. lacked observation data in a young stage, than other sites of Chiba Forest owing to later first observation year (Table 1).

Table 6 shows the extrapolation values and observed values of mean DBH at the reference ages of 110 years old for Chiba Forest and 90 years old for Chichibu Forest for all sites. In five sites of Chiba Forest, extrapolation

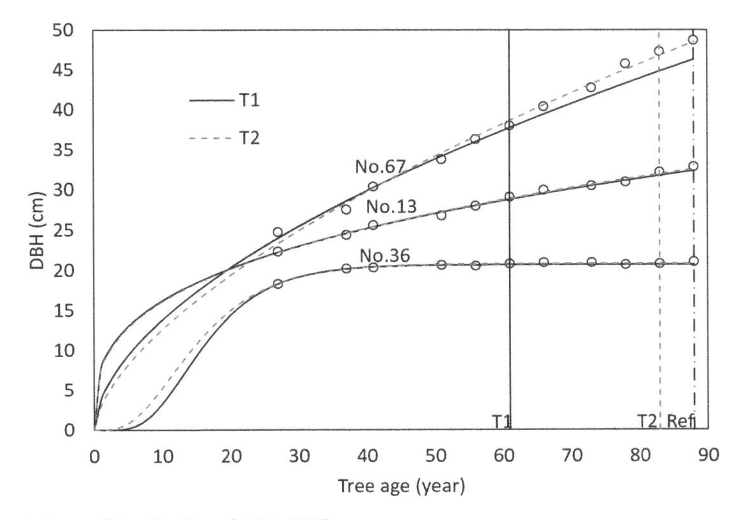

Figure 3. Fitting result for three sample trees of No. 36, 13 and 67 in 005B.
DBH data are stored up to the reference age of 88 (Ref) and growth curves are fitted at two fitting age points of 61 (T1) and 83 (T2).

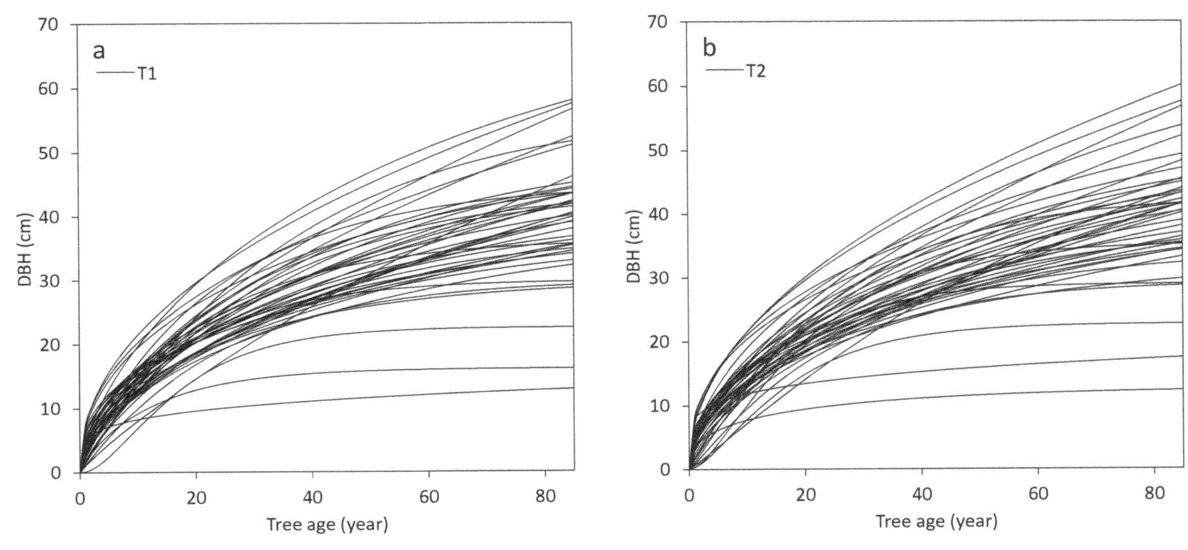

Figure 4. All fitted growth curves for a total of 43 target trees at two fitting age points of 60 (T1) and 81 (T2) in 032D.

Table 4. Prediction bias and root mean squared error (RMSE) between extrapolated and observed DBH in five sites of Chichibu Forest.

	Prediction bias (%) (RMSE)	
Site	60(T1)	80(T2)
005B (n = 52)	−6.28↘ (2.89)	−2.15 (1.07)
032D (n = 43)	−3.78↘ (2.32)	−2.70 (1.33)
036B (n = 104)	−10.87↘ (5.14)	−1.95 (1.25)
048A (n = 121)	−6.51↘ (3.38)	−1.29 (0.88)
503A (n = 188)	−5.83↘ (3.17)	−2.88 (1.45)

Arrows represent increase (↗) or decrease (↘) of prediction biases (%) between age points.

Table 5. Result of Friedman test (a) and Scheffé paired comparison (b) in five sites of Chichibu Forest.

a.

	Mean rank of DBH				
Site	60(T1)	80(T2)	Obs	Chi-squared value	P value
005B	1.17	2.08	2.75	65.12	0.00**
032D	1.58	1.70	2.72	33.81	0.00**
036B	1.03	2.18	2.79	166.21	0.00**
048A	1.23	2.17	2.60	118.83	0.00**
503A	1.30	1.83	2.87	238.05	0.00**

b.

	Chi-squared value (*P* value)		
Site	60(T1)-80(T2)	60(T1)-Obs	80(T2)-Obs
005B	21.24 (0.00)**	64.65 (0.00)**	11.78 (0.00)**
032D	0.29 (0.86)	27.92 (0.00)**	22.51 (0.00)**
036B	69.23 (0.00)**	161.00 (0.00)**	19.08 (0.00)**
048A	52.76 (0.00)**	113.87 (0.00)**	11.61 (0.00)**
503A	26.07 (0.00)**	229.88 (0.00)**	101.13 (0.00)**

$^*P < 0.05$, $^{**}P < 0.01$.

values increased from 60 to 80 and from 80 to 100 years and were largest at 100 years old. Similarly, for all five sites of Chichibu Forest, extrapolation values increased from 60 to 80 and were largest at 80 years old. In five sites of Chiba and all sites of Chichibu Forests, as fitting age increased, the extrapolation values drew closer to the observed values.

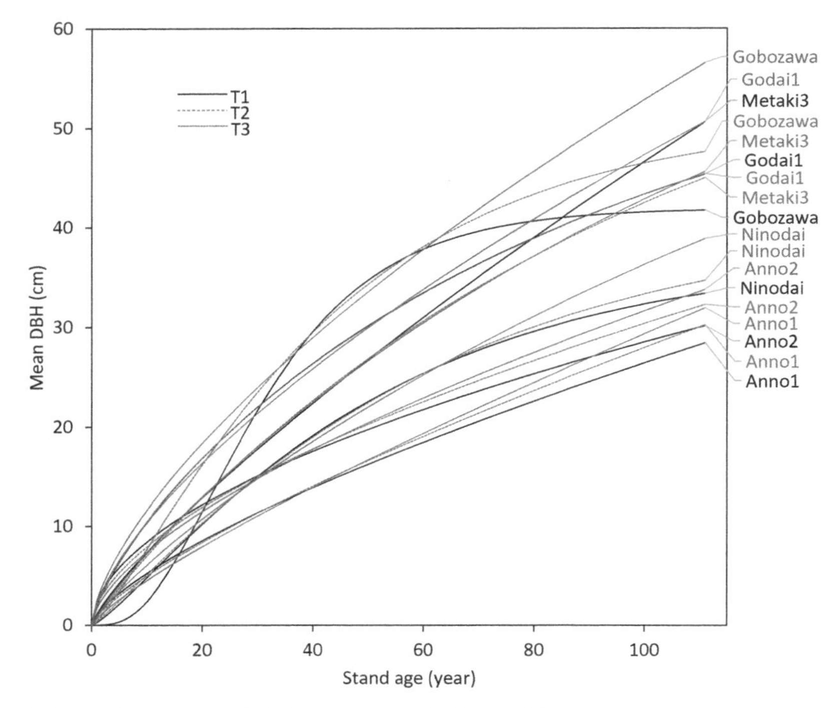

Figure 5. Fitting result of mean DBH growth curves at each fitting age point in six sites of Chiba Forest.

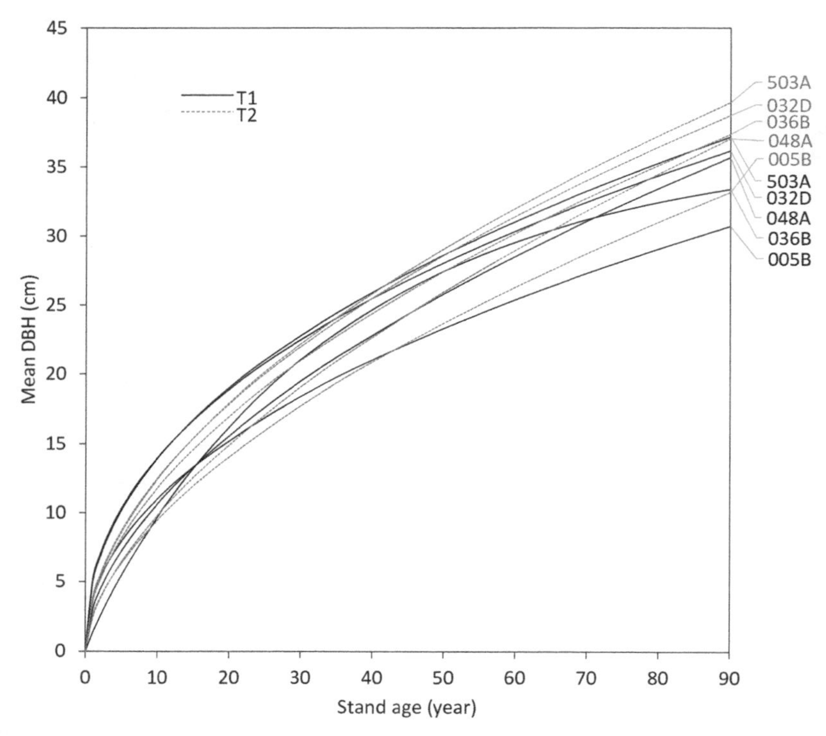

Figure 6. Fitting results of mean DBH growth curves at each fitting age point in five sites of Chichibu Forest.

Discussion

Individual tree-level analysis

In all sites, negative prediction biases at reference age points, according to the growth curves, got smaller from the fitting age points of 80 to 100 years old in Chiba Forest (Table 2) and from 60 to 80 years old in Chichibu Forest (Table 4). These results meant that growth curves tended to shift upward between these fitting age points and that extrapolation values got closer to observation values. Particularly these increases of extrapolation values were statistically significant in Annno1, Gobozawa and Godai1 of Chiba Forest (Table 3 (b)) and 005B, 036B, 048A and 503A of Chichibu Forest (Table 5(b)). These results also imply, as several previous studies pointed out (Osumi et al. 2000; Takeuchi and Ito 2003; Takeuchi 2005; Masaki et al. 2015), that growth of many Sugi trees did not get slower at older ages, specifically from 80 to 100 years old in Chiba Forest and from 60 to 80 years old in Chichibu Forest. An alternative explanation was that growth predictions at older ages tended to underestimate actual growth as shown in Tables 2 and 4 with negative prediction biases in most cases.

In addition, the RMSEs between extrapolated and observed values got smaller as fitting ages became older in

Table 6. Extrapolated and observed values of mean DBH at reference ages of 110 years old for Chiba Forest and 90 years old for Chichibu Forest.

	Mean DBH at reference age			
	Prediction bias % (RMSE)			
Site	60(T1)	80(T2)	100(T3)	Obs
Chiba Forest				
Anno1	27.9↗	29.6↗	31.2	32.8
	−15.0(4.9)	−9.8(3.2)	−4.9(1.6)	
Anno2	29.8↗	31.9↗	33.4	34.9
	−14.5(5.0)	−8.6(3.0)	−4.4(1.5)	
Gobozawa	41.7↗	47.6↗	56.6	57.5
	−27.8(16.0)	−17.5(10.1)	−2.0(1.2)	
Godai1	45.3↗	45.4↗	50.7	52.7
	−14.02(7.39)	−13.95(7.35)	−4.0(2.1)	
Metaki3	49.5↘	44.3↗	44.9	46.0
	7.7(3.5)	−3.7(1.7)	−2.5(1.1)	
Ninodai	33.4↗	34.7↗	38.9	40.4
	−17.4(7.0)	−14.2(5.7)	−3.8(1.5)	
Chichibu Forest				
005B	30.4↗	32.7	-	34.0
	−10.5(3.6)	−3.6(1.2)		
032D	35.3↗	37.6	-	40.9
	−13.7(5.6)	−8.0(3.3)		
036B	33.4↗	37.3	-	38.9
	−14.1(5.5)	−3.9(1.5)		
048A	35.2↗	36.5	-	37.2
	−5.3(2.0)	−1.9(0.7)		
503A	36.2↗	38.5	-	40.7
	−11.0(4.5)	−5.5(2.2)		

Prediction bias and root mean squared error (RMSE) between extrapolated and observed mean DBH were given.
Arrows represent increase (↗) or decrease (↘) of extrapolated DBH between age points.

all sites of Chiba (Table 2) and Chichibu (Table 4) Forests though there were still significant differences between predicted and observed values at most fitting age points (Tables 3(b) and 5(b)). It meant that the accuracy of growth predictions at older ages improved due to the accumulation of sufficient growth data up to older ages.

There were, however, some exceptions in Chiba Forest. In Gobozawa, Godai1 and Ninodai sites, negative prediction biases got bigger in 60 to 80 years olds (Table 2) and significant differences were found in their extrapolation values (Table 3(b)). These results showed tendencies of underestimates got stronger in this period, which implied that many trees had small periodic annual increments over the course of this period. It is possible that these underestimates and small annual increments have some relevance to climate change with regards to increases in temperature and amounts of precipitation (Fang et al. 2014; Pretzsch et al. 2014), as well as the effects of thinning (Nishizono 2010), etc.

Stand level analysis

In all other sites except Metaki3 of Chiba Forest, extrapolation values of mean DBH at reference ages using growth curves reached higher as the fitting age grew older (Table 6), which implied that the growth of Sugi stands does not become slower at older ages. In addition, the difference between extrapolated values and the observed values got smaller as the fitting age became older at these sites (RMSE in Table 6), which implied that the accuracy of growth predictions at older ages improved by accumulating growth data up to a sufficiently old age. From another point of view, growth predictions at older ages tended to underestimate actual growth if growth data were not accumulated up to older ages (Prediction bias in Table 6).

Though results thus far were almost the same as those from the individual tree level, it is necessary to consider, at a stand level, that mean DBH tended to become larger owing to the effects of self-thinning and artificial low thinning as stands grew older. In other words, mean DBH became larger when small tree data were removed owing to mortality as stands became older; hence, the mean DBH growth curve shifted upward (Figures 5 and 6). In this relation, the case of Metaki3, i.e. higher extrapolation value at T1 than those at T2 and T3, was caused by a sudden increase of mean DBH owing to artificial low thinning at 55 years old just 3 years before T1.

Conclusion

This study showed that the growth of Sugi did not get slower at older ages at both the individual tree level and the stand level using long-term growth observation data in Chiba and Chichibu Forests at the University of Tokyo Forests. To discuss the growth of old Sugi forest plantations in an empirical manner as this study attempts to do, it is essential to accumulate enough time-series growth data to cover younger to older age groups.

In the future, we plan to conduct further analysis and research on topics such as correlations between periodic annual increments and other factors such as weather, terrain, management, and tree-related variables such as crown length in the study sites; comparison of prediction accuracies when more flexible functions such as Levakovic and Sloboda (Zeide 1993) with four parameters are fitted; and comparison of fitted growth functions among layers on stratified DBH data.

Acknowledgments

We would like to thank current and former staff members at the University of Tokyo Chiba Forest and the University of Tokyo Chichibu Forest for their substantial ongoing efforts for experimental plot measurements. We are grateful to three anonymous reviewers and editors for their helpful and useful comments on an earlier version of this manuscript.

Disclosure statement

No potential conflict of interest was reported by the authors.

Funding

This study was supported by the Japan Society for the Promotion of Science (JSPS) KAKENHI Grant Number [JP18K05742] and JSPS Core-to-Core Program, B. Asia-Africa Science Platforms.

ORCID

Takuya Hiroshima http://orcid.org/0000-0001-8391-1018
Toshiaki Owari http://orcid.org/0000-0002-9227-4177

References

Cheng CP, Yeh HT, Cheng SS, Guan BT. 2019. Long-term growth records of *Cryptomeria japonica* plantations at National Taiwan University Experimental Forest, Taiwan. In: Kamata N, Kuraji K, Owari T, Guan BT, editors. Developing a network of long-term research field stations to monitor environmental changes and ecosystem responses in Asian forests. Tokyo: The Univ Tokyo For Press; p. 233–242.

Fang J, Kato T, Guo Z, Yang Y, Hu H, Shen H, Zhao X, Kishimoto-Mo AW, Tang Y, Houghton RA. 2014. Evidence for environmentally enhanced forest growth. PNAS. 111(26):9527–9532. doi:10.1073/pnas.1402333111.

Forestry Agency. 2018. A survey of forest and forestry statistics. Tokyo: Japan forest foundation; p. 260.

Forestry and Forest Products Research Institute (FFPRI). 1996. Long term forest monitoring system (Growth and yield experiment report No.20). FFPRI; p. 45.

Hosoda K, Iehara T, Mitsuda Y, Nishizono T, Ishibashi S, Takao G, Takahashi M, Tanaka K, Hirata Y, Kodani E, et al. 2009. Time-series data of the growth and yield experimental sites surveyed in FY2001-2005 (Growth and yield experiment report no.24). Bull FFPRI. 8:187–203.

Hosoda K, Iehara T, Takao G, Nishizono T, Takahashi T, Ishibashi S, Takahashi M, Furuya N, Kodani E, Tanaka K, et al. 2014. Time-series data of the growth and yield experimental sites surveyed in FY2006-2010 (Growth and yield experiment report no.25). Bull FFPRI. 13:225–254.

Masaki T, Mori S, Kajimoto T, Hitsuma G, Sawata S, Mori M, Osumi K, Sakurai S, Seki T. 2006. Long-term growth analyses of Japanese cedar trees in a plantation: neighborhood competition and persistence of initial growth deviations. J For Res. 11(4):217–225. doi:10.1007/s10310-005-0175-6.

Masaki T, Osumi K, Seki T, Mori S, Kajimoto T, Hitsuma G, Yagihashi T, Shibata M, Noguchi M. 2015. Long-term growth of a planted forest of Japanese cedar at Soehatazawa Experimental Forest under various thinning intensities of trees 45–104 years old. Bull FFPRI. 14:65–72.

Matsue K. 2019. Inventory data of Sugi (*Cryptomeria japonica* D.Don) permanent plot on spacing effect in Utsunomiya university forests at Funyu (III). Bull Utsunomiya Univ For. 55:53–60.

Matsumoto M, Nakajima T, Hosoda K. 2011. Improvement of LYCS, a software for construction of local yield tables. J Jpn For Soc. 93 (4):187–195. doi:10.4005/jjfs.93.187.

Matsushita M, Tanaka K, Hitsuma G, Yagihashi T, Noguchi M, Shibata M, Masaki T. 2015. A novel growth model evaluating age-size effect on long-term trends in tree growth. Funct Ecol. 29 (10):1250–1259. doi:10.1111/1365-2435.12416.

Mitsuda Y, Hosoda K, Iehara T. 2013. Parameterization of a forest stand growth model using long-term field survey plot data. Proc Inst Stat Math. 61:307–322.

Mitsuda Y, Hosoda K, Iehara T. 2017. Comparison of growth responses to climatic conditions of Sugi (*Cryptomeria japonica*) and Hinoki (*Chamaecyparis obtusa*) using a carbon balance-based growth model. FORMATH. 16:32–42. doi:10.15684/formath.16.004.

Nagumo H, Shiraishi N, Tanaka M. 1981. Systematic method constructing an yield table for Sugi even-aged stand: A case study in experimental plots of the Tokyo University Forest in Chiba. Bull Univ of Tokyo For. 71:269–330.

Nakajima T, Matsumoto M, Shiraishi N. 2011. Modeling diameter growth and self-thinning in planted Sugi (Cryptomeria japonica) stands. O For Sci J. 4:49–56.

Nishizono T. 2010. Effects of thinning level and site productivity on age-related changes in stand volume growth can be explained by a single rescaled growth curve. For Ecol Manag. 259(12):2276–2291. doi:10.1016/j.foreco.2010.03.002.

Nishizono T, Hosoda K, Iehara T, Takao G, Saito H, Ishibashi S, Takahashi M, Furuya N, Kodani E, Saito K, et al. 2019. Time-series data of growth and yield experimental sites surveyed in FY2011–2015 (Growth and yield experiment report no. 26). Bull FFPRI. 18:231–273.

Niwa Y, Chishima T, Oomura K, Aikawa M, Igarashi Y, Yoshida Y, Saito T. 2014. Growth records on the artificial forest permanent plots in the University of Tokyo Chichibu Forest (2011, 2012). Misc Inform Univ Tokyo For. 56:147–190.

Oomura K, Aikawa M, Igarashi Y, Sawada H, Yoshida Y, Saiki M, Oohata S, Chishima T, Haraguchi R. 2012. Growth records on the artificial forest permanent plots in the University of Tokyo Chichibu Forest (2014–2010). Misc Inform Tokyo Univ For. 52:25–185.

Oomura K, Sawada H, Oohata S. 2004. Growth records on the artificial forest permanent plots in the Tokyo University Forest in Chichibu. Misc Inform Tokyo Univ For. 43:1–192.

Oomura K, Sawada H, Oohata S, Fujiwara A. 2005. Growth records on the artificial forest permanent plots in the Tokyo University Forest in Chichibu (supplement). Misc Inform Tokyo Univ For. 44:211–249.

Osumi K, Mori M, Sakurai S, Saito K, Sato S, Seki T. 2000. Long term growth records of old-aged sugi (*Cryptomeria japonica*) plantations in Akita Prefecture, North-eastern Japan. J Jpn For Soc. 82:179–187.

Osumi S, Ishikawa Y. 1983. Applicability of the Richards' growth function to analysis of growth of tree. Sci Rep Kyoto Prefectural Univ Agric. 35:49–76.

Owari T, Toyama K, Suzuki SN, Hiroshima T, Ishibashi S. 2019. Long-term growth records of *Cryptomeria japonica* plantations at the University of Tokyo Forests, Japan. In: Kamata N, Kuraji K, Owari T, BT G, editors. Developing a network of long-term research field stations to monitor environmental changes and ecosystem responses in Asian forests. Tokyo: The Univ Tokyo For Press; p. 219–231.

Pretzsch H, Biber P, Schütze G, Uhl E, Rötzer T. 2014. Forest stand growth dynamics in Central Europe have accelerated since 1870. Nat Commun. 5(1):4967. doi:10.1038/ncomms5967.

Shiono J, Suzuki M, Kawata S, Matsumura N. 2013. Growth analysis of 200 year old Sugi plantation forest: case study of Todo Sugi stand in Hirakura Experimental Forest, Mie University. Chubu For Res. 61:129–132.

Shiraishi N. 1985a. An analysis of diameter distributions in even-aged stands and its application for growth prediction (I) The mechanism and trend of changes in skewness. J Jpn For Soc. 67:133–140.

Shiraishi N. 1985b. An analysis of diameter distributions in even-aged stands and its application for growth prediction (II) Some considerations on the changes in diameter variance. J Jpn For Soc. 67:305–310.

Shiraishi N. 1986. Study on the growth prediction of even-aged stands. Bull Univ of Tokyo For. 75:199–256.

Sloboda B. 1984. Possibilities of mathematically predicting timber production in commercial forests. Bull Nagoya Univ For. 7:261–279.

Suzuki M, Tatsuhara S, Yamanaka C, Karakama I, Ide Y. 1999. Records on the growth of stands in the Tokyo University Forest in Chiba II: development of the stands from 1976 to 1996. Misc Inform Tokyo Univ For. 38:1–71.

Takao G, Minowa M. 1993. A stand growth model of coniferous plantation in the light of the reduction in respiration per unit stem volume. Bull Univ of Tokyo For. 89:113–153.

Takatoku K, Haraguchi R, Omura K, Igarashi Y, Fujihira K. 2019. Growth records on the artificial forest permanent plots in the University of Tokyo Chichibu Forest (2014–2017). Misc Inform Univ Tokyo For. 61:27–33.

Takeuchi I. 2005. The growth of diameters and stand stem volumes in old man-made Sugi (*Cryptomeria japonica*) stands. J Jpn For Soc. 87 (5):394–401. doi:10.4005/jjfs.87.394.

Takeuchi I, Ito H. 2003. Height growth in old manmade Sugi (*Cryptomeria japonica*) stands. J Jpn For Soc. 85:121–126.

Takeuchi K, Hasegawa S. 1975. Records on the growth of stands in the Tokyo University Forest in Chiba. Misc Inform Tokyo Univ For. 19:69–175.

Tanaka K. 1986. A stochastic model of diameter growth in an even-aged pure forest stand. J Jpn For Soc. 68:226–236.

Tanaka K. 1988. A stochastic model of height growth in an even-aged pure forest stand-Why is the coefficient of variation of the height distribution smaller than that of the diameter distribution? J Jpn For Soc. 70:20–29.

Tanaka K. 1991. Shifts of the height-diameter curve in a stand and an application of the modified HENRICKSEN equation. J Jpn For Soc. 73:172–177.

Taniguchi S, Kayatani K. 1994. Analysis of tree growth using the Richards function fitted (I) Applicability of growth of the Japanese cedar (*Cryptomeria japonica*) plus tree clones. Trans Kansai Br Jpn For Soc. 3:147–150.

Yamamoto H, Ito K, Ohata S, Sasaki K, Omura K. 1988. Records on diameter increment of experimentally thinned plots in the Tokyo University Forest in Chichibu. Misc Inform Tokyo Univ For. 26:1–156.

Yoshida S, Imanaga M, Umata H. 1992. Periodic inventory data of permanent plots in Kagoshima University Forests at Takakuma(I): abstracts of permanent plots. Bull Kagoshima Univ For. 20:223–226.

Zeide B. 1993. Analysis of growth equations. For Sci. 39:591–616.

Predicting individual tree growth of high-value timber species in mixed conifer-broadleaf forests in northern Japan using long-term forest measurement data

Kyaw Thu Moe and Toshiaki Owari

ABSTRACT

Quantifying individual tree growth of economically high-value timber species is important for the simulation and development of forest management options. Long-term permanent plot data provides crucial information of forest stand dynamics that can be used to predict individual tree growth. In this study, we developed individual tree basal area growth models of three high-value timber species: monarch birch (*Betula maximowicziana*), castor aralia (*Kalopanax septemlobus*), and Japanese oak (*Quercus crispula*) in a cool temperate mixed forest in northern Japan using long-term measurement data (1968–2016) collected in permanent plots. Data included species, diameter at breast height, and survival status, and stand management history. We applied linear mixed-effects modelling to predict the individual tree basal area growth as a function of individual tree size, competition, and forest management. Model prediction followed by leave-one-out cross validation revealed a correlation between predicted and observed basal area increments with *r* values of 0.62, 0.73, and 0.70 and root mean square errors values of 10.44, 7.91, and 11.62 cm^2/year for monarch birch, castor aralia, and Japanese oak, respectively. The individual tree growth models developed in this study will provide valuable information for species-specific forest management of economically high-value timber species.

Introduction

High-value timber species are those that produce high-quality wood, used especially in the veneer and furniture industries (Oosterbaan et al. 2009). Despite their spatial occurrence at very low densities (Schulze et al. 2008), high-value timber species play a significant economic role in forest management and are increasingly important elements of forest production (Hemery et al. 2008). In uneven-aged mixed conifer-broadleaf forests in northern Japan, monarch birch (*Betula maximowicziana* Regel), castor aralia (*Kalopanax septemlobus* (Thunb.) Koidz), and Japanese oak (*Quercus crispula* Blume) are important producers of high commercial value timber (Owari et al. 2016). The supply of high-quality timber from these tree species is exclusively dependent on the cutting of large trees within the mixed forests. Forest management practices that ensure their sustainable production play important role in managing high-value timber species.

In uneven-aged conifer-broadleaf mixed forests in northern Japan, selection cutting system has been practicing as a common management system since the early twentieth century (Yasuda et al. 2013). In addition, single-tree management system has been practicing for the management of high-value timber species in northern Japan, especially in the University of Tokyo Hokkaido Forest (UTHF) since 1965 (Shibata 1988; Yamamoto 1990). Under single-tree management system, large-sized trees with high timber quality and value were individually selected and registered, as superior trees, including their size, tree vitality, and spatial position; and these registered trees are periodically monitored for harvest at optimal time (Owari et al. 2016). The information on how long a tree of certain size take to reach a desirable size is necessary for reliable application of the single-tree management system. Quantifying the tree growth of high-value timber species will provide useful information for single-tree management practice, since it will allow the estimation of time to reach desirable size, as well as the simulation of various silvicultural practices (Orellana et al. 2016).

Individual tree growth models help explore the forest management alternatives, as they are flexible in predicting tree growth in stands with diverse structure, species composition and management history (Orellana et al. 2016). Tree growth models that use individual trees as the basic unit for modeling were also widely used in many different regions (Adame et al. 2008; Zhao et al. 2013; Rohner et al. 2017; Tenzin et al. 2017; Schelhaas et al. 2018). In mixed conifer-broadleaf forest in northern Japan, Tatsumi et al. (2016) quantified the neighborhood competition on the diameter growth of 38 tree species, including high-value timber species, using two times DBH measurement data. Using the tree ring data of 76 large-sized monarch birch trees, Shibano et al. (1995) examined the diameter growth of monarch birch trees in mixed conifer-broadleaf forest in northern Japan. Other studies, such as Noguchi and Yoshida (2009) and Fukuoka et al. (2013), examined the effects of selection cutting on individual tree growth and dynamics of Japanese oak. However, a simple and practically applicable tree growth model of high-value timber species was not widely studied, and data from long-term measurement plots in particular has not yet been used for the growth model development.

Forest trees, including high-value timber species, are slow growing and it may take several decades to detect their radial growth pattern (Pretzsch et al. 2019). In such case, long-term and repeated measurement data is indispensable offering robust empirical dataset to develop individual tree growth models for high-value timber species. Several studies derived individual tree growth information from tree ring data (Shibano et al. 1995; Cunha et al. 2016; Tenzin et al. 2017). However, growth measurement using tree ring data is relatively costly, and need extensive resources, time, and effort. Moreover, historical information of stands that are important in individual tree growth process may not be able to include in growth modeling using tree ring data. On the other hand, long-term and repeated measurement data provide information on the past stand conditions and management history (Pretzsch et al. 2019) corresponding to tree growth process that are important for individual tree growth modeling (Noguchi and Yoshida 2009; Pretzsch et al. 2019). Therefore, the empirically derived data can provide valuable information for developing simple and practically applicable individual growth models for high-value timber species.

In this study, we aimed to develop practically useful growth models for three high-value timber species growing in northern Japan. The long-term data from forest measurement plots was used to predict the individual tree growth of high-value timber species and to determine the time required for high-value timber species to reach desirable size.

Materials and methods

Study site

We conducted this study in the University of Tokyo Hokkaido Forest (UTHF) (Figure 1). The UTHF, which has an area of 22,717 ha, is located in the central part of Hokkaido Island, in northern Japan; it is a pan-mixed forest lying in a transition zone between cool temperate and sub-boreal forest ecosystems (Tatewaki 1958). The mean annual temperature and annual precipitation are 6.3°C and 1,210 mm, respectively, and snow usually covers the ground from late November to early April with a maximum depth of 83 cm (Owari et al. 2016). Uneven-aged mixed forests with coniferous and broad-leaved tree species are the main vegetation cover of the UTHF. *Abies sachalinensis* is one of the dominant tree species, and other common tree species include *Picea jezoensis, Tilia japonica, Acer pictum* var. *mono, Q. crispula, K. septemlobus, Ulmus laciniata*, and *B. maximowicziana*. The understory is often occupied by dense evergreen dwarf bamboos cover (*Sasa senanensis* and *Sasa kurilensis*).

Long-term and large-scale experiments of stand-based forest management system have been conducted since 1958 in the UTHF. Selection system, in which trees are periodically selected and harvested from a large area with a tree removal rate of 10–17%, has been implemented as the main silvicultural system in the UTHF (Owari et al. 2016).

Data source

Permanent plots were established throughout the UTHF. The UTHF has a total of 96 permanent plots, many of which were established in the 1960s to record long-term growth and stand development for the management of uneven-aged mixed forests (Owari 2013). A stratified purposive sampling scheme was employed for the plot establishment to represent the major stand types, soil, and terrain conditions (Ishibashi and Hirokawa 1986). Within these plots, diameter at breast height (DBH) measurements of all trees with DBH ≥ 5 cm are performed by UTHF staff at regular, in most case, 5-years interval with 0.1 cm precision. However, the durations between two consecutive measurements varied from 3 to 12 years. All trees are tagged with identification numbers (IDs) on metal plates nailed to steel rods to ensure that DBH measurements are repeated on the same trees. For current study, we used a long-term data set of 31 permanent sample plots located in the stand managed by selection system. The plot data used in this study contained measurement data from 1968 to 2016. Thus, several observations were available for the same trees over time. Plot size ranged from 0.22 to 1.00 ha; plot data included species, DBH, and survival status of tree with DBH ≥ 5 cm. Year of harvest and DBH of harvested trees were also included in plot data. The plot measurements were carried out 8–11 times during 1968–2016. Most of the plots were subjected to three to five times of selection harvest.

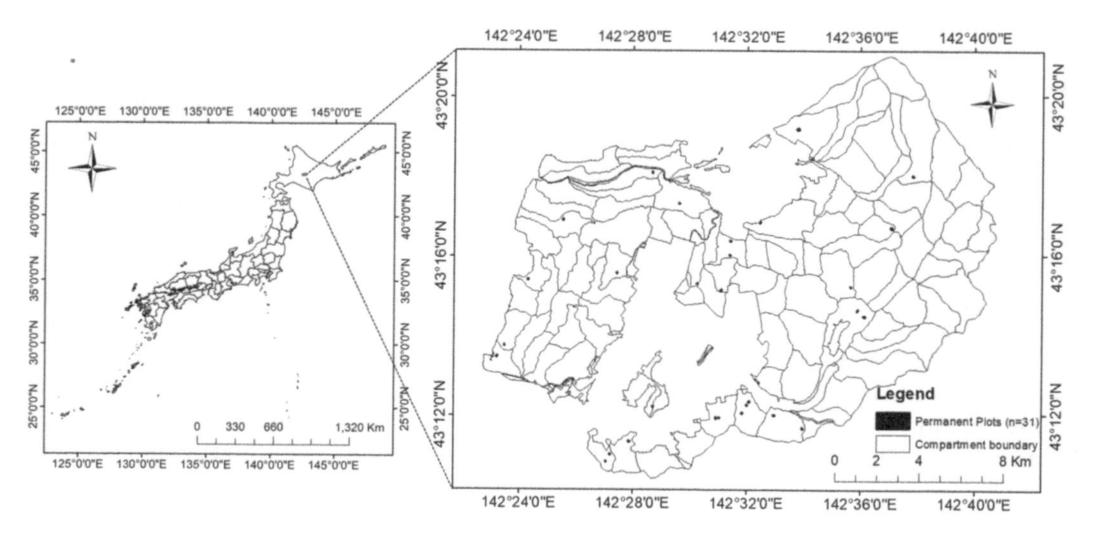

Figure 1. Locations of the permanent plots.

Data preparation

Our analyses were based on the single-tree DBH data collected in the permanent plots. We used data from 168 monarch birch trees, 484 castor aralia trees, and 219 Japanese oak trees for model development. The frequency distribution of DBH among all observations is shown in Figure 2. The dependent variable was individual tree basal area increment (BAI; cm^2/year), which was calculated from the two consecutive DBH measurements on the same living tree, as verified using individual tree IDs. Some studies have indicated a preference for diameter increment models (Schelhaas et al. 2018); however, Vanclay (1994) reported that both are essentially the same because one can be derived from the other. Negative BAI values were excluded from the analysis as measurement error. Tree BA generally increases with an asymmetrical sigmoidal function through time with a slower rate in the younger trees, rapidly increasing at establishment, and then declining during senescence (Tomé et al. 2006). Theoretically, tree BAI can never reach zero because the creation of new tree rings is essential for water transport (Schelhaas et al. 2018); however, we included observations of zero BAI because they may represent to poor growth conditions due to environmental factors. BAI values > 100 cm^2/year were excluded from the analysis as outliers because BAI differences with BAI values > 20 cm^2/year represent < 0.01% of the total observations for all species.

In addition, we derived stand variables normalized by area, including total number of trees (T-tree; tree ha^{-1}), number of conifer trees (N-tree; tree ha^{-1}), number of broadleaf trees (L-tree; tree ha^{-1}), total stand BA (T-BA; m^2 ha^{-1}), conifer BA (N-BA; m^2 ha^{-1}), broadleaf BA (L-BA; m^2 ha^{-1}), and basal of trees larger than target trees (BAL; m^2 ha^{-1}). These variables were derived from the first measurement of the two consecutive DBH measurements of the permanent plots (e.g. when the DBH measurements were carried out in 2005 and 2010, we used the measurement data of 2005 to derive stand variables).

The study permanent plots are located in selection stands where selection harvests are carried out with cutting cycle of 15–20 years (10–20 years until 2005). Attention was paid to be spatially unbiassed when marking trees for selection harvest and larger trees are more likely to be marked than smaller ones while dominant species, i.e., *A. sachalinensis*, is more likely to be marked (Owari et al. 2010). In our previous study (Moe and Owari 2020), we analyzed the BA harvest of high-value timber species, conifer, and broadleaf species. We divided the study period of 48 years into five intervals with approximately 10 years in each interval. We found that small number of trees and BA of high-value timber species were harvested, and more conifer BA were harvested than broadleaf BA (Moe and Owari 2020). The removal of trees by selection harvest may affect the growth of remaining trees. We, therefore, calculated basal area of harvested trees (BA-Har; m^2 ha^{-1}) that may positively affect the growth target trees.

Individual tree BAI model

Individual tree BAI models were fitted separately for three target high-value timber species. Our analysis used initial tree size, competition, and forest management variables as independent variables. Tree size variables included initial DBH, square of initial DBH, and logarithm of initial DBH. Distance-dependent and distance-independent competition indices were generally used in individual tree growth modeling (Contreras et al. 2011; Pokharel and Dech 2012; Cunha et al. 2016; Rohner et al. 2017). Distance-dependent index accounts for spatial position of individual trees, while distance independent index does not require the spatial position of individual trees. Both indices may provide the comparable accuracy of growth prediction (Kahriman et al. 2018; Kuehne et al. 2019). On the other hand, distance-independent competition index can be derived easily from the long-term and repeated measurement data. Therefore, we used distance-independent competition index in our model. Stand level variables, such as tree density and basal area, were generally considered to reflect stand scale competition (Kuehne et al. 2019; Wang et al. 2019). In this study, we considered stand-level variables, such as T-tree, N-tree, L-tree, T-BA, N-BA, L-BA, and BAL as competition variables. We further considered BA-Har as the forest management variable.

Mixed-effects modeling

Repeated measurements of the same trees in long-term permanent plots result in a hierarchical data structure; such data lack independence among observations and are highly spatially and temporally correlated (Calama and Montero 2005; Adame et al. 2008). The mixed-effects approach has been widely used in individual tree growth modeling for repeated measurement data because it handles spatial and temporal correlation by incorporating variables as fixed, random or both effects in the model (Kiernan et al. 2008; Uzoh and Oliver 2008; Pokharel and Dech 2012; Wang et al. 2019).

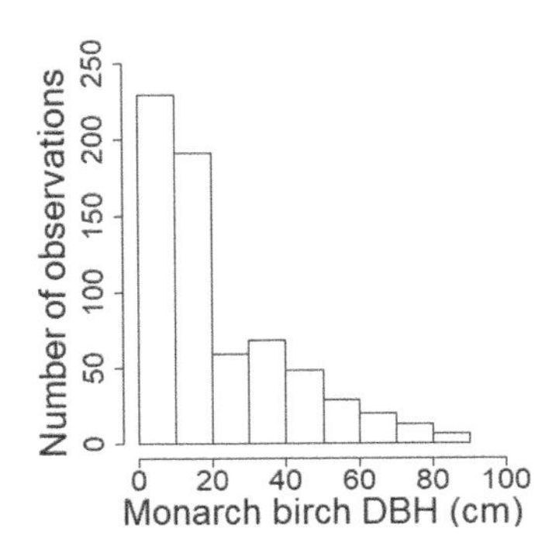

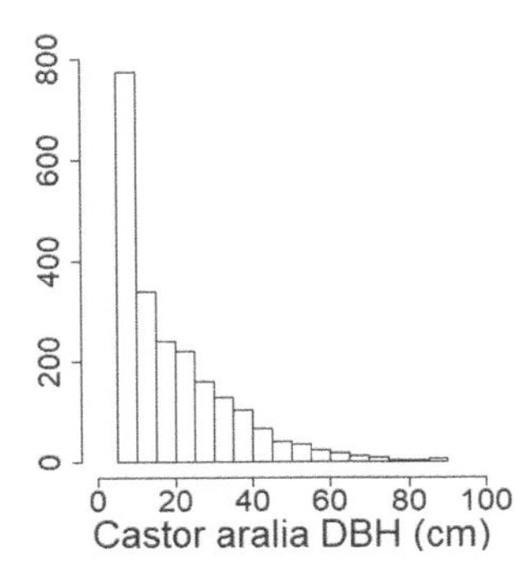

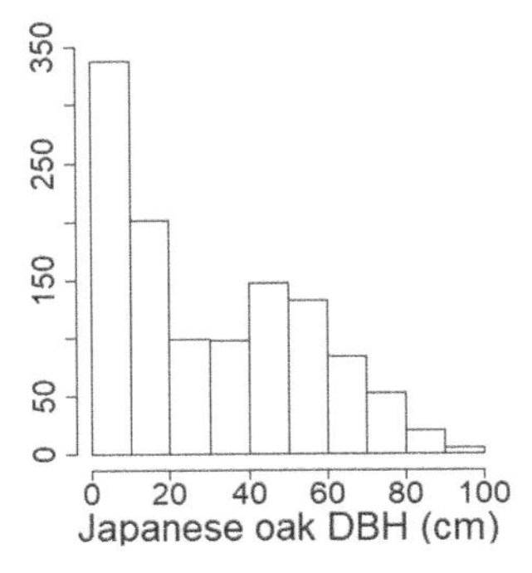

Figure 2. Frequency distribution of trees used for model development.

Using mixed-effects modeling approach, initial tree size, stand structure, and management variables were included as fixed effects, and plots, trees, and measurement years were included as random effects. Thus, the individual tree BAI model is as follow:

$$\ln\left(BAI_{ijk}+1\right) = \beta_0 + \beta_1 DBH_{ijk} + \beta_2 DBH^2{}_{ijk} + \beta_3 \log DBH_{ijk} + \beta_4 BAL_{ijk} + \beta_5 \text{T-Tree}_{jk} + \beta_6 \text{N-tree}_{jk} + \beta_7 \text{L-tree}_{jk} + \beta_8 \text{T-BA}_{jk} + \beta_9 \text{N-BA}_{jk} + \beta_{10} \text{L-BA}_{jk} + \beta_{11} \text{BA-Har}_{jk} + \text{Tree}_i + \text{Plot}_j + \text{Measurement year}_k \quad (1)$$

where BAI_{ijk} is the basal area increment of the tree i in plot j in year k; DBH_{ijk} is the initial DBH of the tree i in plot j measured in year k; BAL_{ijk} is the total BAL of tree i in plot j in year k; T-tree_{jk}, N-tree_{jk}, L-tree_{jk}, T-BA_{jk}, N-BA_{jk}, and L-BA_{jk} are the stand variables of the plot j in year k; and BA-Har_{jk} is the selectively harvested BA of the plot j in year k. Tree_i, Plot_j, and Measurement year_k are random effects parameters for tree i in the plot j at year k. $\beta_0 - \beta_{11}$ are fixed effects parameters to be estimated.

years for a tree to reach a target size as follows (Cunha et al. 2016; Tenzin et al. 2017):

$$t = \left[\ln(BA_{i+n}) - \ln(BA_i)\right] / \ln(1 + PBAI_i\%), \quad (2)$$

where t is the time (year), ln is the natural logarithm, BA_i is the initial tree BA, BA_{i+n} is the target tree BA. $PBAI_i\%$ is the BAI productivity potential for the ith tree, calculated as:

$$PBAI_i\% = (\text{Predicted } BAI_i / BA_i) * 100, \quad (3)$$

where predicted BAI_i is the BAI of the ith individual tree predicted from Equation (1).

Equation (2) is based on compound interest law. Many natural phenomena follow the compound interest law (Han et al. 2014) and it was widely applied in forestry, e.g., estimation of growth period for a tree to reach a certain size (Cunha et al. 2016; Tenzin et al. 2017). It considered the interest rate, i.e., growth rate in our case, to predict the value in the future, i.e., DBH. The prediction of tree DBH in a given year is based on growth rate calculated from the final model of Equation (1). Even though the past forest stand conditions were considered in predicting the growth rate, the changes in future forest stand conditions could not be considered in the estimation of number of years for a tree to reach a certain DBH.

Data analysis

Data analysis was carried out in R Software (R Core Team 2019) with "lme4" (Bates et al. 2020) and "lmerTest" (Kuznetsova et al. 2020) packages. The best models were selected using backward stepwise selection method based on Akaike's information criterion (AIC). However, we only included variables with variance inflation factor (VIF) <5 in the models to avoid multicollinearity and overfitting of the models. Marginal and conditional R^2 was used to evaluate the goodness of fit of the selected models following Nakagawa and Schielzeth (2013). Because our dataset contained relatively few observations given the size distribution of individual trees (Figure 2), it was impractical to perform cross-validation by dividing the dataset into training and validation datasets, which would impose an uneven distribution of tree sizes in both datasets. Therefore, we used the leave-one-out cross validation approach, which allowed us to exclude one observation and fit the selected model to the remaining observations. Root mean square error (RMSE) and r values were calculated to compare observed BAI and predicted BAI.

From forest management perspectives, it is important to estimate the time required for a certain tree to reach target size. Based on the Equation (1), we predicted the number of

Results

Observed basal area increment (BAI)

The relationship between initial tree DBH and observed BAI is shown in Figure 3, and Table 1 shows the correlation between observed BAI and explanatory variables used in the model development. A significant positive correlation was found between initial tree DBH and observed BAI ($p < 0.001$), with correlation coefficients of 0.56, 0.77, and 0.72 for monarch birch, castor aralia, and Japanese oak, respectively. As a pioneer species, monarch birch had a higher BAI at a smaller DBH size; as DBH increased, the growth decreased. Castor aralia and Japanese oak exhibited more stable BAI.

Model fitting, parameter estimation and goodness of fit

The estimated parameters using the individual tree BAI model (Equation (1)) for each species are listed in Table 2. Variables selected in the final models were only included in the table. For each species, a mixed-effects model including individual trees, plots, and measurement year as random factors obtained lowest AIC values and was selected as the final model. High R^2 values of the selected models for fixed

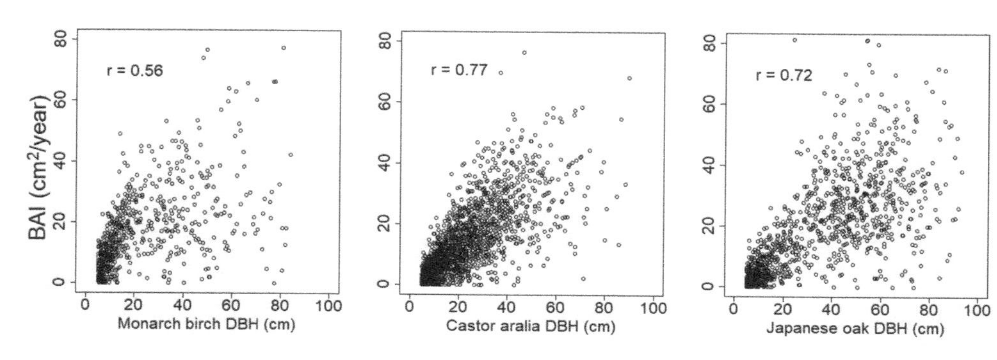

Figure 3. Relationships between initial tree diameter at breast height (cm) and observed basal area increment (cm^2/year).

Table 1. Correlation between observed basal area increment and explanatory variables.

Variable	Monarch birch	Castor aralia	Japanese oak
DBH (cm)	0.56***	0.77***	0.72***
BAL (m^2 ha^{-1})	−0.62***	−0.65***	−0.65***
T-tree (tree ha^{-1})	ns	−0.23***	−0.10**
N-tree (tree ha^{-1})	0.08*	−0.24***	ns
L-tree (tree ha^{-1})	−0.15***	−0.10***	−0.16***
T-BA (m^2 ha^{-1})	0.22***	ns	ns
N-BA (m^2 ha^{-1})	0.15***	−0.21***	−0.15***
L-BA (m^2 ha^{-1})	ns	0.21***	0.10**
BA-Har (m^2 ha^{-1})	ns	ns	ns

Significant code: *** $p < 0.000$, ** $p < 0.001$, * $p < 0.05$, ns represents not significant.
DBH = diameter at breast height, BAL = basal area of trees larger than target trees, T-tree = total number of trees, N-tree = number of conifer trees, L-tree = number of broadleaf trees, T-BA = total basal area, N-BA = conifer basal area, L-BA = broadleaf basal area, and BA-Har = basal area of harvested trees.

Table 2. Estimated parameters of individual tree BAI models for three high-value timber species.

Variable		Monarch birch	Castor aralia	Japanese oak
Intercept	β_0	4.00***	2.92***	2.82***
DBH (cm)	β_1	−0.01	0.02***	0.02***
BAL (m^2 ha^{-1})	β_4	−0.07 ***	−0.04***	−0.04***
N-tree (tree ha^{-1})	β_6	−2.1e-05	−3.7e-04*	-
L-tree (tree ha^{-1})	β_7	−5.7e-04**	−3.8e-04***	−1.7e-04
N-BA (m^2 ha^{-1})	β_9	-	-	− 0.02**
BA-Har (m^2 ha^{-1})	β_{11}	0.007	0.01	0.07*
AIC		1231.3	3742.9	2087.8
R^2 − marginal		0.39	0.51	0.61
R^2 − conditional		0.77	0.80	0.85

Significant code: *** $p < 0.000$, ** $p < 0.001$, * $p < 0.05$. DBH = diameter at breast height, BAL = basal area of trees larger than target trees, N-tree = number of conifer trees, L-tree = number of broadleaf trees, N-BA = conifer basal area, BA-Har = basal area of harvested trees, AIC = Akaike's information criterion.

(marginal R^2) and random (conditional R^2) factors indicated an acceptable fit the data (Table 2). Negative coefficient value was observed for monarch birch DBH while significant positive coefficients were observed for castor aralia and Japanese oak DBH. For all species, significant negative coefficients of BAL were observed. Significant negative coefficient of conifer tree density was observed for castor aralia, and negative coefficients of broadleaf tree density were observed for monarch birch and castor aralia. Conifer basal area showed significant negative coefficient for Japanese oak.

Model prediction for BAI and years to reach target DBH

Figure 4 shows the relationship between observed and predicted BAI for three high-value timber species. Model prediction produced BAI RMSE of 10.44, 7.91, and 11.62 cm^2/year; significant positive correlations were detected between observed and predicted BAI, with *r* values of 0.62, 0.73, and 0.70 for monarch birch, castor aralia, and Japanese oak respectively ($p < 0.001$ for all species).

The derived models of Equation (1) were used to predict the time required for a tree of a given initial DBH to reach an expected target DBH using Equation (2). The Equation (1) was predicted based on the best model described in Table 2 for all species. It can be assumed that variables related to initial tree size, stand, and management were included for the prediction of time using Equation (2). As an example, we estimated the time for a given tree with DBH = 30 cm to reach DBH = 50 cm and 70 cm. The predicted duration for a tree with DBH = 30 cm to reach DBH = 50 cm are 29, 28, and 48 years in average and 48, 46, and 80 years in average to reach DBH = 70 cm for monarch birch, castor aralia and Japanese oak respectively (Table 3 and Figure 5).

Discussion

We used a linear mixed-effects model including fixed effects and random effects parameters to predict individual tree growth using a long-term repeated measurements dataset. The individual tree growth models developed in this study exhibited acceptable predictive accuracy (Table 2). We selected explanatory variables in consideration of statistical fitting and biological importance to individual tree growth.

BAI of monarch birch followed a sigmoidal relationship with initial tree DBH, whereas those of castor aralia and Japanese oak increased steadily as DBH increased. The effect of DBH on BAI was positive and significant in all species except for monarch birch (Table 2). Negative coefficient of DBH was observed for monarch birch, even though it was not significant, meaning that the BAI of monarch birch decreased with increasing DBH. This pattern could be explained by Figure 3, showing that the BAI of monarch birch became larger in the smaller DBH and then declined after reaching certain DBH size. Even though BAI for monarch birch was underestimated in larger DBH, the R^2 and RMSE values indicated the acceptable prediction power.

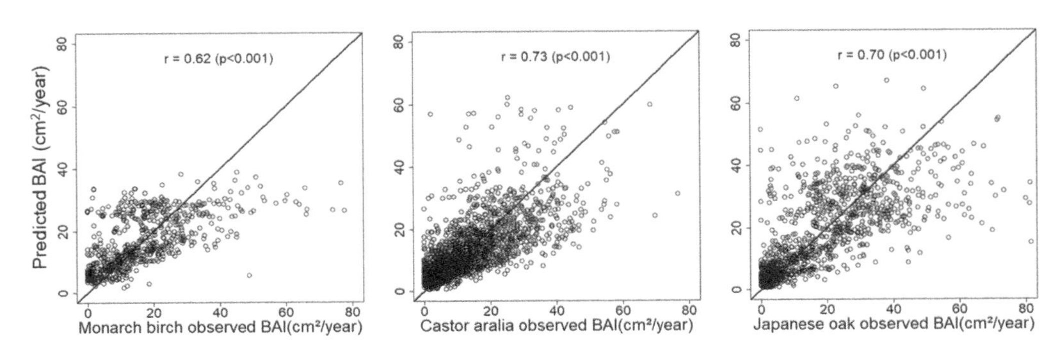

Figure 4. Observed and predicted basal area increment (cm^2/year) for three high-value timber species.

Table 3. The predicted number of years for a tree with 30 cm of initial DBH to reach target DBH of 50 cm and 70 cm.

	Average years (SD)	
Species	50 cm DBH	70 cm DBH
Monarch birch (n = 168)	29(40)	48(65)
Castor aralia (n = 484)	28(20)	46(32)
Japanese oak (n = 219)	48(37)	80(61)

SD stands for standard deviation.

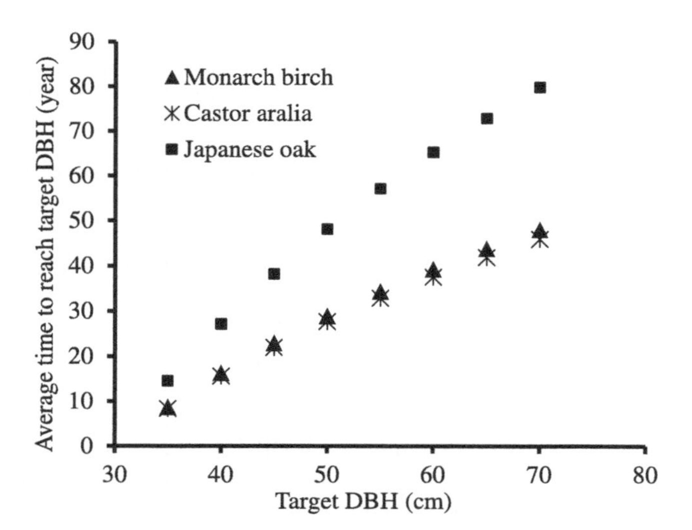

Figure 5. The predicted years for a tree with 30 cm of initial DBH to reach target DBH. Each marker represents the average time (years) to reach the target DBH.

We included stand variables related to tree density and basal area as competition variables in our individual tree growth models. We detected negative relationships between BAI and stand variables, i.e., broadleaf tree density, conifer tree density, and conifer basal area, suggesting that trees in dense stands exhibit slower growth than those in sparsely populated stands. Using the long-term thinning experiments data, Lhotka (2017) also reported the negative effect of tree density on the growth of individual trees. From the practical forest management perspective, these stand variables could be manipulated for improved growth of target trees through the use of various silvicultural interventions.

In the selected models (Table 2), stand variables related to tree density (i.e. N-tree and L-tree) were selected more often than variables related to BA. However, BAL, a stand-level variable related to BA, were selected in the final models for all species. The inclusion of BAL in the all selected models indicated that individual tree BAI could be explained better by BAL than by BA. We found significant negative relationships between BAL and BAI for all three targeted high-value timber species (Table 2). As BAL increases, individual tree BAI decreases. These results are biologically meaningful, since BAL accounts for a subject tree's social ranking and the stand density simultaneously (Schröder and Gadow 1999). When there are higher numbers of trees that are larger than subject tree in an area, the BAI of subject trees will be lower. Similar results have been obtained in recent previous studies in different forest types using different growth modelling approaches (Contreras et al. 2011; Rohner et al. 2017; Ruslandi and Putz 2017; Schelhaas et al. 2018).

General expectation of selection harvest include increased growth of remaining trees (Yoshida et al. 2006). Previous studies indicated that the canopy gaps created by selection harvest improved the growth of remaining trees especially that of smaller trees (Yoshida and Kamitani 1998; Yoshida et al. 2006; Amaral et al. 2019). In the current study, we observed positive coefficients of BA-Har for all high-value tree species, although the coefficients were not significant (Table 2). The result of no significant coefficient of BA-Har can be explained by the fact that BA-Har is a stand scale variable and the gap created by selection harvest may not represent the intensity of canopy gap around the target individual trees that included in the model development.

The models developed in this study would be useful tools for predicting the growth of high-value individual trees and may have potential to be applied in forest management. Shibano et al. (1990) examined the relationship between the DBH and wood quality of monarch birch and suggested to harvest trees with DBH > 60 cm, when the heartwood ratio is expected to be greater than 60%. According to Owari et al. (2016), DBH threshold to register as superior tree has been set to 50 cm under single-tree management system. From a practical forest management perspective, key question is the length of time a tree of certain size requires to reach such desirable DBH. As shown in Table 3 and Figure 5, the BAI model allows predicting the time to reach a target DBH. As an example, we estimated the time of a tree with 30 cm DBH to reach 50 cm DBH and 70 cm DBH for all species (Table 3) using derived BAI models (Equation (1) and Table 2). Japanese oak is predicted to take longer time than the other two species to reach the target DBH. Since, such information was scarce, BAI models developed in this study can be used for this purpose, and it allows planning for harvest and sustainable production of high-value timber species. In our models, however, we implicitly assumed that stand-structure variables (e.g. BAL, T-tree) are not subject to change over time. As a given tree grows higher, it will overtop the surrounding trees. Consequently, it will most likely become less affected by the competition which might positively affect its growth. It should be careful when interpreting our results, since the assumption may have caused the overestimation of years to reach target DBH.

The individual tree growth models developed in this study will provide useful information for forestry practitioner. The variables used for model development can be derived simply and easily from long-term and repeated measurements data. Further, variables in this study do not require the data of tree coordinates and distance between trees. Similar models can be developed for the other species because our long-term plot data included every tree species within the UTHF permanent plots with DBH ≥ 5 cm.

Conclusion

In this study, we demonstrated the power of long-term UTHF measurement dataset for predicting individual tree growth useful for forest management purpose. Individual tree BAIs were predicted from a long-term plot measurement dataset using a linear mixed-effects modeling approach. Initial tree size, competition, and management variables were considered in the models; the results showed reasonable predictive accuracy. However, the model was unable to include some important factors affecting tree growth such as natural disturbance, soil, elevation, slope, slope direction, and climatic data. Therefore, it should be generalized carefully in other regions considering possible change in species composition and stand conditions, which might alter ecosystem functions of the forests. The models produced in this study could be improved by the application of advanced data collection techniques such as airborne Light Detection and Ranging (LiDAR) and unmanned aerial vehicle (UAV) which may allow quantifying tree crown competition at individual tree level (Ma et al. 2018; Versace et al. 2019). For example, Ma et al. (2018) examined the growth and competition at individual tree level with the use of bi-temporal LiDAR data. Using similar approach with low cost UAV data, it would be one of the potentials to improve growth prediction of target tree species.

Acknowledgments

The authors would like to thank the current and former technical staff of the University of Tokyo Hokkaido Forest for their great efforts and contributions in field measurements of long-term permanent plots. We also would like to express our thanks to editors and three anonymous reviewers for their comments and suggestions to significantly improve the manuscript.

Disclosure statement

Authors declare no conflict of interest.

Funding

This work was supported by the Japan Society for the Promotion of Science [KAKENHI 17H01516 and JPJSCCB20190007].

ORCID

Kyaw Thu Moe http://orcid.org/0000-0002-3125-237X
Toshiaki Owari http://orcid.org/0000-0002-9227-4177

References

Adame P, Hynynen J, Cañellas I, Del Río M. 2008. Individual-tree diameter growth model for rebollo oak (*Quercus pyrenaica* Willd.) coppices. For Ecol Manage. 255(3-4):1011–1022. doi:10.1016/j.foreco.2007.10.019.

Amaral MRM, Lima AJN, Higuchi FG, Dos Santos J, Higuchi N. 2019. Dynamics of tropical forest twenty-five years after experimental logging in central amazon mature forest. Forests. 10(2):89. doi:10.3390/f10020089.

Bates D, Maechler M, Bolker B, Walker S, Christensen RHB, Singmann H, Dai B, Scheipl F, Grothendieck G, Green P, et al. 2020. Linear mixed-effects model using "Eigen" and S4, R Package Version 1.1-23. https://github.com/lme4/lme4/. (accessed on 30 April 2020).

Calama R, Montero G. 2005. Multilevel linear mixed model for tree diameter increment in Stone Pine (*Pinus pinea*): a calibrating approach. Silva Fenn. 39:37–54.

Contreras MA, Affleck D, Chung W. 2011. Evaluating tree competition indices as predictors of basal area increment in western Montana forests. For Ecol Manage. 262:1939–1949.

Cunha T, Finger CAG, Hasenauer H. 2016. Tree basal area increment models for *Cedrela, Amburana, Copaifera* and *Swietenia* growing in the Amazon rain forests. For Ecol Manage. 365:174–183.

Fukuoka S, Oikawa N, Tokuni M, Isozaki Y, Goto S. 2013. Effects of selection cutting on population dynamics, *Quercus crispula* in a conifer-hardwood mixed forest in the University of Tokyo Hokkaido Forest. Bull Univ Tokyo For. 129: 1–14. (in Japanese with English summary).

Han ZQ, Liu T, Sun QM, Li R, Xie JB, Li BL. 2014. Application of compound interest laws in biology: reunification of existing models to develop seed bank dynamics model of annual plants. Ecol Modell. 278:67–73.

Hemery G, Spiecker H, Aldinger E, Kerr G, Collet C, Bell S 2008. COST Action E42: growing valuable broadleaved tree species, 40. http://www.valbro.uni-freibur.

Ishibashi S, Hirokawa T. 1986. An analysis of data on selection forest in the Tokyo University Forest in Hokkaido. Trans Annu Meet Kanto Branch Jpn For Soc. 37: 15–18. (in Japanese).

Kahriman A, Ahin AS, Sönmez T, Yavuz M. 2018. A novel approach to selecting a competition index: the effect of competition on individual-tree diameter growth of Calabrian pine. Can J For Res. 48:1217–1226.

Kiernan DH, Bevilacqua E, Nyland RD. 2008. Individual-tree diameter growth model for sugar maple trees in uneven-aged northern hardwood stands under selection system. For Ecol Manage. 256:1579–1586.

Kuehne C, Weiskittel AR, Waskiewicz J. 2019. Comparing performance of contrasting distance-independent and distance-dependent competition metrics in predicting individual tree diameter increment and survival within structurally-heterogeneous, mixed-species forests of Northeastern United States. For Ecol Manage. 433:205–216.

Kuznetsova A, Brockhoff PB, Christensen RHB, Jensen SP 2020. "lmerTest": tests in linear mixed effects models, R package version 3.1-2. https://github.com/runehaubo/lmerTestR. (accessed on 30 April 2020).

Lhotka JM. 2017. Examining growth relationships in *Quercus* stands: an application of individual-tree models developed from long-term thinning experiments. For Ecol Manage. 385:65–77.

Ma Q, Su Y, Tao S, Guo Q. 2018. Quantifying individual tree growth and tree competition using bi-temporal airborne laser scanning data: a case study in the Sierra Nevada Mountains, California. Int J Digit Earth. 11:485–503.

Moe KT, Owari T. 2020. Sustainability of high-value timber species in mixed conifer–broadleaf forest managed under selection system in northern Japan. Forests, 11:484.

Nakagawa S, Schielzeth H. 2013. A general and simple method for obtaining R^2 from generalized linear mixed-effects models. Methods Ecol Evol. 4:133–142.

Noguchi M, Yoshida T. 2009. Individual-scale responses of five dominant tree species to single-tree selection harvesting in a mixed forest in Hokkaido, northern Japan. J For Res. 14:311–320.

Oosterbaan A, Hochbichler E, Nicolescu VN, Spiecker H. 2009. Silvicultural principles, goals and measures in growing valuable broadleaved tree species. Die Bodenkultur. 60:45–51.

Orellana E, Filho AF, Netto SP, Vanclay JK. 2016. A distance-independent individual-tree growth model to simulate management regimes in native Araucaria forests. J For Res. 22:30–35.

Owari T. 2013. Sustainable and adaptive forest management and data infrastructure under the stand-based silvicultural system. Proc Inst Stat Math. 61: 201–216. (in Japanese with English summary).

Owari T, Inukai H, Koike Y, Minowa Y, Nakajima T. 2010. Single-tree selection techniques in the stand-based forest management system. Trans Meet Hokkaido Branch Jpn For Soc. 58: 101–104. (in Japanese).

Owari T, Okamura K, Fukushi K, Kasahara H, Tatsumi S. 2016. Single-tree management for high-value timber species in a cool-temperate mixed forest in northern Japan. Int J Biodivers Sci Ecosyst Serv Manag. 12:74–82.

Pokharel B, Dech JP. 2012. Mixed-effects basal area increment models for tree species in the boreal forest of Ontario, Canada using an ecological land classification approach to incorporate site effects. Forestry. 85:255–270.

Pretzsch H, Del Río M, Biber P, Arcangeli C, Bielak K, Brang P, Dudzinska M, Forrester DI, Klädtke J, Kohnle U, et al. 2019. Maintenance of long-term experiments for unique insights into forest growth dynamics and trends: review and perspectives. Eur J For Res. 138:165–185.

R Core Team. 2019. R: The R Project for Statistical Computing; R Foundation for Statistical Computing: Vienna, Austria. Available online: https://www.r-project.org/ (accessed on 6 January 2020).

Rohner B, Waldner P, Lischke H, Ferretti M, Thürig E. 2017. Predicting individual-tree growth of central European tree species as a function of site, stand, management, nutrient, and climate effects. Eur J For Res. 137:29–44.

Ruslandi CWP, Putz FE. 2017. Tree diameter increments following silvicultural treatments in a dipterocarp forest in Kalimantan,

Indonesia: a mixed-effects modelling approach. For Ecol Manage. 396:195–206.

Schelhaas M, Hengeveld GM, Heidema N, Thürig E, Rohner B, Vacchiano G. 2018. Species-specific, pan-European diameter increment models based on data of 2.3 million trees. For Ecosyst. 5:21.

Schröder J, Gadow KV. 1999. Testing a new competition index for Maritime pine in northwestern Spain. Can J For Res. 29:280–283.

Schulze M, Grogan J, Landis RM, Vidal E. 2008. How rare is too rare to harvest? Management challenges posed by timber species occurring at low densities in the Brazilian Amazon. For Ecol Manage. 256:1443–1457.

Shibano S, Iguchi K, Kimura N, Watanabe S. 1990. Hartwood rate trunk of large *Betula maximowicziana* timbers. Trans Meet Hokkaido Branch Jpn For Soc. 38: 203–205. (in Japanese).

Shibano S, Kasahara H, Kimura N, Fukushi K, Iguchi K, Oakmura K, Takahashi Y. 1995. Processes of diameter growth for large trees of *Betula maximowicziana*: growth declining and dead trees at the Tokyo University Forest in Hokkaido. Trans Meet Hokkaido Branch Jpn For Soc. 106: 263–264. (in Japanese).

Shibata S. 1988. Studies on the management of natural forests: an experiment of natural forest management in the Tokyo University Forest in Hokkaido. Bull Tokyo Univ For. 80: 269–397. (in Japanese with English summary).

Tatewaki M. 1958. Forest ecology of the islands of the north Pacific ocean. J Fac Agric Hokkaido Univ. 50:371–486.

Tatsumi S, Owari T, Mori AS. 2016. Estimating competition coefficients in tree communities: a hierarchical Bayesian approach to neighborhood analysis. Ecosphere. 7:e01273.

Tenzin J, Tenzin K, Hasenauer H. 2017. Individual tree basal area increment models for broadleaved forests in Bhutan. Forestry. 90:367–380.

Tomé J, Tomé M, Barreiro S, Paulo JA. 2006. Age-independent difference equations for modelling tree and stand growth. Can J For Res. 36:1621–1630.

Uzoh FCC, Oliver WW. 2008. Individual tree diameter increment model for managed even-aged stands of ponderosa pine throughout the western United States using a multilevel linear mixed effects model. For Ecol Manage. 256:438–445.

Vanclay J. 1994. Modelling forest growth and yield: applications to mixed tropical forests. Wallingford UK: CAB International.

Versace S, Gianelle D, Frizzera L, Tognetti R, Garfì V, Dalponte M. 2019. Prediction of competition indices in a Norway spruce and silver fir-dominated forest using lidar data. Remote Sens. 11:2734.

Wang W, Chen X, Zeng W, Wang J, Meng J. 2019. Development of a mixed-effects individual-tree basal area increment model for oaks (*Quercus* spp.) considering forest structural diversity. Forests. 10:474.

Yamamoto H. 1990. Studies on an integrated computer-based system of forest management in natural selection forest. Bull Tokyo Univ For. 83: 31–142. (in Japanese with English summary).

Yasuda A, Yoshida T, Miya H, Harvey BD. 2013. An alternative management regime of selection cutting for sustaining stand structure of mixed forests of northern Japan: a simulation study. J For Res. 18:398–406.

Yoshida T, Kamitani T. 1998. Effects of crown release on basal area growth rates of some broad-leaved tree species with different shade-tolerance. J For Res. 3:181–184.

Yoshida T, Noguchi M, Akibayashi Y, Noda M, Kadomatsu M, Sasa K. 2006. Twenty years of community dynamics in a mixed conifer-broad-leaved forest under a selection system in northern Japan. Can J For Res. 36:1363–1375.

Zhao L, Li C, Tang S. 2013. Individual-tree diameter growth model for fir plantations based on multi-level linear mixed effects models across southeast China. J For Res. 18:305–315.

Evaluating relationships of standing stock, LAI and NDVI at a subtropical reforestation site in southern Taiwan using field and satellite data

Chiang Wei, Jiquan Chen, Jing-Ming Chen, Jui-Chu Yu, Ching-Peng Cheng, Yen-Jen Lai, Po-Neng Chiang, Chih-Yuan Hong, Ming-Jer Tsai and Ya-Nan Wang

ABSTRACT

In this study, we evaluate the relationships between the standing stock, field-measured LAI, and NDVI from remotely sensed images and in situ measurements at plantation forests in the subtropics–tropics region of southern Taiwan. The purpose is to facilitate assessing the biomass of reforestation sites in large areas applying the possible stock-LAI-NDVI relationships analyzed in this study. 15–16 years old forest in one square kilometer area with 14 tree species was tested at different spatial scales. In addition, we also assess the relationship of plots with pure tree species for the effect mixed tree species. By long-term monitoring, intensive measurement for 5 years and analysis at different spatial scales, the results show the correlation coefficient of stock-LAI is not significant while that of stock-NDVI is 0.5639, 0.7230 and 0.9283 as the spatial scale enlarges. Negative stock-LAI correlations found for three tree species but all the stock-NDVI correlations for six specific tree species are positive. If the multi-regression is applied, the correlation coefficient of stock-LAI-NDVI is higher than that of the stock-LAI and stock-NDVI, which reaches to the 0.6470, 0.7680 and 0.9995 at the plot, block and site level, respectively; the correlation coefficients of six specific tree species are also larger at the plot level.

Introduction

The policy of reforestation for landscape scenery in Taiwan was established on 31 August 2001 and has been implemented since 1 January 2002. This policy resulted in a total of 10,000 ha (original goal was 25,100 ha) of forest plantations by the end of 2007 (Chen and He 2008). The benefits of the reforestation include land protection, conservation of natural resources, landscape preservation, and sustaining biodiversity. This economic-efficient approach appears effective for environmental protection, while enhancing carbon sequestration, improving the air quality, and mitigating the greenhouse effects. This policy for reforestation aligns well the requirements of the Kyoto Protocol such as monitoring of variations in carbon dioxide flux and helps to improve the environmental performance of Taiwan in its role as a global partner. The assessment of reforestation across Taiwan was recently produced by Lin et al. (2010), but the authors mainly evaluated regarding the policy and reforestation area and bonus per area. Liu et al. (2019a) also conducted an overall assessment of reforestation at landslide-prone areas in Taiwan.

To assess the biomass in reforestation sites, forest structural and spectral indices obtained through field measurement and remote sensed satellite data could be used as surrogates of standing stock. Among field-measured structural indices, leaf area index (LAI) is defined as one-sided green leaf area per unit of ground surface area, and is a key parameter for physical and biological processes of plant canopies, such as photosynthesis, respiration, transpiration, carbon and nutrient cycling, and rainfall interception (Chen et al. 1991; Chen and Black 1992; Wei et al. 2017). LAI is a required input variable in many climate and ecological models as a critical parameter for understanding plant development (Yang et al. 2008). Among satellite-based spectral indices, the normalized difference vegetation index (NDVI), which was formulated after a normalized difference spectral index (Tucker 1979), has been a widely used index that can be derived from satellite imagery (Rouse et al. 1973; Casanova et al. 1998). The advantages of using NDVI are the availability of the satellite data acquisition, acceptable spatial resolution, wide-range, short re-visit time, and low cost compared to other options such as light detection and ranging (LiDAR) data.

Numerous studies of the relationships between LAI or NDVI and biomass were reported during the last two decades (Zheng et al. 2004; le Marie et al. 2011; Manna et al. 2014; Gaia et al. 2017). In the literature, these relationships have been mostly calculated for mature forests and growing crops, with few studies attempted for young plantation. Studies for forests in the subtropical zone are particularly rare and urgently needed (Xavier and Vettorazzi 2004). If the relationships are established and well-correlated with each other, standing stock at different spatial scales can be estimated by the indices and indirectly and efficiently retrieved to save the resources of time, budget, and manpower.

In this study, by using field measurement and remotely sensed satellite data, we examined the stock–LAI and stock–NDVI relationships at different spatial scales in a reforestation area of southern Taiwan. The species-specific relationships were also assessed to see the differences between tree species used in reforestation sites. Since NDVI has a saturation problem around high biomass, it may lead to weak NDVI correlations with standing stock (Huete et al. 2002; Liao et al. 2011). It has been reported that NDVI is influenced by atmospheric correction, the viewing angle of the sensors, and circumstances when LAI is below a value of about 2–4, which may be viewed as being due to the variation in the bare soil component (Carson and Ripley 1997). Therefore, in addition to the evaluation of the relationship between stock-LAI and stock-NDVI separately, we also assessed the multi-regression of stock-LAI-NDVI both from under and above the canopy.

Materials & methods

We developed a working framework that includes several sequential steps (Figure 1). In the first step, the study site was delineated into 16 blocks and 64 plots. SPOT imagery was georeferenced to the site to calculate NDVI for each plot. Then the standing stock (hereafter stock) and LAI were estimated annually. In the second step, the variation and correlation between the stock, LAI, NDVI and at different spatial scales was examined and also by considering species effects. Our final step is to assess the model performance. Because there are 14 tree species in such small study site (1 km^2), so it is the major motive for the authors to evaluate the relationship of stock-LAI-NDVI.

Site description

Our study site in Pingdong (PD) is located in Hai-Feng Section No.176 (22°31′ N, 120°36′ E) in southern Taiwan, near the Tropic of Cancer. This site belonged to the Wan-Long Farmland of the Taiwan Sugar Corporation prior to plantation in 2002, and covered 290.66 ha at 60 m a.s.l. (Figure 2). After the declaration of the reforestation policy, the farm was converted to plantation forest in 2002. The local soils are Entisols, with more than 60% of the site covered with sandstone on a mild slope of about 5 °. The average temperature is 25.1°C, with a maximum of 28.4°C in July and a minimum of 20.1°C in January. The average annual rainfall is 2,022 mm (data from the Forest Bureau). Since 2002, 14 species of trees have been planted in 25 clusters with a density of 1,500 seedlings per hectare over the 161 ha land area.

To evaluate the carbon sequestration for reforestation, the National Taiwan University Experimental Forest (NTUEF) established an eddy covariance flux tower in February 2008 that has been continued since April 2008. By January 2018, the tree height at PD site ranged from 1.7 to 16.8 m, and the diameter at breast height (DBH) ranged from 2.4 to 32.4 cm. Based on logged data from the flux tower, the CO_2 concentration ranged from 388 to 405 ppm, and net ecosystem production (NEP) was ~ 0.33 Mg C $year^{-1}$ ha^{-1}.

Stock assessment

Following the protocols of the Forest Inventory and Analysis (FIA) (USDA Forest Service 2016), a 1 km^2 area centered around at the flux tower was divided into 16 blocks (Figure 2). A 40.16 m radius sample region (light green) within each block was further divided into four circular plots (orange circle, radius 3.66 m) in the center, with three additional ones on the perimeter that were separated by a 120 degree angle from the north (Figure 3). The plot was located using the geographic coordinate by the GPS. The plot boundary was delineated by the tape

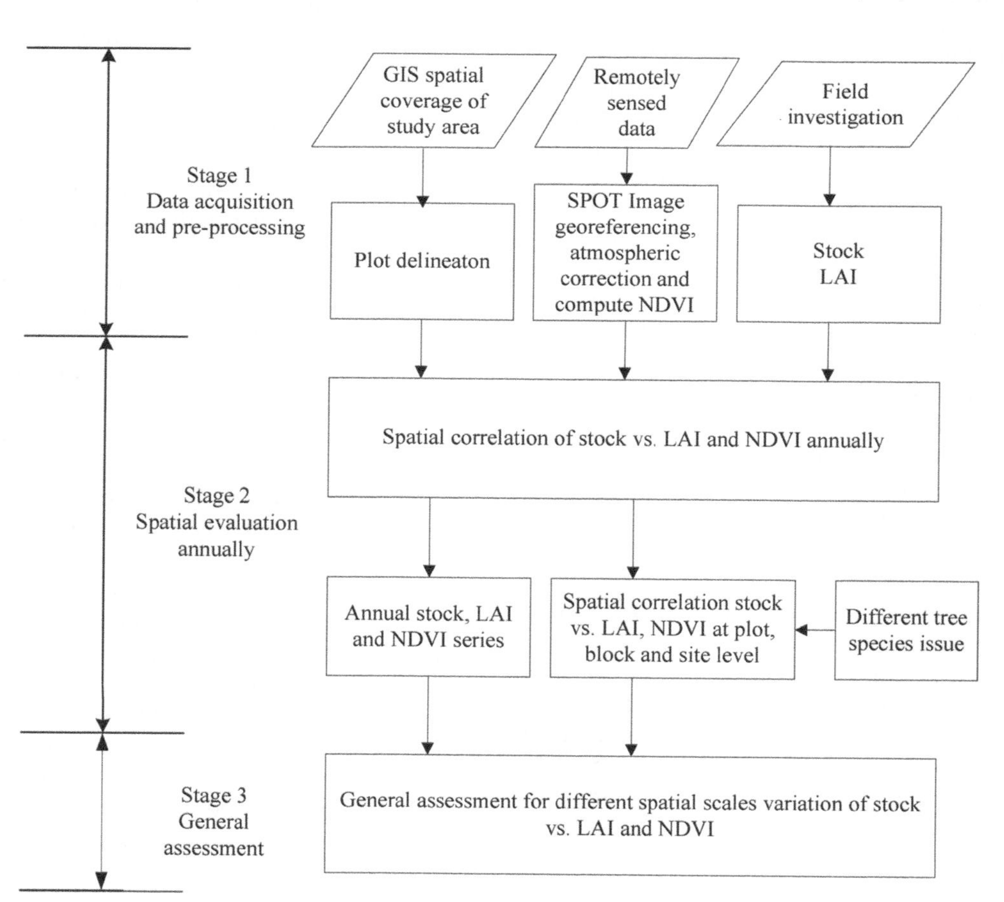

Figure 1. Flowchart of methodology in this study.

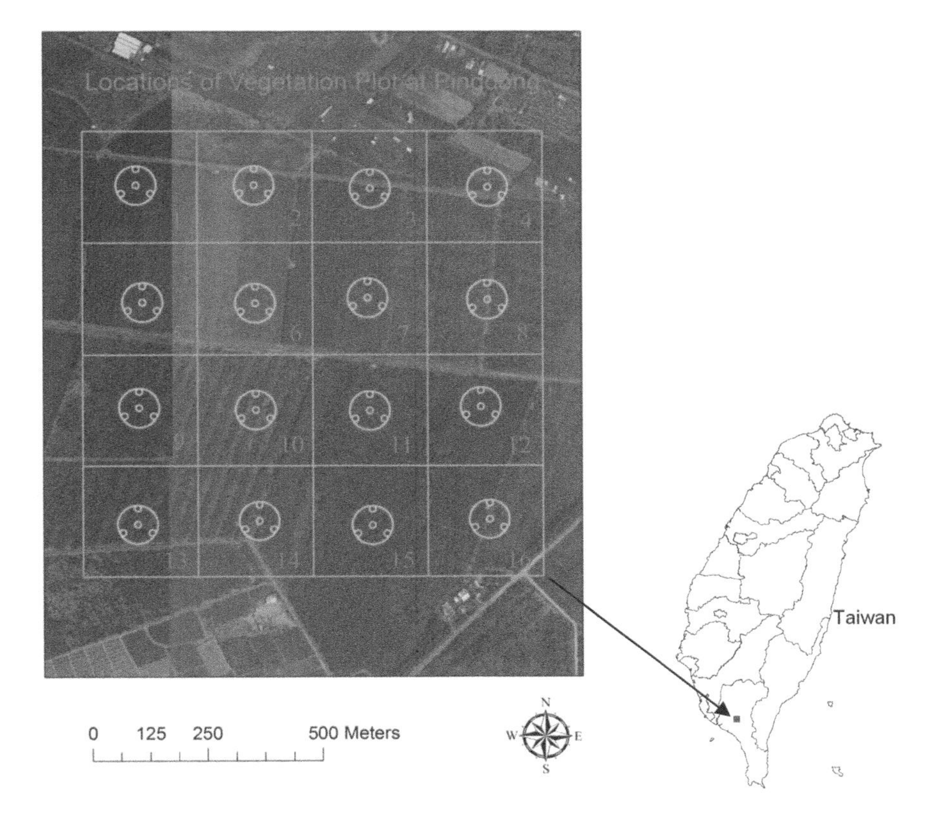

Figure 2. Location of Wan-Long farm in Pingdong, southern Taiwan.

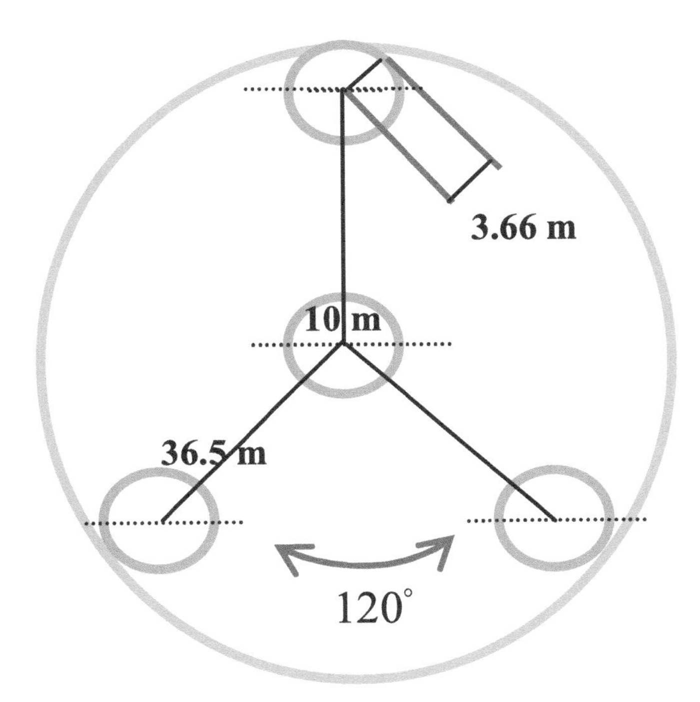

Figure 3. Diagram of FIA plot design.

measure. All the four centers of the plot in each block were also marked with the plastic foundation pile. The DBH and height of individual tree (all marked with a silver tap) inside the 64 plots have been measured annually in mid January since 2011. The stock (V) as (FAO 2015):

$$V = BHF = \pi r^2 HF = \pi D^2 HF/4 \qquad (1)$$

where B is the basal area, D is the DBH, H is the tree height, r is the radius equal to half of DBH, and F is the form factor. DBH was measured at 1.3 meter high from the ground using caliper and tree height was measured using Haga altimeter. The investigation of all trees inside the 64 plots in 2011 is listed in Table 1. Due to the lacks in locally-developed biometric equations, the cubic volume of wood for standing trees was estimated with a form factor of 0.45 for broadleaf trees (Taipei City Government, 2011). The stock at plot level is calculated by the sum of all individual stock divided by area of the plot (42.08 m^2) while the block level is the average stock of four plots. The stock at site level is the average of 16 blocks.

Leaf area index (LAI)

A full-frame hemispherical digital camera with an 8 mm fisheye lens was set at the center of each plot at 1.2 m above the ground to take multiple photos. The average LAI of the plot was calculated from three measurements along the two ends of a 10 m transect in an east-west direction shown in Figure 3. The measurements were collected before 0800 h or after 1600 h to avoid direct solar radiation during May 2–4, 2011; January 24–25, 2013; February 6–7, 2014; and February 11–13, 2015, the LAI was not investigated in 2012.The canopy structure and gap light transmission indices were used to calculate LAI with the Gap Light Analyzer (Frazer et al. 1999). The block LAI was assigned by the average of LAI value of four plots in this block. The LAI at site level is the average of 16 blocks. Satellite-based LAI products are not included in this study because the common used spatial resolution is 500 m and 1 km which is far larger than the satellite-based NDVI product (20 m in this study), which were not suitable to be included for stock-LAI relationship at different spatial scales. In addition, satellite-derived LAI products and their biases were reported to exhibit large discrepancies and could lead to substantial

Table 1. The investigation of stock of all 64 plots at Pingdong site in 2011.

Plot No.	Tree species				Number of trees	Stock (m^3 ha^{-1})
1–0	*Terminalia catappa*				18	21.43
1–1	*Terminalia catappa*				12	22.04
1–2	*Terminalia catappa*				18	7.52
1–3	*Terminalia catappa*				15	19.13
2–0	*Swietenia macrophylla*				14	32.50
2–1	*Swietenia macrophylla*				16	39.40
2–2	*Swietenia macrophylla*				14	15.29
2–3	*Zelkova serrata*				12	2.53
3–0	*Terminalia catappa*	*Pterocarpus indicus*			19	18.43
3–1	*Swietenia macrophylla*				7	21.11
3–2	*Terminalia catappa*	*Pterocarpus indicus*			19	36.05
3–3	*Pterocarpus indicus*	*Terminalia catappa*			15	20.48
4–0	*Fraxinus formosana*				14	40.67
4–1	*Swietenia macrophylla*				10	12.65
4–2	*Cinnamomum camphora*	*Bischofia javanica*	*Zelkova serrata*		12	18.38
4–3	*Fraxinus formosana*				23	13.02
5–0	*Melia azedarach*				13	3.51
5–1	*Melia azedarach*				15	8.53
5–2	*Melia azedarach*				19	16.25
5–3	*Melia azedarach*				8	0.61
6–0	*Swietenia macrophylla*				16	11.34
6–1	*Swietenia macrophylla*				15	19.07
6–2	*Swietenia macrophylla*				18	9.25
6–3	*Swietenia macrophylla*				18	15.09
7–0	*Terminalia catappa*	*Pterocarpus indicus*	*Fraxinus formosana*		17	8.36
7–1	*Pterocarpus indicus*	*Terminalia catappa*			23	13.28
7–2	*Terminalia catappa*	*Pterocarpus indicus*			26	6.09
7–3	*Terminalia catappa*	*Pterocarpus indicus*			23	4.64
8–0	*Fraxinus formosana*				19	10.02
8–1	*Fraxinus formosana*				18	14.40
8–2	*Pterocarpus indicus*	*Sapindus saponaria*	*Swietenia macrophylla*	*Zelkova serrata*	20	14.09
8–3	*Fraxinus formosana*				13	3.23
9–0	*Pterocarpus indicus*				14	13.33
9–1	*Fraxinus formosana*	*Pterocarpus indicus*			23	13.51
9–2	*Pterocarpus indicus*				20	15.74
9–3	*Pterocarpus indicus*				16	15.53
10–0	*Pterocarpus indicus*	*Millettia oraria*			17	10.26
10–1	*Melia azedarach*	*Pterocarpus indicus*			14	16.06
10–2	*Pterocarpus indicus*				18	14.21
10–3	*Pterocarpus indicus*				11	8.59
11–0	*Zelkova serrata*				10	1.86
11–1	*Zelkova serrata*				10	8.24
11–2	*Zelkova serrata*				14	3.03
11–3	*Zelkova serrata*				10	2.18
12–0	*Zelkova serrata*				16	6.23
12–1	*Zelkova serrata*				18	6.96
12–2	*Zelkova serrata*				18	12.10
12–3	*Terminalia catappa*				24	37.18
13–0	*Zelkova serrata*	*Millettia oraria*	*Pterocarpus indicus*		11	3.96
13–1	*Millettia oraria*	*Fraxinus formosana*	*Pterocarpus indicus*		20	6.39
13–2	*Pterocarpus indicus*	*Millettia oraria*	*Swietenia macrophylla*		22	16.18
13–3	*Fraxinus formosana*	*Zelkova serrata*	*Millettia oraria*	*Pterocarpus indicus*	27	12.72
14–0	*Pterocarpus indicus*	*Melia azedarach*			15	16.96
14–1	*Pterocarpus indicus*	*Melia azedarach*			6	4.12
14–2	*Cassia fistula*				20	25.21
14–3	*Pterocarpus indicus*	*Melia azedarach*			14	15.08
15–0	*Pterocarpus indicus*				9	23.57
15–1	*Zelkova serrata*	*Pterocarpus indicus*			7	7.16
15–2	*Pterocarpus indicus*				18	19.70
15–3	*Pterocarpus indicus*				20	26.76
16–0	*Zelkova serrata*				16	10.81
16–1	*Zelkova serrata*				11	6.02
16–2	*Zelkova serrata*	*Pterocarpus indicus*	*Bischofia javanica*		21	19.48
16–3	*Zelkova serrata*				22	10.86

uncertainty when simulated for carbon and water fluxes (Liu et al., 2019b).

SPOT imagery

We used red band and near infrared data of SPOT (Satellite Pour l'Observation de la Terre, which is a commercial high-resolution optical imaging earth observation satellite system operating from space) series imagery to calculate NDVI for each plot. In this study, we use SPOT 4 and SPOT 5 satellite imagery according to the nearest time for field measurement (Table 2). SPOT imagery was collected according to the time of field measurements (stock and LAI) except 2011. SPOT imagery was collected between January and February when the weather was more stable and cloud-free than in other months. The radiometric conditions during these months also vary less. The imagery was directly received and processed by the Center for Space and Remote Sensing Research (CSRSR), National Central University, Taiwan. According to the information provided from the CSRSR, the georeferencing errors of SPOT 4 and SPOT 5 were 6 and 4 m,

Table 2. Attribute data of satellite imagery used in this study.

No.	Satellite	Date of image acquisition	Original spatial resolution (m)	Georeference level	Lowest digital number of the image: Green	Red	Near IR
1	SPOT-5	2011.01.27	10	3	52	36	31
2	SPOT-4	2012.01.19	20	3	38	23	8
3	SPOT-5	2013.01.19	10	3	57	41	35
4	SPOT-5	2014.01.23	10	3	50	33	18
5	SPOT-5	2015.02.12	10	3	49	36	19

* Georeference level 3 means a precision-corrected image with ground control points and digital terrain model.

respectively. The SPOT imagery (orthoimage) was extracted according to the corresponding coordinates. Because the ground pixel size of 2012 SPOT 4 imagery is 20 m, other SPOT images were resampled using nearest neighbor method to 20 m, resulting in 2,500 pixels within the study area.

Correction for the atmospheric effects

A number of different methods, such as the dark object subtraction (DOS, aka the histogram minimum method) (Chavez 1988) and relative radiometric normalization (Jensen 1983; Song et al. 2001) were applied to correct for atmospheric effects. We assumed that the lowest digital number (DN) represented the values contributed by upwelled radiances, and it was therefore subtracted from the original digital values of the five images. The lowest digital numbers of the five images are listed in Table 2 and were processed in subsequent NDVI computations.

Normalized differential vegetation index (NDVI)

The NDVI is widely used as an indicator for change in ground vegetation (Kriegler et al. 1969; Rouse et al. 1973; Cohen 1991). Because green vegetation reflects infrared but absorbs red light, a decrease in NDVI indicates that the vegetation area has decreased. In contrast, increasing NDVI suggests expansion of the vegetation. The NDVI was calculated as:

$$NDVI = \frac{(NIR - R)}{(NIR + R)}, \tag{2}$$

where, R is the DN (Digital Number) of red light (Band 2) and NIR (Band 3) is the DN of near infrared light, and their wavelength region lies between 0.61–0.68 μm and 0.788–-0.89 μm, respectively. The corresponding NDVI values of 64 plots (orange color) were assigned by the nearest pixel value of NDVI to the center of the circular plot. The block NDVI was assigned by the average of NDVI value of four plots in this block. The NDVI at site level is the average of 16 blocks.

The relationships between stock, LAI, and NDVI

Due to mixed tree species in a single plot, the relationship between stock, LAI and NDVI may vary at different spatial scales. In this study, we assessed the relationship at three levels: plot, block and site. At each level, the stock-LAI, stock-NDVI is correlated with the corresponding values. In order to consider the radiance both above and under the canopy, the multi-regression of stock with LAI and NDVI is tested to integrate the advantages of both indices at different spatial scales. Furthermore, the multi-regression is also tested for the specific tree species only at plot level.

Results and discussion

Annual variation in stock, LAI and NDVI at different spatial scales

The standing stock increased between 2011 and 2015 at the site level as Figure 4(a). The stock volume ranged from 10 m^3 ha^{-1} to 100 m^3 ha^{-1} except block 5 and 11. The trees in block 5 (*Melia azedarach*) and block 11 (*Zelkova serrata*) grew comparatively slower than other tree species. In addition, only 44 trees were found in block 11 (3.83 m^3 ha^{-1}) in 2011, compared to 50–60 trees in other blocks, and only 21 trees were found in block 11 in 2015.

The average LAI increased in 2013 and slightly decreased in 2014 and 2015, whereas the LAI for blocks 1, 5, and 11 continuously decreased from 2011 because many trees in these blocks died in 2013 and 2014. The variation of all blocks and the average is shown in Figure 4(b).

The average NDVI of all 16 blocks oscillated between −0.06 and 0.99 as Figure 4(c). The mechanism of decrease in NDVI may result from the radiation variation of the SPOT imagery, or shading caused by tree or ground litter/vegetation. It should be noted that although DOS had adjusted NDVI, it only accounts for atmospheric scattering.

Stock–LAI–NDVI relationships at different spatial scales

The relationship between the stock, LAI and NDVI at the plot, block and site level from 2011 to 2015 are shown in Figure 5 and listed in Table 3. The correlation between stock and NDVI were higher than those between stock and LAI at all spatial levels. The correlation coefficient lies between 0.5639 and 0.7230 and 0.9283. The correlation between stock and LAI at the block level was higher than that at the plot level, with the correlation coefficient increased from 0.4365 to 0.4460, but it decreased to −0.5352 at the site level; the average LAI at the site level decreased slightly in 2014 and 2015 for previously discussed reasons. Another possible reason of negative correlation coefficient found at the site level because less data (n = 4) was regressed compared to the plot (n = 256) and site level (n = 64). It is clear that the correlation between the stock and NDVI is higher than LAI at all spatial levels. At the plot level, the effect of mixed tree species may exist, while this effect is not significant at the block level. The outliers in high stock but low LAI and NDVI may be due to the tree species *Swietenia macrophylla* that has large DBH and height but smaller crown, whereas *Melia azedarach* has a smaller DBH and height but a wider crown span. The other mixing effect may come from vegetation under the trees or background contamination (e.g. soil moisture content variation under the tree) (Kim et al. 2011). The multi-regression result of stock-LAI-NDVI at three spatial levels

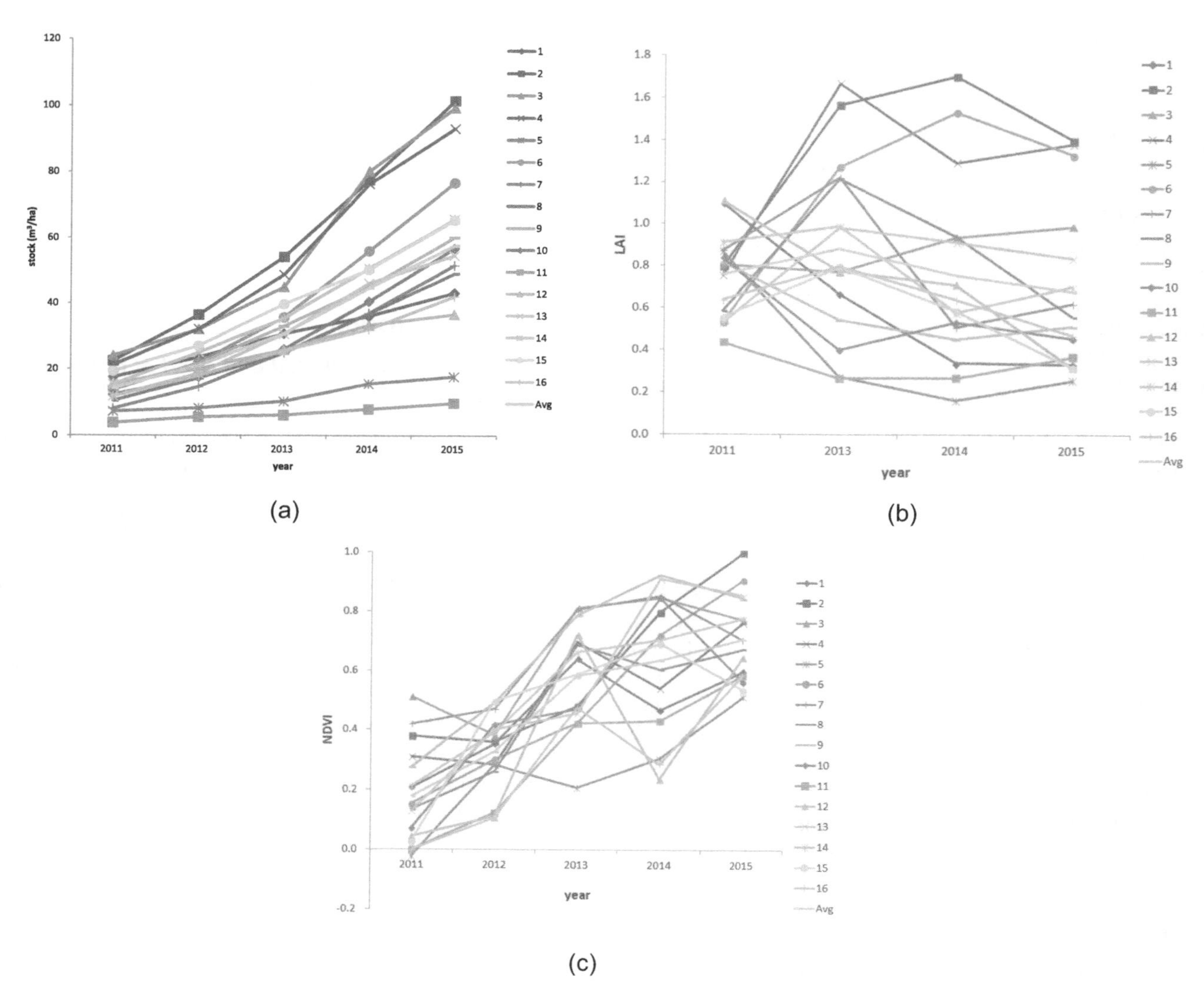

Figure 4. Variation in (a) stock, (b) LAI, and (c) NDVI for all 16 blocks at the Pingdong site.

is also listed in Table 3. The correlation coefficient of stock-LAI-NDVI is higher than that of the stock-LAI and stock-NDVI which reaches to the 0.647, 0.768 and 0.999 at the plot, block and site level, respectively. The possible reason may lead to the different mechanism for these two indices: the LAI measured the closure of the associated crown understory. However, the NDVI sensed the reflectance of canopy but failed to indicate the vertical direction of the tree structure. In this study, we do not separate the correlation of these two indices but associated to the stock.

In addition, the negative correlation between stock and LAI should be addressed here. The drop of LAI of all plots is not always due to perish of standing trees. The defoliation period mainly lies between October and December. However, the new leaves may grow until spring. Except 2011, our field survey mainly was investigated in January and February when before the major growing seasons. However, the leaves of falling still exists shift of timing in each block and may cause the decrease of LAI though the stock is increasing in Figure 4 (b). There is no treatment such as pruning and thinning done during 2011 and 2015. These exhibit for different tree-species in other areas and forest ecosystem, in particular, for two tree species *Swietenia macrophylla* and *Melia azedarach*. The former had larger stock but low LAI and the latter had lower stock but larger LAI in young ages.

Species-specific stock–NDVI–LAI relationship

Since the reforestation in 2002 and the FIA plots were installed in 2011, multiple species have been detected in some plots/blocks. Forty-four plots, including six with pure tree species, were analyzed for the stock–LAI–NDVI relationship (Figure 6(a–f)). The stock–LAI–NDVI in plots with specific tree species shows an irregular correlation between 2011 and 2015. Three species (*Fraxinus formosana*, *Swietenia macrophylla*, and *Zelkova serrata*) had positive stock–LAI correlations. Negative correlation was found for *Terminalia catappa*, *Pterocarpus indicus*, and *Melia azedarach*. However, all six specific tree species show positive stock–NDVI correlation, with correlation coefficient ranging from 0.3048 to 0.7503.The highest correlation coefficient of stock–LAI and stock–NDVI was 0.6860 and 0.7503, respectively. The correlation coefficient of stock–LAI and stock–NDVI for a single species is much higher than that for all tree species at plot level. The lowest correlation lies in the *Pterocarpus indicus* that has high stock but comparatively low LAI value. The possible reason may lead to its foliation period (from October to December depending on the tree species) before the surveying timing. The spatial resolution may also cause effect of mixed tree species within an image pixel; and the temporal shift between SPOT imagery and stock investigation may also result in different conditions

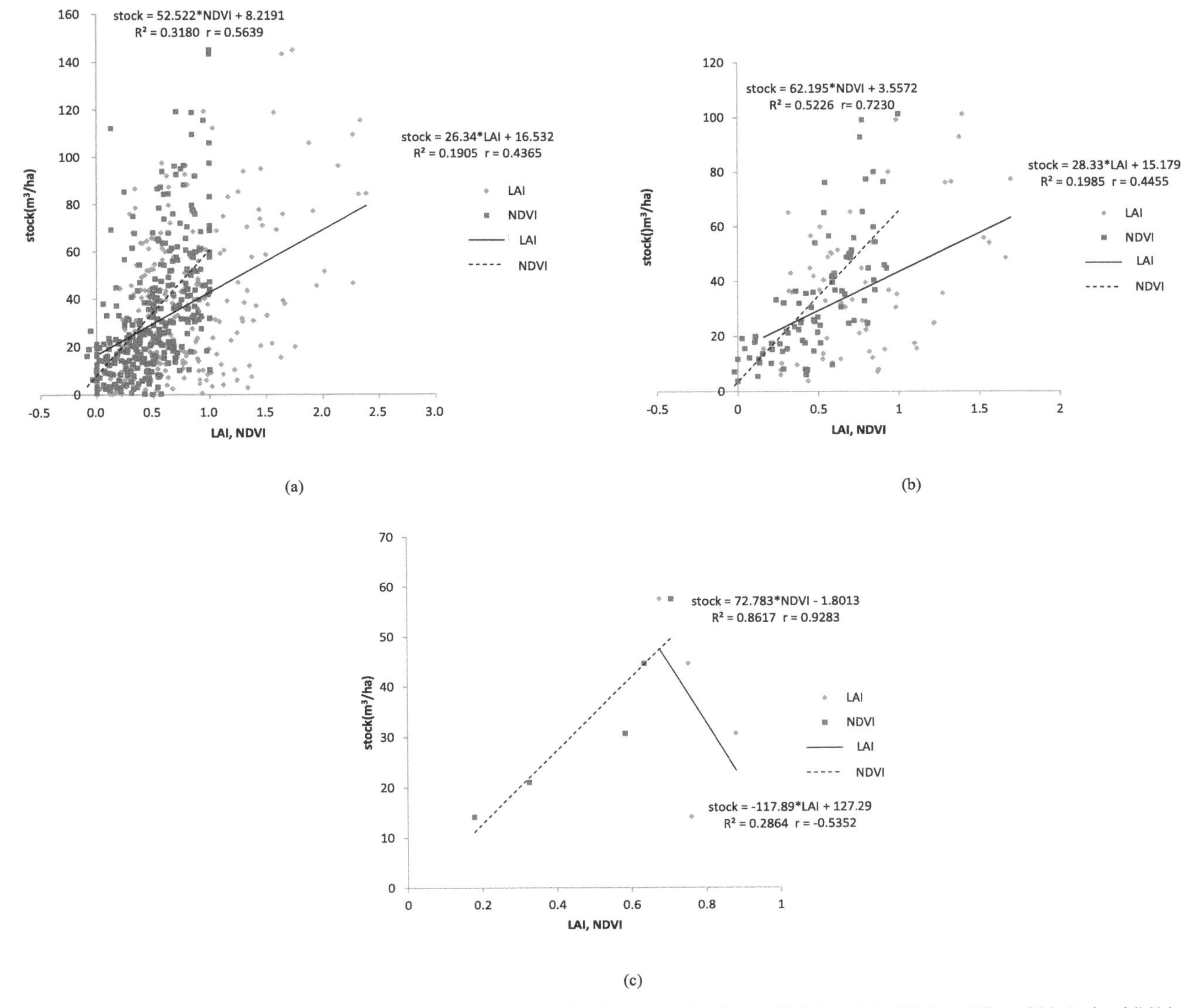

Figure 5. Correlation of stock vs. LAI and NDVI at the (a) plot (LAI (n = 256), NDVI (n = 320), (b) block ((LAI (n = 64), NDVI (n = 80)), and (c) site level (LAI (n = 4), NDVI (n = 5)).

Table 3. Regression of stock vs. LAI, stock vs. NDVI and multi-regression of stock vs. LAI and NDVI at different spatial levels.

Spatial level	Sample Size	R^2	Correlation coefficient	P value	regression formula
stock vs. LAI					
Plot	256	0.1905	0.4365	<0.0001	Stock = 26.34*LAI+16.532
Block	64	0.1985	0.4460	<0.0001	Stock = 28.33*LAI+15.179
Site	4	0.2864	−0.5352	0.4648	Stock = −117.89*LAI+127.29
stock vs. NDVI					
Plot	320	0.3180	0.5639	<0.0001	Stock = 51.5956*NDVI+8.507
Block	80	0.5226	0.7230	<0.0001	Stock = 62.195*NDVI+3.5572
Site	5	0.8617	0.9283	0.0228	Stock = 72.783*NDVI-1.8013
stock vs. LAI and NDVI					
Plot	256	0.4187	0.6470	<0.0001	Stock = 20.5733*LAI +45.1847*NDVI-2.8317
Block	64	0.5898	0.7680	<0.0001	Stock = 18.8342*LAI +56.4427*NDVI-7.2354
Site	4	0.9991	0.9995	0.0294	Stock = −89.8126*LAI +66.8946*NDVI+70.5046

for atmospheric radiation in 2011. The difference in growing curves of independent tree species needs to be considered because all trees were young during the study period (i.e. <16 years). Nevertheless, our results indicated that the stock–LAI–NDVI relationship varies by species, suggesting that species composition should be considered. Multi-regression of stock–LAI–NDVI for six specific tree species is shown in Table 4. Compared with the Figure 6(a–f), all the correlation coefficients are higher than those of the stock-LAI and stock-NDVI. Due to the limitation of SPOT 4 imagery in 2012, the ground resolution of the imagery can be finer to 10 m for SPOT 5 imagery to get more detailed information. For the stock-LAI-NDVI multi-regression, it is noted that all the correlation coefficient of LAI were positive in Table 4 but three among six species were negative in Figure 6. The stock best fits LAI and

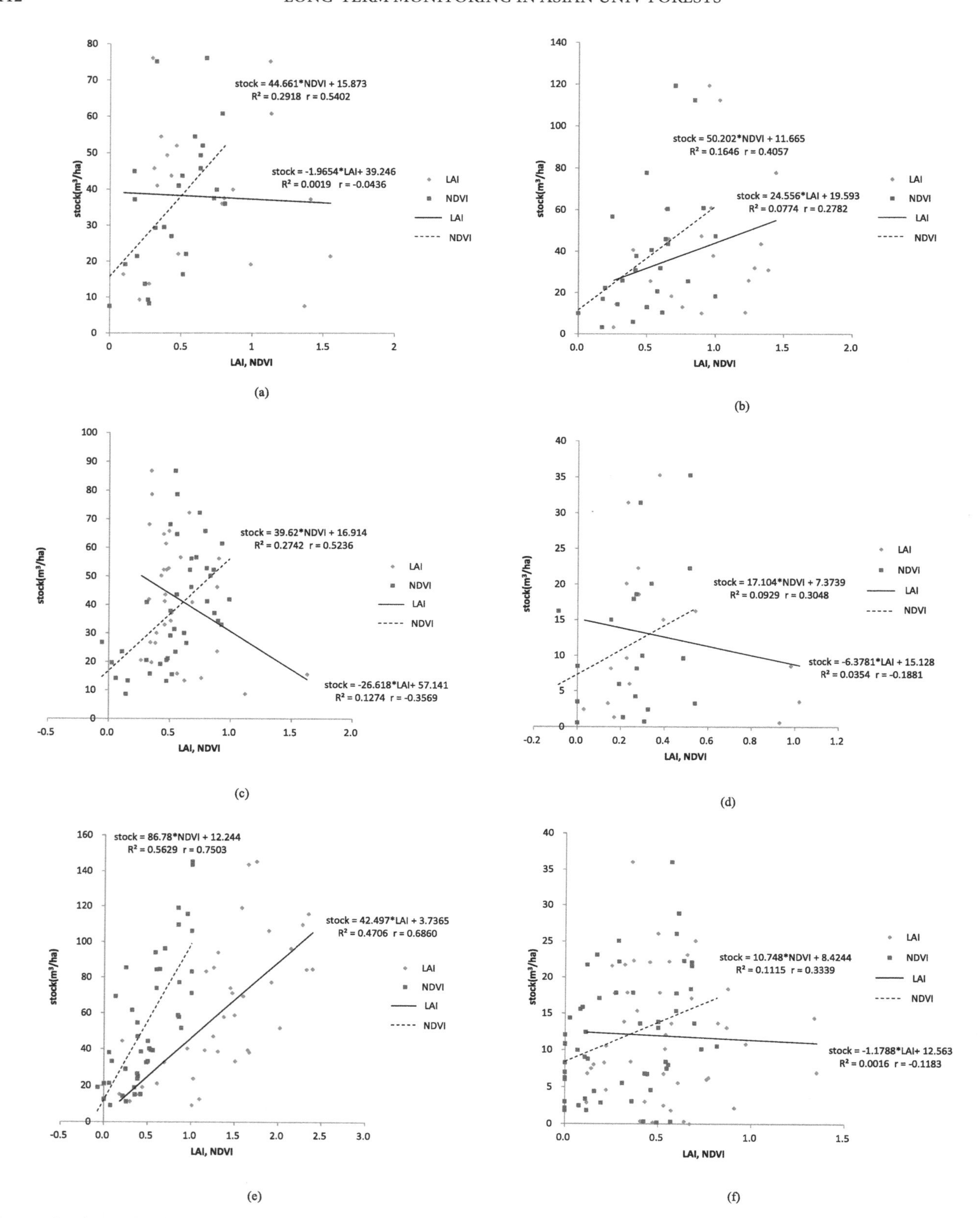

Figure 6. Correlation of stock vs. LAI and NDVI with specific tree species (a) *Terminalia catappa* (LAI (n = 20), NDVI(n = 25)), (b) *Fraxinus formosana* (LAI (n = 20), NDVI(n = 25)), (c) *Pterocarpus indicus* (LAI (n = 32), NDVI(n = 40)), (d) *Melia azedarach* (LAI (n = 16), NDVI(n = 20)), (e) *Swietenia macrophylla* (LAI (n = 36), NDVI (n = 45)), and (f) *Zelkova serrata* (LAI (n = 44), NDVI(n = 55)) at the plot level.

Table 4. Multi-regression of stock vs. LAI and NDVI with pure tree species at the plot level.

Tree species	Sample Size	R^2	Correlation coefficient	P value	Multi-regression formula
Terminalia catappa	20	0.3532	0.5943	0.0246	Stock = 5.6432 + 9.7351*LAI+53.2235*NDVI
Fraxinus formosana	20	0.2242	0.4735	0.1156	Stock = −3.8239 + 22.3971*LAI+42.952*NDVI
Pterocarpus indicus	32	0.3430	0.5867	0.0026	Stock = 34.493 + 19.5753*LAI+33.2311*NDVI
Melia azedarach	16	0.1307	0.3615	0.4024	Stock = 5.2547 + 4.1291*LAI+23.1267*NDVI
Swietenia macrophylla	36	0.6612	0.8131	<0.0001	Stock = −5.8186 + 25.6379*LAI+57.44*NDVI
Zelkova serrata	44	0.1923	0.4390	0.0126	Stock = 1.9618 + 9.3132*LAI+15.4615*NDVI

NDVI but it should be noted that the value range for LAI lies between [0.03, 2.39] and NDVI is [−1, 1] will reflect on the regression coefficient of these two variables.

In addition, short wave infrared band, blue band is not available to analyze other vegetation index such as Normalized Difference Water Index (NDWI) and Enhanced Vegetation Index (EVI). Other vegetation index from high-resolution multispectral imagery from satellite or UAV is feasible to continue the long-term monitoring. The ground survey time can also be adjusted to avoid the foliation period in the future and better stock-LAI- NDVI relationship is expected.

Compared with the findings of similar studies in Taiwan

Liao et al. (2011) assessed the relationship of biomass and NDVI, Transformed NDVI (TNDVI), NDWI, EVI at Ping-Dong of southern Taiwan and found the exponential formula of NDWI with the best correlation ($R^2 = 0.6819$). The result also shows if age of the reforestation forest is too young, with understory vegetation and the crown closure is not complete that may lead to the saturation effect and cause error for estimating biomass by using vegetation index. The average standing stock of *Fraxinus formosana* is 0.0173 m^3 (no tree number), which is larger than the value 0.0157 m^3 measured in this study in 2011. Although the study area covered the 100 ha of this study, the result can only be set as the reference due to the different sampling method for pure tree stand at different surveying time. Hsieh et al. (2011) evaluated the *Fraxinus formosana* reforestation plantation (planted from 2002 to 2009) at Da-Lung and farm of the Taiwan Sugar Corporation in Hualien County of Eastern Taiwan, the average stock (measured between December of 2009 and November of 2010) of *Fraxinus formosana* is 18.13 ± 2.18 m^3 ha^{-1} of 60 sample plots. The linear correlation coefficient between stock and SAVI (Soil Adjusted Vegetation Index) derived from FORMOSAT- II imagery is 0.8670. In this study, the stock of *Fraxinus formosana* measured in 2011 is 16.27 ± 14.30 m^3 ha^{-1} of only five plots, and the correlation coefficient is 0.6700. It is noted that the resolution of FORMOSAT- II imagery is 8 m and the significant large sample size. In this case, the growth condition in different region may differ even for the same tree species.

The results in this study can be set as a reference for plain reforestation at farm area once intensifying cultivation in Taiwan. The farmland or plain reforestation area is often small in size, and with different species in patches, causing additional challenges in estimating and evaluating forest productivity or biomass. Once the relationships between the stock and NDVI are established, we can quickly and easily retrieve standing stock using the satellite-based NDVI at corresponding spatial scales by applying the stock-NDVI relationship. In this case study, we analyzed the correlation between these three variables in a 100 ha area at plot, block, and site levels annually between 2011 and 2015. Additionally, forest inventory should be carefully designed for general investigation in detail. Since we only made one field measurement for each year, the possible seasonal or interannual variations between the stock, LAI, and NDVI are yet to be evaluated. By long-term monitoring and field survey in the future will be expected to yield more convincing and reliable relationship.

Conclusions

We evaluate relationships between the stock, LAI, and NDVI for a subtropical–tropical reforestation plantation in southern Taiwan. The major findings of this study is by long-term monitoring, intensive measurement for 5 years and analysis at different spatial scales, the results show the correlation coefficient of stock-LAI is not significant while that of stock-NDVI increase the spatial scale enlarges. Negative stock-LAI correlations found for three tree species but all the stock-NDVI correlations for six specific tree species are positive. If the multi-regression is applied, the correlation coefficient of stock-LAI-NDVI is higher than that of the stock-LAI and stock-NDVI which reaches to the 0.6470, 0.7680 and 0.9995 at the plot, block and site level, respectively; the correlation coefficients of six specific tree species are also larger at the plot level.

Authors contribution

Chiang Wei performed analysis of the remotely sensed and field data and drafted the manuscript, Jiquan Chen directed the FIA sampling and edited the draft; Jing-Ming Chen initialized the research idea and provided LAI technique, Jui-Chu Yu and Ching-Peng Cheng managed the principal field investigation and data collection, Yen-Jen Lai, Po-Neng Chiang, and Chih-Yuan Hong assisted the field investigation, Ming-Jer Tsai and Ya-Nan Wang supervised the CO_2 flux monitoring project of NTUEF.

Acknowledgments

In addition, field investigation was supported by the CO_2 flux monitoring project of the National Taiwan University Experimental Forest.

Disclosure statement

The authors declare no conflicts of interest.

Funding

The authors would like to thank the Ministry of Science and Technology (former National Science Council) for financial support of this research under the grant Contract No. NSC 99-2918-I-002-027 and NSC 100-2621-M-002-032.

ORCID

Yen-Jen Lai http://orcid.org/0000-0002-3366-8766

References

Carson TN, Ripley DA. 1997. On the relation between NDVI, fractional vegetation cover, and leaf area index. Remote Sens Environ. 62:241–252.

Casanova D, Epema GF, Goudriaan J. 1998. Monitoring rice reflectance at field level for estimating biomass and LAI. Field Crops Res. 55:83–92. doi:10.1016/S0378-4290(97)00064-6.

Chavez PS Jr. 1988. A improved dark-object subtraction technique for atmospheric scattering correction of multispectral data. Remote Sens Environ. 24:459–479. doi:10.1016/0034-4257(88)90019-3.

Chen JM, Black TA. 1992. Defining leaf area index for non-flat leaves. Plant Cell Environ. 15:421–429. doi:10.1111/j.1365-3040.1992.tb00992.x.

Chen JM, Black TA, Adams RS. 1991. Evaluating of hemispherical photography for determining plant area index and geometry of a forest stand. Agric For Meteorol. 56:129–143. doi:10.1016/0168-1923(91)90108-3.

Chen JS, He SM. 2008. The promotion results of reforestation plan for plain scenery and green beautification plan. Agric Policy Rev. 192:

32–37. Council of Agriculture, Executive Yuan, Taiwan. (in Chinese).

Cohen WB. 1991. Response of vegetation indices to changes in three measures of leaf water stress. Photogram Eng Remote Sen. 57:195–202.

FAO. 2015. National forest assessments knowledge reference for national forest assessments-modeling for estimation and monitoring. Accessed on 2 Jan 2016. http://www.fao.org/forestry/17109/en/

Frazer GW, Canham CD, Lertzman KP. 1999. Gap Light Analyzer (GLA), Version 2.0: imaging software to extract canopy structure and gap light transmission indices from true-colour fisheye photographs, users manual and program documentation. New York: Copyright © 1999: Simon Fraser University, Burnaby, British Columbia, and the Institute of Ecosystem Studies, Millbrook.

Gaia VL, Pirotti F, Callegari M, Chen Q, Cuozzo G, Lingua E, Notarnicola C, Papale D. 2017. Potential of ALOS2 and NDVI to estimate forest above-ground biomass, and comparison with lidar-derived estimates. Remote Sens. 9(18). doi:10.3390/rs9010018.

Hsieh HC, Wang DH, Wang TY, Chang JY, Chiu CM. 2011. Applying FORMOSAT-2 image and field survey data to estimate carbon sequestration in *Fraxinus* farm afforestation. J Photogram Remote Sens. 16(2):79–99. (in English with Chinese abstract).

Huete A, Didan K, Miura T, Rodriguez EP, Gao X, Ferreira LG. 2002. Overview of the radiometric and biophysical performance of the MODIS vegetation indices. Remote Sens Environ. 83:195–213. doi:10.1016/S0034-4257(02)00096-2.

Jensen JR. 1983. Urban/suburban landuse analysis. In: Jensen JR, editor. Manual of remote sensing. American Society of photogrammetry. 2nd ed. p.1571–1666, Falls Church, Virginia.

Kim Y, Huete RA, Miura T, Jiang Z. 2011. Spectral compatibility of vegetation indices across sensors: band decomposition with hyperion data. J Appl Remote Sens. 4:043520. doi:10.1117/1.3400635.

Kriegler FJ, Malila WA, Nalepka RF, Richardson W. 1969. Preprocessing transformations and their effects on multispectral recognition. Proc Sixth Int Symp Remote Sens Environ. University of Michigan, Ann Arbor, Michigan, 97–131.

le Marie G, Marsden C, Nouvellon Y, Grinand C, Hakamada R, Stape JL, Laclau JP. 2011. MODIS NDVI time-series allow the monitoring of *Eucalyptus* plantation biomass. Remote Sens Environ. 115:2613–2625. doi:10.1016/j.rse.2011.05.017.

Liao YW, Chen MK, Chen YK, Chung YL, Wu ST. 2011. Use SPOT satellite images to estimate the afforestation carbon storage of Taiwan sugar corporation in Ping-Tung. J Photogram Remote Sens. 16(2):101–113. (in Chinese with English abstract).

Lin JC, Wang PJ, Liu WY. 2010. The practice and effectives of policy for subsidy reforestation in Taiwan. For Res Newsl. 17(2):16–21. Taiwan Forestry Research Institute, Council of Agriculture, Executive Yuan, Taiwan. (in Chinese).

Liu CC, Chen YH, Wu MHM, Wei C, Ko MH. 2019a. Assessment of forest restoration with multi-temporal Formosat-2 imagery. Sci Rep. 9:7279. doi:10.1038/s41598-019-43544-5.

Liu Y, Xiao J, Ju W, Zhu G, Wu X, Fan W, Li D, Zhou Y. 2019b. Satellite-derived LAI products exhibit large discrepancies and can lead to substantial uncertainty in simulated carbon and water fluxes. Remote Sens Environ. 206:174–188. doi:10.1016/j.rse.2017.12.024.

Manna S, Nandy S, Chanda A, Akhand A, Hazra S, Dadhwal VK. 2014. Estimating aboveground biomass in *Avicennia marina* plantation in Indian Sundarbans using high-resolution satellite data. J Appl Remote Sens. 8:e083638. doi:10.1117/1.JRS.8.083638.

Rouse JW, Haas RH, Schell JA, Deering DW 1973. Monitoring vegetation systems in the Great Plains with ERTS. Third ERTS Symp, NASA SP-351 I, 309–317, Remote Sensing Center, Texas A&M University, College Station, Texas.

Song C, Woodcock CE, Seto KC, Lenny MP, Macomber SA. 2001. Classification and change detection using Landsat TM data: when and how to correct atmospheric effects. Remote Sens Environ. 75:230–244. doi:10.1016/S0034-4257(00)00169-3.

Taipei City Government. 2011. Handbook for the survey of permanent plot of forest in Taipei. Geotechnical Engineering Office, Public Works Department, Taipei City Government, Taipei, (in Chinese).

Tucker CJ. 1979. Red and photographic infrared linear combinations for monitoring vegetation. Remote Sens Environ. 8:127–150. doi:10.1016/0034-4257(79)90013-0.

USDA Forest Service. 2016. Forest Investigation and Analysis (FIA) National Core Field Guide Vol. 1: field data collection procedures for phase 2 plots, Ver. 7.1., National Office, U.S. Forest Service, Washington.

Wei Z, Yoshimura K, Wang L, Miralles DG, Jasechko S, Lee X. 2017. Revisiting the contribution of transpiration to global terrestrial evapotranspiration. Geophys Res Lett. 44:2792–2801. doi:10.1002/2016GL072235.

Xavier AC, Vettorazzi CA. 2004. Mapping leaf area index through spectral indices in a subtropical watershed. Int J Remote Sens. 25:1661–1672. doi:10.1080/01431160310001620803.

Yang CM, Liu CC, Wang YW. 2008. Using Formosat-2 satellite data to estimate leaf area index of rice crop. J Photogram Remote Sens. 13:253–260. (in English with Chinese abstract).

Zheng D, Rademacher J, Chen J, Crow T, Bresee M, Le Moine J, Ryu SR. 2004. Estimating aboveground biomass using Landsat 7 ETM+ data across a managed landscape in northern Wisconsin, USA. Remote Sens Environ. 93:402–411. doi:10.1016/j.rse.2004.08.008.

Index

Abies firma 40–42, 44–46
abundant species 65, 70
accuracy assessment 17
air temperature 16, 30, 61, 67, 69
Akaike Information Criterion (AIC) 62
alpha-pinene 57, 58
Amateis, R. L. 85
ambrosia beetles 49, 56, 58, 60, 61, 63, 65, 67
Ananomiya experimental watershed (AEW) 16, 18, 20
annual litterfall 36–38; mass 32–34, 36–38
Antón-Fernández, C. 79, 84, 85
atmospheric effects 109
attractants 50, 56–58

Baramgol 16, 18
bark beetles 49, 56, 58, 60, 67
basal area increment (BAI) 99–102
base temperature 24, 27
Bates, D. M. 81
Beaver, R. A. 60, 67
Box, E. 3
breeding 69, 70, 72, 75
broadleaf plantations 32
bud break 24–26, 28–30
Buras, A. 42
Burkhart, H. E. 85
Buse, A. 75

Cameron, D. M. 84
castor aralia 97, 100, 101
causality test 61
central Taiwan 32, 33, 80
Chamaecyparis obtusa 40, 70
Chen, K. N. 80
Cheng, C. H. 1, 84, 85
Chiba Forest 89, 91, 92, 94, 95
Chichibu Forest 25, 27–30, 58, 89, 92, 94, 95
Chuang, S. T. 80
climate change 4, 8, 10, 12, 24, 41, 46, 56, 69, 70, 75
climate data 6, 8, 42, 61, 71
climate datasets 6, 8
climate subtypes 8, 12
climate variables 42, 43, 45, 61–63, 67
clusters 55, 56, 58, 106
C. obtusa 41, 42, 44–46
Coleoptera 50
collection times 62, 63, 65, 67
combinations 4, 50, 57, 92
confidence intervals 72, 73, 75, 82
coniferous plantations 32, 79, 98
convergent cross mapping (CCM) 61–63, 65, 67
cool temperate forest 49
core sampling 41
Cryptomeria japonica 33, 40–42, 44–46, 79, 88
Cupressaceae species 46
curculionidae 50, 60, 61
curve number (CN) 14–19, 22; determination 15, 18; values 15, 16, 18–20, 22

Dai, A. 42
deer densities 50
degree days 26–28
diameter at breast height (DBH) 33, 51, 79, 80, 89, 91, 95, 98–102, 106, 107
drought indices 41–45
drought response 40, 41, 43–46
Duffková, R. 30
Dufrêne, M. 51

ecosystem responses 69
egg-laying dates 69–76
environmental implications 38
ethanol 50, 51, 57, 58, 60
ethanol-baited traps 60, 61
Eucalyptus spp 40
exotic species 40, 41, 46; plantations 40, 41, 46
explanatory variables 26, 62, 100
extrapolation values 89, 92, 94, 95

Fahlvik, N. 86
Feng, S. 7, 8
fitted Gompertz model 81, 82
Flechtmann, C. 56
Forrester, D. I. 79
Fujimoto, S. 24
Fujisawa, Y. 80
Fukuchi, S. 84
Fukuda, K. 4

Galko, J. 56
GDD models 26–28, 30
generalized linear model (GLM) 62
global climate change 69
Gompertz equation 80
Gompertz models 80, 82, 86
Granger causality index (GCI) 62
Granger causality test 61–63, 65, 67
growing degree days model 24

growth chamber experiments 25–27, 29, 30
growth curves 80, 91, 92, 94, 95
Guan, B. T. 2, 80

Hauser, V. L. 14, 16
Hawkins, R. H. 15, 17
Hennessey, T. C. 37
high-value timber species 97–99, 101, 102
Hiroshima, T. 2
Hjelmfelt, A. T. 14, 16
Hokkaido 25, 27–30, 60
Holdridge, L. R. 3
Horn, L. H. 3, 7
Hsieh, H. C. 113
Hulcr, J. 60

Im, S. 1, 4
indicator species 51, 53–58
indicator species analysis (INSPAN) 51, 53, 57
individual tree BAI models 99, 100
individual tree growth 85, 97, 101, 102; models 97, 98, 101, 102
individual tree-level analysis 89, 91, 94
Indocryphalus pubipennis 58
initial densities 79–82, 84–86
insect collection 50
insect trapping 50
interannual litterfall variation 33, 34, 37, 38
Irikawa catchment 50, 54, 57
Ishiguri, F. 80, 85

Jacob, D. 7, 8
Japanese oak 97, 100–102
Jeong, M. S. 2
Jiang, Z. H. 79, 85
Jones, O. R. 16
Jung, J. B. 1

Kamata, N. 1, 16, 25, 26
Kasetsart University (KU) 4, 5, 8, 10
Kikuzawa, K. 29
Kim, S. K. 45
Kira, T. 24
Korea Forest Research Institute 40, 41, 45
Kuraji, K. 4

Lai, Y. J. 1, 5
Lam, T. Y. 2
Lardizabal, M. L. 5
Lawrence, D. 36
leaf area index (LAI) 4, 5, 36–38, 58, 62, 102, 105–107, 109–111, 113
leafing phenology 24, 25, 30
Legendre, P. 51
Lhotka, J. M. 102
Liao, Y. W. 113
Lin, J. C. 105
Lin, K. C. 37
Lindelow, A. 57, 58
linear mixed-effect models 72, 73, 101
litterfall 32, 33, 36–38; mass 32–34, 37, 38; seasonality 33, 34, 36, 37; variation 34, 37, 38
Löyttyniemi, K. 60, 67
Lu, E. Y. 37

Macedo-Reis, L. E. 60
Masaki, T. 84, 88
mixed conifer-broadleaf forests 97
mixed-effects modeling 99
mizunara oak 24
Moe, K. T. 2
monoculture plantation 37
Montgomery, R. J. 14
multiple regression models 27, 29

Nakagawa, S. 100
Nam, Y. 26
Nambu University Forest 41, 70
National Taiwan University (NTU) 4, 7, 10
normalized difference vegetation index (NDVI) 105, 106, 108–111, 113
northern Japan 25, 97, 98

Oliver, W. W. 79
Osumi, K. 84, 88
Owari, T. 2, 102

permanent plots 86, 98, 99, 102
permutational multivariate analysis of variance (PERMANOVA) 51
Phua, M. H. 5
physiological traits 45
Picea sitchensis (Bong.) Carr. 40
Pinheiro, J. C. 81
Pinus radiata D. Don 40
plantations 32, 33, 37, 38, 41, 50, 51, 54, 57, 58, 79, 84
Polygraphus proximus Blandford 54
population cycles 60, 65
pre-breeding period temperatures 69, 70, 72, 74, 75
probabilistic method 15, 16, 18–22

Quercus crispula Blume 24–30, 97

rainfall 14–18, 33, 61–63, 65, 67
reforestation 105, 106, 110
Reukema, D. L. 79
root mean square errors (RMSEs) 6, 17, 20, 89, 91, 92, 94, 95, 100
R software 61
runoff relationship 17

Saito, T. 50, 51
Sanguansub, S. 1, 60, 61
Schielzeth, H. 100
Schroeder, L. M. 57–58
seasonality 60, 62
seasonal litterfall variation 33
seasonal tropical forest 60, 67
Seoul National University (SNU) 4, 7, 8, 10
Shibano, S. 97, 102
Shirasaka experimental watershed (SEW) 16
short disturbance time 37, 38
site description 106
soil conservation service curve number determination 14
spatio-temporal variation 69
species-specific response 45
SPOT imagery 106, 108, 109
Springer, E. P. 14
stand basal area 79, 81, 84, 86
stand level analysis 89, 92, 95
stock assessment 106
stock-LAI-NDVI 106, 109, 110, 113
Sueus niisimai 58
sugi 79–81, 84, 85, 88, 89, 95
Sugihara, G. 61

Tan, P. H. 9
Tanaka, N. 5, 25
Tantasirin, C. 5
target trees 89, 91, 92, 99, 102

Tatsumi, S. 97
Thornthwaite, C. W. 3
Tokyo Chiba Forest 4, 88, 89
Tokyo Chichibu Forest 4, 25, 49
tree mortality 50, 58
tree-ring chronology 41
Trewartha, G. T. 3, 7
Tsai, M. J. 5
Tseng, Y. C. 9
Tsushima, S. 80
typhoon disturbances 32–38

U-Bukmoongol 16–18
Universiti Malaysia Sabah (UMS) 4, 5, 8, 10
University of Tokyo 4, 10
UTokyo 4, 7, 10

Vanclay, J. 99
varied tits 69–73, 75, 76

Walter, H. 3
Wang, S. Y. 80
Wang, T. T. 85
watersheds 14, 16–22
Wei, C. 2
wood-boring Coleoptera 60
Worldclim 6–8; datasets 7, 8, 12; data validation 6

Xitou 32, 33, 36–38, 89

Yamamura, R. 5

Zhang, H. 36